STRUCTURAL MODELLING AND OPTIMIZATION: A General Methodology for Engineering and Control

ELLIS HORWOOD SERIES IN ENGINEERING SCIENCE

The Ellis Horwood Engineering Science Series has two objectives; of satisfying the requirements of post-graduate and mid-career education and of providing clear and modern texts for more basic undergraduate topics in the fields of civil and mechanical engineering. It is furthermore the editors' intention to include English translations of outstanding texts originally written in other languages, thereby introducing works of international merit to English language audiences.

STRENGTH OF MATERIALS
J. M. ALEXANDER, University College of Swansea.

TECHNOLOGY OF ENGINEERING MANUFACTURE
J. M. ALEXANDER, R. C. BREWER, Imperial College of Science and Technology, University of London, J. R. CROOKALL, Cranfield Institute of Technology.

VIBRATION ANALYSIS AND CONTROL SYSTEM DYNAMICS
CHRISTOPHER BEARDS, Imperial College of Science and Technology, University of London.

COMPUTER AIDED DESIGN AND MANUFACTURE
C. B. BESANT, Imperial College of Science and Technology, University of London.

STRUCTURAL DESIGN AND SAFETY
D. I. BLOCKLEY, University of Bristol.

BASIC LUBRICATION THEORY 2nd Edition
ALASTAIR CAMERON, Imperial College of Science and Technology, University of London.

ADVANCED MECHANICS OF MATERIALS 2nd Edition
Sir HUGH FORD, F.R.S., Imperial College of Science and Technology, University of London and J. M. ALEXANDER, University College of Swansea.

ELASTICITY AND PLASTICITY IN ENGINEERING
Sir HUGH FORD, F.R.S. and R. T. FENNER, Imperial College of Science and Technology, University of London.

TECHNIQUES OF FINITE ELEMENTS
BRUCE M. IRONS, University of Calgary, and S. AHMAD, Bangladesh University of Engineering and Technology, Dacca.

STRUCTURAL DESIGN OF CABLE-SUSPENDED ROOFS
L. KOLLAR, City Planning Office, Budapest and K. SZABO, Budapest Technical University.

CONTROL OF FLUID POWER, 2nd Edition
D. McCLOY, The Northern Ireland Polytechnic and H. R. MARTIN, University of Waterloo, Ontario, Canada.

DYNAMICS OF MECHANICAL SYSTEMS 2nd Edition
J. M. PRENTIS, University of Cambridge.

ENERGY METHODS IN VIBRATION ANALYSIS
T. H. RICHARDS, University of Aston, Birmingham.

ENERGY METHODS IN STRESS ANALYSIS: With an Introduction to Finite Element Techniques
T. H. RICHARDS, University of Aston, Birmingham.

STRESS ANALYSIS OF POLYMERS 2nd Edition
J. G. WILLIAMS, Imperial College of Science and Technology, University of London.

STRUCTURAL MODELLING AND OPTIMIZATION:

A General Methodology for Engineering and Control

D. G. CARMICHAEL, B.E., M.Eng.Sc., Ph.D.
Department of Civil Engineering
University of Western Australia

ELLIS HORWOOD LIMITED
Publishers · Chichester

Halsted Press: a division of
JOHN WILEY & SONS
New York · Chichester · Brisbane · Toronto

First published in 1981 by

ELLIS HORWOOD LIMITED

Market Cross House, Cooper Street, Chichester, West Sussex, PO19 1EB, England

The publisher's colophon is reproduced from James Gillison's drawing of the ancient Market Cross, Chichester.

Distributors:

Australia, New Zealand, South-east Asia:
Jacaranda-Wiley Ltd., Jacaranda Press,
JOHN WILEY & SONS INC.,
G.P.O. Box 859, Brisbane, Queensland 40001, Australia

Canada:
JOHN WILEY & SONS CANADA LIMITED
22 Worcester Road, Rexdale, Ontario, Canada.

Europe, Africa:
JOHN WILEY & SONS LIMITED
Baffins Lane, Chichester, West Sussex, England.

North and South America and the rest of the world:
Halsted Press: a division of
JOHN WILEY & SONS
605 Third Avenue, New York, N.Y. 10016, U.S.A.

British Library Cataloguing in Publication Data
Carmichael, D. G.
Structure modelling & optimization. –
(Ellis Horwood series in engineering science)
1. Structure, theory of – Mathematical models
I. Title
624.171'0724 TA645

Library of Congress Card No. 81–4238 AACR2

ISBN 0–85312–283–0 (Ellis Horwood Ltd., Publishers – Library Edn.)
ISBN 0–85312–300–4 (Ellis Horwood Ltd., Publishers – Student Edn.)
ISBN 0–470–27114–0 (Halsted Press)

Printed in Great Britain by R. J. Acford, Chichester.

To my parents

A. Fraser Carmichael and Edna K. Carmichael

Table of Contents

Author's Preface

Despite advances in the development of sophisticated mathematical tools, confidence in the treatment of complicated structural systems, and the development of a certain order in the theory of structures (whether in analytic or synthetic modes), there still exist untidy thinking and lack of general understanding in both the modelling and design processes. Clarification of these processes is conceivable with the adoption of a format and thinking akin to systems theory where the aim is to provide a common basis and unified conceptual framework for studying system behaviour through generalizations and an ordering of knowledge. (The notion 'system' is used in the sense of sets of interacting elements or a transformation of 'input' data into 'outputs'.)

Modelling

The possibility of the formulation of mathematical models for structures which are meaningful and at the same time of wide applicability is offered through the medium of systems theory; fundamental to a systems theory is the establishment of suitable behaviour models expressing the interaction or interdependence of a system's components in a rational manner. Such a definite approach for structures has previously been obscured by their essentially associative (non-flow) nature. The bulk of systems concepts have been developed for sequential (flow) systems, and hence the relevance (apart from certain analogies) to structural systems is not immediately apparent. Both flow and non-flow types, however, can be shown to share a common systems basis.

Design

As the modelling process in associated engineering branches has been restructured by systems approaches, so too has the design process been restructured by forcing an awareness on the designer to reassess his assumptions, goals and decisions. The approaches have enabled an objective approach to the formulation and the efficient solution of design problems. In these associated engineering branches where the service performance of the system controls the design process, the systems approach has proven to be powerful. It remains to show its validity in the field of structures, where a feedback learning cycle emanating from constructed designs is unfortunately absent, or at most piecemeal, and the service conditions are uncertain. As suitable models are central to the conceptual foundations of systems theory, so suitable mathematical methods and thinking are central to the quantitative treatment of systems. In this respect, the philosophy of optimal control systems theory will be useful for the structural design problem, as it exploits the composition of the system design problem.

The book is divided into four parts. Part A on modelling discusses within the framework of both single level and multilevel systems theories, the equations and principles of structural mechanics. Part B discusses design, and in conjunction with A exploits the systems viewpoint to provide a unification and generalization of the modelling and design stages of the total structural design process. The relevance of, and motivation for, using systems concepts in these contexts are examined along with the historical setting of the present approach. The emphasis at all times is on the development of a rational and systematic approach. Using the conceptual foundation of a formal control systems theory and identifying the principal entities of state and control, a broad class of structural systems is reduced to canonical models, and the components of the design problem are delineated. The development of A and B is from a fundamental viewpoint, at all times appealing to the physical nature of the structural system or the design process.

Part C delves into the specific optimization techniques in a deterministic sense. Within an optimal control systems theory notation, the topics of mathematical programming, dynamic programming, Pontryagin's principle, variational calculus, singular control, multicriteria optimization, multilevel optimization, Lyapunov theory in design, and energy and 'optimality criteria' based approaches are discussed.

Part D gives a Closure for the book. (Several related topics have been omitted for reasons of space. In particular a game theoretic treatment, sensitivity, and probabilistic optimization have been left out. Active control, being distinct from conventional structural design, is not discussed, although similar methodologies and techniques may be used.) Examples are used to introduce or highlight much of the philosophy. Extensive notes, comments and bibliographies are given on each of the topics. An attempt is made in the book to bring together a lot of the literature on structural optimization, scattered as it is throughout professional journals and monographs, and to show its relation to an optimal control systems format to the structural design problem. An extensive reference list is given.

The book is aimed at the graduate student and reference text level, although considerable material is extracted from the text by the author for both undergraduate and graduate lectures in structural mechanics. It is hoped that the text is accessible to control theorists, mathematicians, structural engineers and structural theorists alike.

This monograph owes much to the author's association with Professor Douglas H. Clyde (Western Australia) and Professor David G. Elms (Canterbury). The (largely unpublished) foundation ideas of Professor Douglas Clyde on the monograph subject as well as a close personal association, are acknowledged in particular.

Acknowledgements

The following material has been reproduced with permission of the publishers:

Figs. 1.1, 1.2, 1.3 and 11.1 from a paper by the author and D. H. Clyde appearing in *Structural Control*, edited by H. H. E. Leipholz, North-Holland Publishing Company, Amsterdam/S. M. Publications, Waterloo (1980).

Fig. 7.5 from a paper by the author appearing in *Archives of Mechanics (Archiwum Mechaniki Stosowanej)*, Vol. 30, No. 6 (1978), Polish Scientific Publishers, Warsaw.

D. G. Carmichael

Perth, January 1980

Notation

SYMBOLS

$\subset$	is a subset of
$\in$	is an element or member of, belongs to
$\triangleq$	equals by definition, denotes
$=$	equals, is equivalent to
$<(>)$	less (greater) than
$\leq(\geq)$	less (greater) than or equal to
$/$	a symbol cancelled thus, denotes the negation of the symbol meaning
$\simeq$	equals approximately
$\forall$	for all
$\times$	Cartesian product
$[a, b]$	closed interval $a \leq y \leq b$
(a, b)	open interval $a < y < b$
$(a, b]$	semiopen interval $a < y \leq b$
	rounded bracket inplies strict inequality
$\delta(\ )$	Dirac delta
δe	small variation in e
Π	product
Σ	sum
ext	extremum
max	maximum
min	minimum
$\|\ \|$	absolute value
$\|\ \ \|$	norm
$\oint_c$	integral over a closed path c, arc length σ
$\|J(\ )\|$	Jacobian determinant
∇	gradient vector operator $\left(\frac{\partial}{\partial e_1}, \frac{\partial}{\partial e_2}, \ldots\right)$

Braces denote a set or a family: for $e \in \Xi$

$\{e\}$ is the set whose generic element is e

$\{e; A(e)\}$ is the set with element e having property A.

A sequence $e_1, e_2, \ldots, e_m$ is denoted $\{e_i\}$ if the range of indices is clear.

$p(\cdot)$ probability density function

$F(\cdot)$ probability distribution function

$P\{\cdot\}$ probability of an event

$E\{\cdot\}$ expectation operation

$P\{A \mid B\}$ conditional probability; conditioned on the occurrence of the event B

E^m m dimensional Euclidean space (Euclidean m-space) of m tuples with the norm of an element $e = \{\xi_1, \xi_2, \ldots, \xi_m\}$ defined as

$$\| e \| = \left[\sum_{i=1}^{m} | \xi_i |^2 \right]^{1/2}$$

$\partial_l e$ with $l = (l_1, l_2, \ldots)$, relates to a collection of partial derivatives of e, each with respect to $y_1, y_2, \ldots$ to the respective orders $l_1, l_2, \ldots$; the overall order of each derivative is $L = l_1 + l_2 + \ldots$, and $l_1, l_2, \ldots$ assume the ranges $0 \leq l_i \leq L$, $i = 1, 2, \ldots$ depending on the particular derivative. e.g. with only two parameters y_1 and y_2 and with $L = 3 = l_1 + l_2$ $(0 \leq l_1, l_2 \leq 3)$ this gives a collection of four derivaties

$$\frac{\partial^3 e}{\partial y_1^3}, \qquad \frac{\partial^3 e}{\partial y_1^2\, \partial y_2}, \qquad \frac{\partial^3 e}{\partial y_1\, \partial y_2^2}, \qquad \frac{\partial^3 e}{\partial y_2^3}$$

The notation $\partial_l e$ implies that one or more of these derivatives exists.

CONVENTIONS

(i) All vectors are column vectors. Vectors in general are lower case letters. Components of vectors are subscripted.

(ii) Matrices in general are upper case letters. Components of matrices are doubly subscripted (a_{ij}, i'th row, j'th column).

(iii) Differentiation, integration or other mathematical manipulations, when applied to vectors or matrices, are applied to all elements of those vectors or matrices respectively.

(iv) Scalar quantities are noted in the text and may be upper or lower case letters.

(v) Arguments of scalar-valued or vector-valued functions or functionals are placed in parenthesis or omitted where confusion is not possible. Similar notation is used to denote the value of a function at a given value of the independent variable(s).

(vi) Indexing variables are h, i, j, k, l, α and β and take whole number values $1, 2, 3, \ldots$. Subscripts and superscripts may sometimes be used as mnemonics, but this form should be clear from the context. Superscripts L, R denote left and right interval limits; superscripts a, b denote boundary curves.

(vii) A variable with a superposed caret ^ is the optimal form of that variable in the sense of the context. Transpose is denoted by a superscript T. Inverse (reciprocal) is denoted by a superscript −1. A superposed dot denotes differentiation.

PRINCIPAL CHARACTERS

A, B, C, D	matrices
D	spatial domain, boundary ∂D
E	Weierstrass function
f, F	function, system equation
g, θ	function, end criterion
G, ϕ	function, domain criterion, criterion
h	function, response equation, constraint inequation
H	Hamiltonian
J	optimality criterion
k	discretization index
L	Lagrangian
m	constraint counter; number of response coordinates
M	boundary function
n	number of state coordinates
N	total discrete intervals; number of criteria
r	number of control coordinates
R	feasible region
S	set of end states; optimal return function
t	time
T	time domain
u	control variable
U	admissible region of controls
V	admissible region in state-control product space; Lyapunov function
x	state variable
X	admissible region of states
y	spatial coordinate; general independent variable
Y	time-position space; domain with boundary ∂Y
z	response variable
Δ	discrete interval
λ	costate variable; Lagrange multiplier
σ	switching function; arc length
Σ	closed curve, arc length σ
ω	probability parameter
Ω	sample space
κ	singularity order
π	interaction variable
γ	interaction function

Part A
Modelling

Chapter 1

A Basis for Modelling

1.1 AN HIERARCHICAL MULTILEVEL SYSTEM REPRESENTATION FOR STRUCTURES

The concept of a system provides for system representation as an assemblage of subsystems. As such a structure may be viewed as an hierarchical multilevel system with the subsystems for example corresponding to the structure, member, element and material levels (Fig. 1.1). Alternatively substructures, member segments, cross-section layers and related ideas may be interpreted as subsystems. Subsystem description (input–output relationship) is in terms of a constitutive relationship, while subsystem interaction is in terms of equilibrium and compatibility relationships. The three sets of relationships, when combined, define the subsystem description at the next higher level (Fig. 1.2). That is, on any given level, the behaviour is studied in terms of that level's constitutive relationship, while the manner in which subsystems on that level interact to form a higher level system is studied on the higher level.

Referring to Fig. 1.1, the subsystem boxes represent the constitutive relationship at the given level. Three notions, namely control, state, and response, have been introduced here and require explanation. For the present purpose, qualitative explanations will be sufficient; complete definitions will be given later. Subsystem controls refer to the material and geometrical properties of the subsystem components and the distribution of these properties over space and their variation over time. The state relates to an internal behaviour description of the subsystem and the response to an external behaviour description. A distinction between the 'inputs' is required; as with the response, the given information on the state follows from the environment–system interaction, but the control derives from the designer. For most systems problems, the given state information is usually regarded as known. In the systems design problem the control is free to be varied.

To fix the ideas, consider the illustration in Fig. 1.3. This illustration is given in the sense of Fig. 1.1 and is for the case of structure nodal

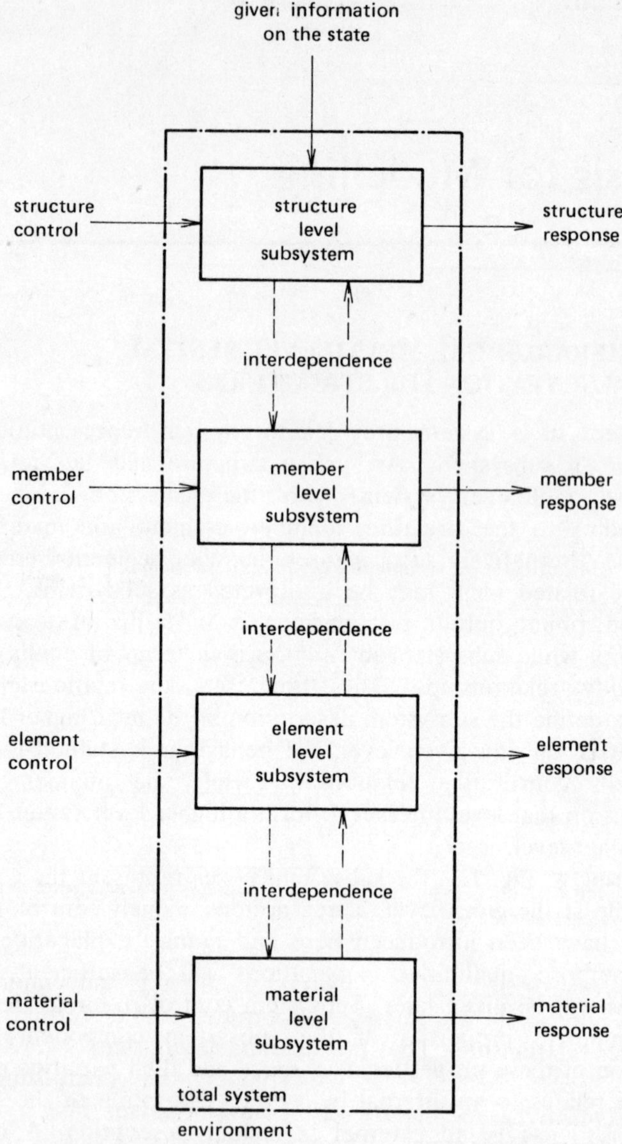

Fig. 1.1 An hierarchical multilevel representation.

loading. Related relationships may be written for other known information on the state; for example for the case of prescribed nodal displacements the stiffnesses are replaced by flexibilities. Notice that there is in general an order of magnitude change of the information at each level.

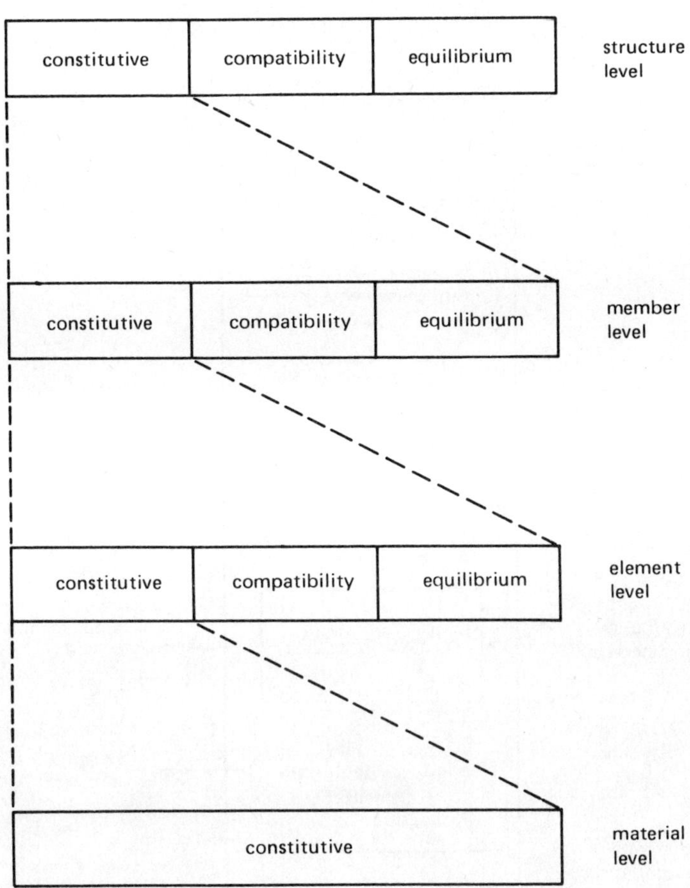

Fig. 1.2 Relationship between levels. A system on a given level is a subsystem on the next higher level.

The directed paths in Fig. 1.1 and 1.3, although conventionally used to denote flows of the relevant quantities, are here used to imply dependence relationships. They facilitate the description of a system as sets of input–output pairs and are convenient when generalizing systems concepts (which have primarily been developed for flow systems) to structures (non-flow systems). The use of the terms 'higher' and 'lower' when referring to levels is interpreted in the sense of the orientation of Figs 1.1, 2, 3.

It is seen that no levels are isolated; when considering any one level, the two adjacent levels must be taken into account. The interdependence between subsystems is indicated in Fig. 1.1 by two-way arrows between boxes. The downward directed arrow represents information from higher levels that is needed to solve the lower level

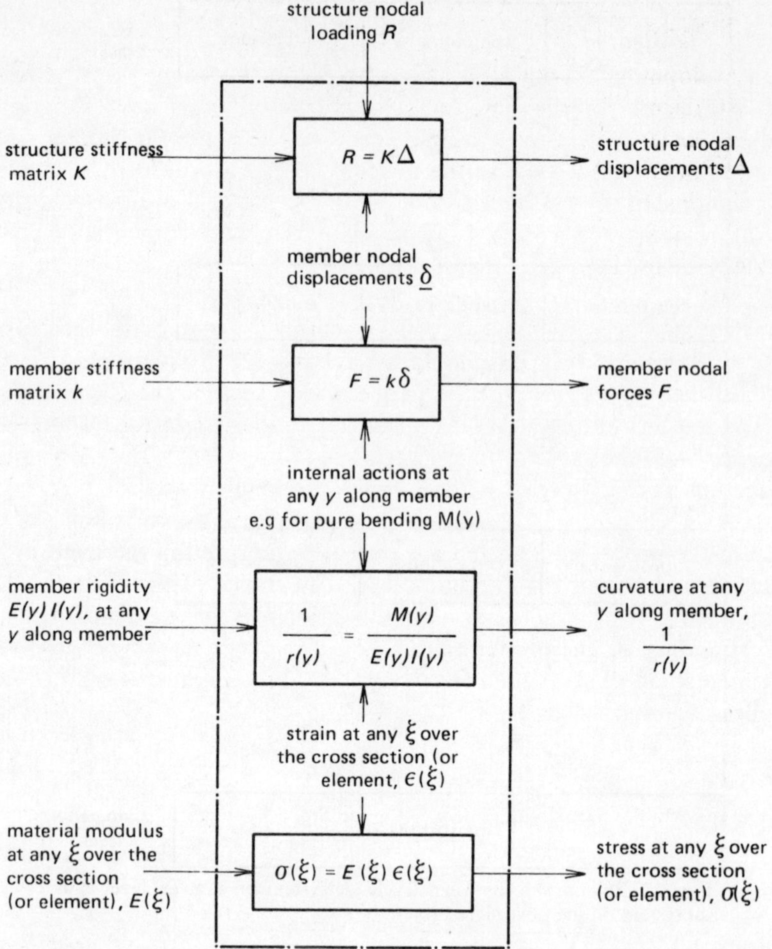

Fig. 1.3 Illustration of elastic modelling. Structure subjected to loading at nodal points.

problem; upper levels define the bounds within which the lower levels function. The upward directed arrow shows that the construction (and behaviour) of the higher levels depends on the lower level construction (and behaviour). Control may be applied, and exchanges with the environment may occur at all levels. Changes in controls on higher levels are manifested by parameter changes on lower levels. Understanding of the structural system functioning improves on ascending the hierarchy, while the detail unfolds on descending the hierarchy (Fig. 1.2). Explanations of the total system behaviour are possible in terms of the lower levels and their interrelationships.

1.2 A SINGLE LEVEL SYSTEM REPRESENTATION

The development of multilevel systems theory has only taken place in the last decade and is ongoing. Usable results are now starting to emerge. Historically attention has been directed at the far simpler single level problem with a view to the internal composition of the system and the relationship of this composition to the levels of a multilevel system. It still remains convenient both conceptually and computationally in many cases to aggregate the subsystems and work with a single level (Fig. 1.4).

The equations of conventional structural mechanics in their usual form, are regarded as unsuitable as a basis for a structures oriented systems theory, and as a first step towards such a theory, a revised model is introduced. Three distinct entities—control, state and response—of the system may again be identified. (The conceptual distinction has, in fact, existed all along, although it was sometimes lost sight of in earlier work.) Conventional structural assumptions are not altered; the processes involved are one of reinterpreting the traits of the structure and one of reworking models. The choice of the revised model is founded on an examination of the principles of mechanics and an understanding of their interrelationships. The model will permit ready statements of the fundamental systems problems of analysis and synthesis (design, optimization).

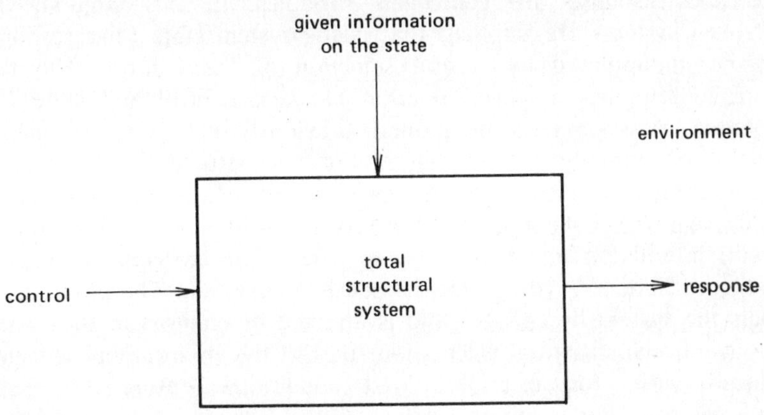

Fig. 1.4 Single-level structure representation.

1.3 VARIOUS SINGLE LEVEL MODEL FORMS

1.3.1 Basic Notions

The use of inductive arguments to establish the conceptual framework offered by control systems theory as a rational basis for the modelling of structures, and particular examples to emphasize certain physical and conceptual entities (control, state and response), is perhaps the most useful way. The utility of these entities as measures of generalization and uniformity of structural description as well as their relationship to a design and understanding viewpoint may then be discussed, and, to extend the theory by general inference, all other related structural systems will be required to share these qualities. This leads on to a generalization of the modelling results in Chapters 2 and 3.

By way of introduction, several essential concepts of control systems theory may be identified:

Control variables contain the information relating to the physical properties (flexural stiffness, axial stiffness, . . .) of the various components of the system. They exert the control on the behaviour of the system and may be freely chosen (manipulated) by the designer. In this sense they are 'input' into the model by the designer.

State variables contain all the information regarding the internal behaviour or state (deflections, induced moments, . . .) of the system.

The system **response** indicates the level of outward behaviour (deflection, . . .) of the system. Response variables may or may not be identified directly with state variables. Generally the response, being a relevant measure of the state, will comprise part of the state description.

It follows that the state relates the 'input' control to the 'output' response and determines the response uniquely for a given control. Both state and response are **controlled** variables. In this context, only **controlled systems** are implied; that is the system state (and response) may be manipulated by careful selection of the control. The term 'controlled' implies a causal relation between control and state (and response). A **system** as mentioned previously may be conveniently thought of initially as an interaction of structural elements or input–output transformations. A more explicit meaning is not required at this stage. A collection of elements is insufficient to describe the system; interaction has also to be specified. The **environment** may be taken to include everything not defined as the system. The environment affects the system by changes and is affected by changes in the system. In conventional structural calculations part of the environment is usually replaced with, for example, load conditions, enforced structure displacements and others which are known for any given environment–system arrangement. Another form of system–environment interaction is the usual notions of boundary and terminal conditions.

Following from these definitions of system and environment, it is apparent that any given system may be reduced to subsystems. The hierarchical multilevel system of Fig. 1.1 (or 1.2) follows, with the subsystems delineated at each level of behaviour. The notions of state, response and control extend to all levels such that materials, dimensions, geometry, rigidities, . . . may all be considered controls, while stresses, strains, curvatures, . . . may all be considered states at various levels of the total structure hierarchy. In some cases the response and state may obey a one-to-one transformation, and the distinction in this case between response and state disappears superficially. However, for consistency of terminology on all levels, the distinction will be maintained. The concept of state relates best to systems variable in space and/or time, and to which a control is introduced and a response (or output) calculated.

The fundamental systems problems of analysis, synthesis (design, optimization) and identification (investigation) may now be introduced in relation to this terminology.

Analysis procedures regard the control variables to be given, with the only true variables being the state variables. Synthetic type techniques attempt to assign the control variables so as to give a desired state (direct synthesis) or to optimize some design goal (optimal synthesis, optimal control, optimization). Both the analysis and synthesis problems require the *a priori* specification of the system model; however, identification procedures determine the form of the system model for given input–output characteristics. They are commonly called 'black box' problems, implying a complete or partial lack of knowledge of the organization of the model. The theory of control embraces these fundamental problems. The relevance to the theory of structures is apparent.

1.3.2 Ordinary Differential Equation Models

To demonstrate the notion of state, consider the Bernoulli–Euler beam constitutive relationship of the form

$$\frac{d^2}{dy^2}\left[D(y)\,\frac{d^2 w(y)}{dy^2}\right] = q(y) \qquad y \in [y^L, y^R]. \tag{a}$$

For a given control D (denoting flexural rigidity), and loading q, the solution of this equation (the response displacement w) is completely resolved at any position $y \in [y^L, y^R]$, when a combination of four—depending on the individual problem—of the total possible static (stress) and/or kinematic (displacement) boundary conditions are specified (shared) between y^L and y^R. It will be recalled that the kinematic boundary conditions relate to

(i) the deflection w, and
(ii) the rate of deflection, dw/dy,

while the static boundary conditions relate to

(iii) the internal moment (proportional to the second derivative of w), and
(iv) the internal shearing force (proportional to the third derivative of w).

These four quantities will be referred to as the **state** of the beam at y^L and y^R. However, it will be noted that the interval limits y^L and y^R are arbitrary, and in fact the four quantities may be specified at any position y for a solution to be gained of (a). Hence the state could be defined at each position y along the beam. In this sense the state (at any y) contains the minimal amount of information required to determine the state at some other position y', for any given control.

Provided the state is known at any position y, the response may be evaluated for a given control; the state relates the input control to the output response and uniquely determines the response for a given control. It is the necessary information required to determine the response completely. The boundary conditions (or 'end' conditions, implying a visualization of the interval $[y^L, y^R]$) are known values of state at certain positions along the beam (here the left and right ends) and are sufficient to define the values of state for all y. (For a more general structural theory than considered here, loading (surface traction or static boundary condition) too may be considered as an 'end' condition on the states which also become more general than considered here. Boundary conditions (static and kinematic) represent an interaction of the system and environment as mentioned earlier.)

The state may alternatively be thought of as representing the internal behaviour of the beam. As such it would then appear reasonable that to exercise control over the system, information about the state would be more useful than a single quantity representing the gross or outward system behaviour. (In this case the response is the deflection w.) Established structural practice eliminates all but one 'behaviour variable' (generally the response variable) and proceeds to solve for this (in the form of (a)); systems concepts define additional behaviour variables (for example quantities (i) to (iv)) that incorporate this one variable (for example quantity (i)) and are collectively denoted as the state. The outward behaviour follows straightforwardly from a knowledge of the state and control.

The difference between working with the internal behaviour of the system (that is the state) and the outward behaviour (response) will be seen to be twofold. Firstly, as discussed above, control may be applied more efficiently by working internally to the system and increasing the flexibility of the designer/system interaction. Secondly, it will be shown that the state concept appears more rational as it exploits the basic composition of the structural system equations (in this case equation (a)). The hierarchy proposition of section 1.1 will then be seen in a still more favourable light. Structures may be adequately described by their outward behaviour characteristics, but for proper functional understanding a description in terms of lower levels is required.

For the beam example presented above, having decided on the choice of state variables parameterizing the input–output transformation (a), this same equation may be reworked slightly and interpreted in a standard form. The advantages of the standard form will be apparent and are emphasized, following its introduction.

Corresponding to the state quart-tuple, new variables $\{x_i;\ i = 1, \ldots, 4\}$ are introduced

$$x_1 \triangleq w \qquad x_2 \triangleq \frac{\mathrm{d}w}{\mathrm{d}y} \qquad x_3 \triangleq D\,\frac{\mathrm{d}^2 w}{\mathrm{d}y^2} \qquad x_4 \triangleq \frac{\mathrm{d}}{\mathrm{d}y}\left(D\,\frac{\mathrm{d}^2 w}{\mathrm{d}y^2}\right) \tag{b}$$

which define a four-dimensional state space in which $x_1, \ldots, x_4$ are coordinates. Then by differentiation and with control $u \triangleq D$, equation (a) may be written as four simultaneous first-order equations. Isolating each derivative $\mathrm{d}x_i/\mathrm{d}y$ on the left-hand sides:

$$\begin{aligned}
\frac{\mathrm{d}x_1}{\mathrm{d}y} &= \frac{\mathrm{d}w}{\mathrm{d}y} = x_2 \\
\frac{\mathrm{d}x_2}{\mathrm{d}y} &= \frac{\mathrm{d}^2 w}{\mathrm{d}y^2} = \frac{x_3}{u} \\
\frac{\mathrm{d}x_3}{\mathrm{d}y} &= \frac{\mathrm{d}}{\mathrm{d}y}\left(D\,\frac{\mathrm{d}^2 w}{\mathrm{d}y^2}\right) = x_4 \\
\frac{\mathrm{d}x_4}{\mathrm{d}y} &= \frac{\mathrm{d}^2}{\mathrm{d}y^2}\left(D\,\frac{\mathrm{d}^2 w}{\mathrm{d}y^2}\right) = q
\end{aligned} \tag{c}$$

Equations (c) are equivalent to the original system equation (a). Equations (c) will be referred to as the **state equations** (or **system model equations** or **system equations**) and belong to a frequently used standard (canonical, normal) form.

$$\mathrm{d}x(y)/\mathrm{d}y = f[x(y), u(y), y]. \tag{1.1}$$

In (1.1) the state and control variables are clearly distinguished. (In general an n'th order differential equation will require n quantities to specify the state of the system model, and n first-order equations will result.)

The response will also be taken to conform to a standard form (though now algebraic rather than differential) referred to as **response (output) equations**.

$$z(y) = h[x(y), u(y), y]. \tag{1.2}$$

For the example above, the response w equals the state x_1 directly and is clearly a special case of (1.2).

The general form of (1.1) and (1.2) may be obtained from intuitive arguments on the roles played by u, x and z in the description of any system. Equations (1.1) and (1.2) (together with listed end-state conditions) specify the **model of the system** (abbreviated to (state) model or system where no confusion may occur). Frequently only the state equations will be referred to as the system model, with the response equation implied but not stated.

Certain characteristics of equations (1.1) and (1.2) will be apparent. The right-hand sides only contain the state variables $x_i(y)$, controls $u_j(y)$ and constants of the system such as $q(y)$. f and h are vector-valued functions of the state vector $x(y)$, control vector $u(y)$ and independent variable y. System constants (for example loading and frequently materials and certain geometry terms when not required as controls) are omitted from the standard form of (1.1) and (1.2). In general these constants will be given for any given situation. The state variable form corresponds with the so termed normal form of the theory of differential equations, and the equations are said to be normalized.

The representation (1.1) is advantageous in that it allows a common description of all systems (of the class considered), while standard numerical solution techniques of differential equations, techniques which usually are only valid for first-order equations, may be invoked.

Restricting the discussion to (1.1) for the moment (with the knowledge that the response z follows straightforwardly from (1.2) for given state) certain points require amplification. Derivatives of the state (only) appear only on the left-hand side. The state is assumed to be defined for a given control u belonging to an admissible class of functions. (The matter of mathematically admissible functions is discussed in a later section, but for the present, it is noted that normal engineering structures satisfy the admissibility requirement on u.) The state at any position y of a system defined by the n differential equations (1.1) may be represented by a point in the n-dimensional state space. (The state space is the set of all $x(y)$.) The locus of these points describes the state over the y interval.

This reduction process of the constitutive relationship, equation (a), illustrates a general procedure to be followed, namely the introduction of simpler equations (c) which may be cast into a general system model class (equations (1.1)). Note that the choice of the detail in the simpler equations is not unique, but in the present context the transformations will be introduced such that the resulting first-order differential equations have a well-defined physical significance in terms of relationships of equilibrium, compatibility and constitution. This breakdown is applicable for static behaviour and dynamic behaviour where space derivatives occur on the left-hand side; clearly for dynamic behaviour and with time derivatives chosen on the left-hand side, the equations will assume a different interpretation (though still meaningful physically), but this will be discussed later. (The development of a suitable mathematical model, being the first step in the analytic or synthetic treatment of structures is critical. Any choice of variables satisfying the mathematics of (1.1) would have been acceptable. The lack of physical significance of the variables and equations involved in this case, however, holds little intuitive appeal, although computationally it may be advantageous. The reader is referred to Chapter 2 for amplification of these comments.)

The three basic relationships (equilibrium, compatibility and constitution) in the above beam example are readily identified: (i) equations $(c)^3$ and $(c)^4$ comprise the equilibrium relationships while (ii) equations $(c)^1$ and $(c)^2$ comprise compatibility and constitution. (It will be appreciated that the states x_1 and x_2 are the conventional generalized displacements while the states x_3 and x_4 are generalized forces.) For statically determinate structures, (i) and (ii) are uncoupled as anticipated and may be solved independently. Conversely (i) and (ii) are coupled in statically indeterminate structures. In general, however, no distinction is necessary between statically determinate and statically indeterminate structures, the latter being the general case. For dynamic problems (and space derivatives chosen on the left-hand side) the equivalent sets of data are (i) equations of dynamical equilibrium and (ii) equations of kinematics and constitution.

The concept of state for the dynamic case (time derivatives chosen on the left-hand side) may be regarded as an axiomatization of Newton's laws of mechanics; the inference of defining momentum as the product of mass and velocity such that mass times acceleration is then the rate of change of momentum, has an analogous control theory interpretation. For example, a vibrating lumped mass:

$$\frac{\mathrm{d}}{\mathrm{d}t}\left(m\,\frac{\mathrm{d}w(t)}{\mathrm{d}t}\right) = F(t) \tag{d}$$

The motion is uniquely determined for all t, if, given the control m (mass) and forcing function $F(t)$, the entities w and $m\,\mathrm{d}w/\mathrm{d}t$ are specified at any time t. The value of t at which these two entities are specified is immaterial. The state is thus the position–momentum pair $(w, m\,\mathrm{d}w/\mathrm{d}t)$. This may be taken as the basic definition of the system. Thus, for deterministic systems, the state at any time t is the minimal amount of information needed to completely determine the behaviour (state) of the system for all other times for any given control.

To extend the concept of state to stochastic systems, the state at any time t is regarded as the information that uniquely determines the probability distributions of behaviour (state) at all other times. By definition this describes a Markov process. This definition for state in stochastic systems is a basic assumption and implies a form of dependence between adjacent states (but not total dependence between all states). In general the system may not have states with these properties, but the assumption allows analogous treatments between the deterministic and stochastic cases. The assumption enables solutions to be found that would otherwise not be possible if full stochastic dependence of states was employed.

1.3.3 Difference Equation Models

A state equation form equivalent to (1.1) exists for the case where the independent variable y takes on only discrete values. The corresponding system is referred to as a **discrete (data) system** as opposed to a **continuous (data) system** where the variables are functions of the continuous independent variable y. (Where the variables are in the form of a pulse train or a numerical code, the system is often referred to as a **sampled data system**. A **digital system** implies the use of a digital computer or a digital sensing element in the system. Both sampled data and digital systems are discrete data systems.)

The standard first-order state vector difference equation form, in analogy with (1.1), and output equation, in analogy with (1.2), are

$$x(k+1) = F[x(k), u(k), k] \qquad k = 0, 1, \ldots, N-1 \tag{1.3}$$

$$z(k) = h[x(k), u(k), k] \qquad k = 0, 1, \ldots, N \tag{1.4}$$

The form (1.3) may be interpreted as a sequence of transitions from the k'th to the $(k+1)$'th state, $k = 0, 1, \ldots, N-1$. With information only available on the states at discrete points, the control $u(k)$ is considered to be maintained constant during each interval and changed in a step manner at these points (Fig. 1.5).

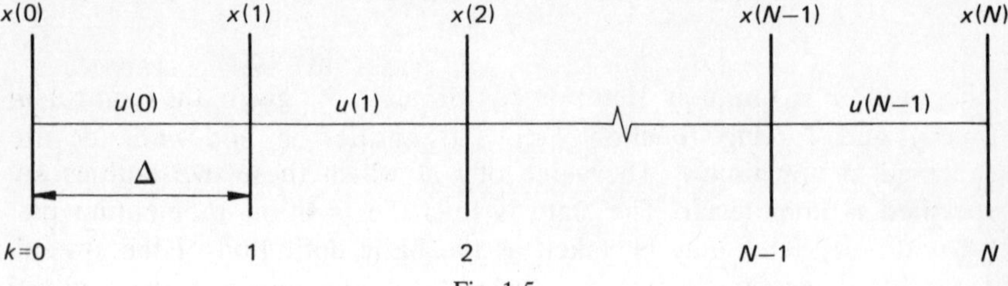

Fig. 1.5

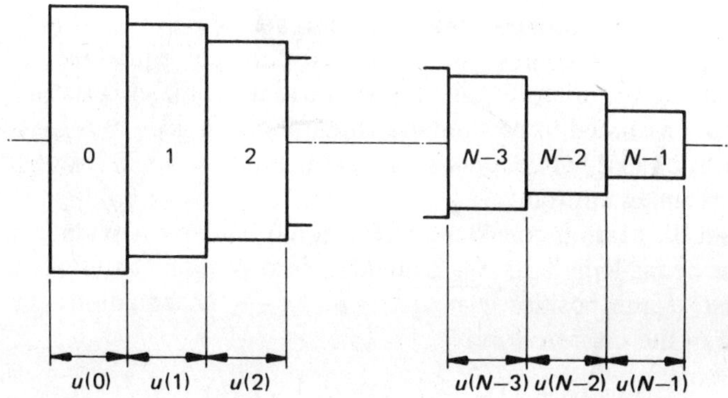

Fig. 1.6

The state is assumed to have Markov properties; that is the state at $k + 1$ depends only on the immediately previous state $x(k)$ and control $u(k)$.

As an illustration of modelling structures according to (1.3) and (1.4) consider an elastic vibrating shaft, formed by the assemblage of N concentric rings (Fig. 1.6).

For segments of constant diameter, the states (rotation ϕ and $JG(\mathrm{d}\phi/\mathrm{d}y)$) are related from one side of a segment to another through

$$\begin{bmatrix} x_1 \\ x_2 \end{bmatrix}_{k+1} = \begin{bmatrix} 1 & L/JG \\ r^2\gamma\omega & 1 \end{bmatrix}_k \begin{bmatrix} x_1 \\ x_2 \end{bmatrix}_k$$

where L is the length of the segment, JG is the torsional rigidity, r is the radius of gyration, γ is the mass per unit length, and ω is the circular frequency of vibration. For the design problem, the controls relate to the geometrical properties JG and r.

A discrete representation of a system in the form of (1.3) and (1.4) may be suitable not only for the case where the system is inherently discrete but also as an approximation to a continuous system as an aid to computations. This latter case is particularly relevant for the stochastic control problem where the discrete version produces a conceptually simpler problem while avoiding the heavy rigour required in the continuous stochastic case. If the interval $[y^{\mathrm{L}}, y^{\mathrm{R}}]$ is discretized while keeping the probability space continuous, the stochastic processes $x(y)$ and $u(y)$ now become random sequences and are completely defined by their 'finite dimensional distributions'.

Using the finite difference relation at k

$$\frac{\mathrm{d}x}{\mathrm{d}y} = \frac{x(k+1) - x(k)}{\Delta} \tag{1.5}$$

over $[y^L, y^R]$ partitioned into N intervals of size $\Delta = (y^R - y^L)/N$, equation (1.1) becomes the vector difference equation (1.3). The behaviour of the discrete and the behaviour of the original continuous models are assumed to be similar as the interval Δ goes to zero. Boundary conditions on (1.1) are expressed at $k = 0$ and $k = N$. The interval Δ need not be assumed constant.

As an illustration consider the Bernoulli–Euler beam state equations (c). The beam length $[0, L]$ is divided into N equal intervals $\Delta = L/N$ such that at any position $y = k$, $k = 0, 1, \ldots, N$, equations (c) may be restated in the discrete form

$$\begin{pmatrix} x_1(k+1) \\ x_2(k+1) \\ x_3(k+1) \\ x_4(k+1) \end{pmatrix} = \begin{pmatrix} x_1(k) \\ x_2(k) \\ x_3(k) \\ x_4(k) \end{pmatrix} + \Delta \begin{pmatrix} x_2(k) \\ x_3(k)/u(k) \\ x_4(k) \\ q(k) \end{pmatrix}. \tag{e}$$

Boundary conditions apply at $k = 0$ and N.

1.3.4 Partial Differential Equation Models

For systems interpreted in the form of equations (1.1), (1.2), (1.3) and (1.4), the underlying mathematical structure is the theory of vector spaces and the space (and time) domain treatment of vector differential and difference equations. The illustrations covered systems described by ordinary differential equations and difference equations, and are referred to as **lumped parameter systems**. The concepts extend readily to systems governed by partial differential equations, referred to as **distributed parameter systems**. By defining suitable function spaces, the formalism of equation (1.1) can be shown to be applicable to these types of systems as well. The spaces in this case are not finite dimensional. However, the present work and in particular the axiomatic-type presentation of state space modelling (Chapter 2) will retain the partial differential form. Equation (1.2), being algebraic, extends directly to the distributed parameter case.

Three standard partial differential state equation forms may be recognized and are outlined in Chapter 2 in detail along with structural examples. Two of the three forms reduce to the standard lumped parameter form (1.1) on reverting to the finite dimensional case.

To produce an analytically less complex system model, for purposes of solution of the design problem, various quantizing procedures may be employed. Essentially these involve either total or part discretization of the independent parameters $\{y_i;\ i = 1, \ldots\}$ over their interval ranges $[y_i^L, y_i^R]$. (Discretization of the dependent functions—that is discretization in level—will not be considered. Variables may be classified according to whether they are discrete or continuous in their parameter set or level (that is, variable space). For example $x(y)$ may be discrete or continuous in (a) the parameter y or (b) the space Ξ, $x \in \Xi$. Equivalent distinctions exist for the stochastic case.)

Consider in relation to the associated design problem:

(i) Reducing the system equations to a form continuous in only one independent variable (and hence discretely lumped in the other independent variables) offers the opportunity to exploit the use of the conceptually simpler lumped parameter solution techniques. The lumped parameter case is a commonly treated case in the literature owing to its conceptual simplicity compared with the distributed parameter case.

(ii) Total Y domain discretization yields a finite dimensional system of difference equations. The approximate system is then equivalent to a multistage system for which multistage decision processes may be used for the solution of the design problem. Most favoured among these are the discrete forms of the maximum principle and dynamic programming. The problem may also be formulated as one in nonlinear programming with the optimality criterion assuming the form of a hypersurface in a suitable (usually control) space bounded by given constraints. Much of the control literature deals with this total Y domain discretization model as a result of its particular relevance to digital computation. Its use is particularly well documented. Solution techniques for the design problem are discussed in Part C.

Discretization implies differential equations reduce to difference equations and integrals to finite summations.

1.3.5 Algebraic (Non-Difference) Equation Models

By far the most common models and the most preferred by engineers are the simple algebraic versions. For example consider a matrix stiffness representation of a framed structure.

$$R = K\Delta \tag{f}$$

where R is the structure nodal loading vector, Δ is the structure nodal displacement vector, and K is the structure stiffness matrix with entries such as EI/L, EA/L, ...

A distinction between behaviour type variables and controls may be drawn. Controls relate to materials and geometry which are at the disposal of the designer to vary such as the elastic modulus, and first and second moments of area. Behavioural variables relate, for example, to the loading and/or displacement depending on the given problem; the distinction between state and response breaks down for algebraic representations.

Generally algebraic models take the form (note: a different F is implied from that in (1.3)):

$$F(x, u) = 0 \tag{1.6}$$

where u is an r-dimensional control vector, x is an n-dimensional state or response vector, and F is a vector-valued function of the arguments shown. Frequently the distinction between control variables and behaviour variables is dropped in optimization studies.

Algebraic models correspond in mathematical terms to the so-called 'static' models of control theory. (The state space forms correspond in mathematical terms to the so-called 'dynamic' models of control theory, the exception being two of the three distributed parameter forms.) Both the algebraic and state space forms may be converted to the 'input–output' forms of classical control theory. However, 'input–output' forms are generally not suitable for a formal optimization theory. Also control theory's distinction between static and dynamic systems will be disregarded as being specific to control problems only and not general enough to describe structural mechanics problems.

1.4 AN OUTLINE

Two chapters on modelling follow, treating single level (Chapter 2) and multilevel (Chapter 3) models respectively. In both chapters, structures are modelled within the framework of a generalized control systems theory. This generalization enables the system to be specified independently of particular cases which then only require the correct recognition of the system elements for definition. The framework of the modelling remains constant for all systems. The presentation is essentially deterministic with follow-up notes on the extension to the stochastic case. The format is an attempt to treat structures as a whole rather than the fragmented approach common in some established texts on mechanics, and leads on to general design ideas in later sections.

Chapter 2 describes single level models in terms of general nonlinear partial differential equations in the four-dimensional space-time domain. The lumped parameter models and the algebraic models will be seen to follow straightforwardly. This specification thus encompasses a broad class of (though obviously not all) models. It is assumed that the system models do not change their properties; that is, adaptive and learning systems are excluded.

The concepts developed are clarified in Chapter 2, and also in later chapters, with illustrations. The illustrations and the development of the theory are offered on a theory of structures level corresponding for example to that involved in reducing the complete continuum mechanics equations to the beam equation. For the full implications of the proposed control systems theory treatment, a general continuum mechanics approach of the form sought by Pister (1972) (or a slightly more specific four-dimensional theory of elasticity (for example Sokolnikoff 1956) approach) would be desirable. The present approach based on a simplified theory of structural behaviour, while losing generality and producing slight inconsistencies (for example surface tractions are state boundary conditions but the approximate form of the beam equation (a) has already eliminated the corresponding state variable and the load there is treated as a constant) does produce tangible results, results which it is felt might be unattainable using a more general theory. Fung (1969), among others, shows the connection between a general and simplified structural theories.

Chapter 2 generalizes the systems modelling ideas introduced in Chapter 1. Chapter 2 introduces the necessary notations and terminology in a semi-informal manner and gives an overview of single level modelling. The fundamental notions of state and control are given precise meaning, and the system model is then defined in terms of particular mathematical relationships of these entities.

Chapter 3 discusses multilevel modelling and system decomposition ideas. Systems are shown to be able to be decomposed vertically and horizontally with the consequent subsystems and subsystem interaction having different characteristics. Subsystems may be modelled via the single level ideas of Chapter 2, while the interaction between subsystems can be shown to be related mathematical relationships of the control and state variables at the relevant levels.

1.5 NOTES, COMMENTS AND BIBLIOGRAPHY

The detail in this chapter follows Carmichael and Clyde (1975). See also Clyde (1970a, 1970b), Pister (1972) and Carmichael and Clyde (1979).

The standard and historically important reference on hierarchical multilevel systems theory is Mesarovic *et al*. (1970). See also Wismer (1971a), Himmelblau (1973), Mahmoud (1977), Lasdon (1970) and Singh (1977) among others.

For the idea of substructures, see for example Przemieniecki (1968) and for segmental analysis in reinforced concrete see for example Warner *et al*. (1976).

The foundation works in the field of multilevel representation of structures, and where motivational material for the systems view may be found, are Clyde (1970a, b). The example in Fig. 1.3 follows Clyde (given according to the sense of Fig. 1.2).

Related ideas on dynamical system models can be found in

MacFarlane (1970) and on general modelling in Rubinstein (1975). Alternative mathematical models, for example, use set theory notation where a system may be described as a mapping from product sets of controls and initial conditions to the set of outputs (Mesarovic and Takahara 1975, Masarovic *et al.* 1970, Klir 1969). Such models are more general than given here but are more restrictive in their application to the design problem. The fundamental forms of models (other than mathematical) are discussed by Rubinstein (1975). Wong and Bugliarello (1970) discuss the introduction of artificial intelligence.

The definition of system/environment follows Hall (1962). For statements of the fundamental systems problems of analysis, synthesis and identification see for example Klir (1969) and Lee (1964). See also Rubinstein (1975) and Rozvany (1966a) for structural examples of analysis and synthesis. Alternative terminology for the word system is plant, process or object.

For a discussion of the state space formulation and lumped parameter system models see Rubio (1971), Elgerd (1967), Tou (1964), MacFarlane (1970), Zadeh (1962), and Ogata (1967, 1970) among others.

For state space arguments in a structures sense see Carmichael and Clyde (1975), Beliveau (1977), C. W. de Silva (1975, 1976) and Pestel and Leckie (1963).

The standard lumped parameter form (1.1) is the starting point for much of the work in control. See Athans (1966) and Paiewonsky (1965) among others.

For the complete model description of lumped parameter systems including the response (output) equation, see for example Porter (1969) and Lee (1964).

The normal form of differential equations is treated in Pontryagin (1962).

For a discussion on the standard lumped parameter form (1.1) see Carmichael (1977b).

For a discussion on the concept of state and Newton's laws see Kalman (1962, 1963a).

For Markov processes see Bharucha-Reid (1960) and Wong (1971).

For an introduction to state space concepts in stochastic systems see Fuller (1960b). In a structures sense see Carmichael (1978a) and Carmichael and Clyde (1976).

The dynamic case of classical mechanics is given for example in Synge (1960), Lanczos (1962) and MacFarlane (1970). See also Ogata (1967). For a system of particles or rigid bodies with k degrees of freedom, the state space (usually known as phase space) is $2k$-dimensional with coordinates $q_1, \ldots, q_k$ and $p_1, \ldots, p_k$ where q_i and p_i are generalized coordinates and momenta respectively.

The equations of motion (using a variational approach rather than the equivalent Newtonian view) can be described by a set of $2k$ first-order differential equations (Hamilton's canonical equations—they are canonical adjoints):

$$\mathrm{d}q_i/\mathrm{d}t = \partial H/\partial p_i$$
$$\mathrm{d}p_i/\mathrm{d}t = -\partial H/\partial q_i \qquad i = 1, \ldots, k$$

where H is the Hamiltonian. The motion is then the path of a point in phase space. (Occasionally time may be included in the definition of phase space, in which case the phase space is the Cartesian product of the above phase space in E^{2k} and the time space $(= E^1)$). In essence the approach is to associate with a system a set of coordinates which define a space, of dimension equal to the order of the system. The behaviour of the system is then represented by a trajectory in this space.

Control theory uses a simple generalization of this. In transferring to the analogous state space in control theory it is noted that the concept of degrees of freedom does not transfer directly yet the concept of phase space does. It is the concept of phase space which has been generalized to the definitions of state space used in control theory. See Fuller (1960a) for an excellent historical survey of state space concepts. See also Zadeh and Desoer (1963) and Tou (1964) on the concept of state. Additional to the idea of state, control theory separates out the control from the other system entities and often interprets this as an input which is varied to give the system a desired response.

Inductive reasoning extends this dynamic basis for the idea of state to the case with a spatial coordinate as the independent variable. Whereas in the dynamic case only positive time has meaning, by suitable definition of axes, both positive and negative spatial coordinate values are possible.

Concepts of state are also known in other branches of applied mathematics and theoretical engineering. They are, for example, an integral part of the field theories of continuum mechanics (for example, Truesdell and Toupin 1960); the mechanical behaviour of materials (for example, Freudenthal 1950); the transfer matrix theory of matrix structural analysis (for example, Pestel and Leckie 1963, Livesley 1964). Their use in control theory, however, appears to be only a relatively recent innovation arising from generalized circuits theory and the above dynamic bases. (Terminology, concepts and symbolism have also been generalized from these two roots wherever needed.) Their use in the present work generalizes the use of state in a structural mechanics context by adopting the framework of control theory.

For a discussion on the discrete system standard form (1.3) as an approximation to the continuous system standard form (1.1) see

Carmichael and Elms (1975), Tabak and Kuo (1971) and Cullum (1969).

Two philosophies relating to discretization and the solution of the design problem may be seen : (a) where the continuous version is maintained in the computations for as long as possible and discretization only takes place at the last stage of the calculations; or (b) where discretization is the first stage in the computations. Thus both the continuous and discrete system models are given above. It is also acknowledged that some systems are inherently continuous and some discrete.

The modelling of a rotating disc as a discrete control system has been considered by Distefano (1974a) and Nagy (1971). Discrete control formulations of trusses may be found in Singaraj and Rao (1972, 1975). The discrete Bernoulli–Euler beam is considered in Carmichael (1978a).

The set of equations (e) obtained through discretization bear a form which is reminiscent of that encountered in the transfer matrix technique of conventional structural analysis. See for example Pestel and Leckie (1963) and Livesley (1964). To illustrate, express (e) in matrix form

$$\begin{pmatrix} x_1 \\ x_2 \\ x_3 \\ x_4 \end{pmatrix}_{k+1} = \begin{pmatrix} 1 & \Delta & & \\ & 1 & \Delta/u & \\ & & 1 & \Delta \\ & & & 1 \end{pmatrix}_k \begin{pmatrix} x_1 \\ x_2 \\ x_3 \\ x_4 \end{pmatrix}_k + \begin{pmatrix} \\ \\ \\ \Delta q \end{pmatrix}_k .$$

This matrix is clearly the transfer matrix for the particular interval $(k, k+1)$ of the beam; for a beam of constant rigidity $u = EI$ and length L, the entries in the matrix become 1, L, L/EI and 0. Transformations, for example as outlined in Livesley, give the equivalent stiffness or flexibility matrices. State equations thus offer a means of deriving stiffness and flexibility matrices alternative to conventional ways. The extension to distributed parameter systems and stochastic finite elements follows.

For descriptions of distributed parameter systems using function space ideas see for example Katz (1964), Yu. V. Egorov (1963, 1966), Falb (1964), Balakrishnan (1963, 1965), Robinson (1971) and Rubio (1971).

For a statement of the three standard distributed parameter forms see Carmichael and Goh (1977).

For a discussion on the order of magnitude difference in complexity between the lumped and distributed parameter case, see Athans (1966) and the survey by Robinson (1971).

Discretization schemes are discussed in Tabak and Kuo (1971) and

Daniel (1971). The behaviour of the discrete system and the original continuous system are assumed to be similar as the interval Δ goes to zero. The validity or consistency of the approximations, as well as questions of stability and convergence, may be found in Wang and Tung (1964) and Wang (1964).

Fel'dbaum (1965) discusses the distinction between discretization in the independent variables y_i and discretization in the variable space. The terminology used there is discrete–continuous, discrete–discrete, and continuous to distinguish the form of discretization.

Optimization studies using algebraic models of structural systems may be found for example in Spunt (1971), Fox (1971), Majid (1972, 1974), Kowalik (1966), Schmit (1974), Gallagher and Zienkiewicz (1973) and Spillers (1975a).

The distinction between behaviour (equivalently state or response) and design (equivalently control) variables in structural optimization has been made by Rozvany (1966a), Sheu and Prager (1968), Kirsch and Moses (1976) and Brotchie (1967) among others.

Various system models, other than state space models, can be found for example in MacFarlane (1970) and include network (or graph) models and transform (or transfer function or input–output) models. These together with the state space models represent the most favoured system models. For graph models used in a structures sense see Fenves (1966a), Fenves and Branin (1963), Fenves and Gonzalez-Caro (1971), Lind (1962) and Spillers (1963, 1971, 1972, 1974, 1975b). See also Spillers and Friedland (1972), Spillers (1966) and Kron's work (Tabarrok and Simpson, 1968).

State space or state variable models of systems are sometimes referred to as 'mechanistic' or 'internal variable' models in comparison with input–output descriptions which in general take little heed of the internal composition of the system. Equivalence of the input–output models and state space models can be shown for systems that are linear which is the domain of the input–output models, although some extensions to nonlinear systems are possible.

The above state equations and associated output equations were given according to the categories lumped parameter/distributed parameter and continuous (nonsampled)/discrete (sampled). Further categorization is popular in control texts along the divisions nonlinear/linear, y-variant (nonstationary, time-variant)/y-invariant (constant coefficient, time invariant, stationary) and deterministic/stochastic (probablistic, random). The standard linear form is

$$\begin{aligned} \mathrm{d}x(y)/\mathrm{d}y &= Ax(y) + Bu(y) \\ z(y) &= Cx(y) + Du(y) \end{aligned}$$

where A is referred to as the system matrix, B the distribution matrix, C the output or measurement matrix, and D the input–output matrix. Where these matrices are functions of y the system is y-variant. For the nonlinear case, the system is y-variant if f and h are functions of y. Equivalent difference forms exist.

Noton (1965) for example gives various ways of discretizing linear systems based on their special properties. See Chapter 12 for notes on the terminology autonomous/non-autonomous and discrete/continuous. Also distributed parameter forms are sometimes described as parabolic, hyperbolic or elliptic if they take on the appropriate form.

The treatment given follows 'modern control theory' lines as opposed to 'classical control theory'. For the distinction between the two see for example Ogata (1967).

For the distinction between associative (non-flow) and sequential (flow) systems as mentioned in the *Preface* see Gosling (1962). Comments on the modelling and design processes in structural mechanics as mentioned in the *Preface* may be found in Clyde (1970a) and Pister (1972).

Chapter 2

Single Level State Space Modelling

2.1 GENERAL

This chapter presents general state space modelling of continuous systems (single level) and covers systems described by the standard lumped parameter form (equations (1.1), (1.2)) as a special case and the standard distributed parameter forms alluded to in Chapter 1. The modelling of discrete systems, being conceptually easier, will be apparent. Algebraic (non-difference) equation models are the only models of the standard types mentioned in Chapter 1 which are not conventionally termed state equation or state space forms, and are also omitted in the following. Their modelling being conceptually easier again will also be apparent.

The use of state and control variables provides a measure of generalization or uniformity to the composition of structural models. The interrelationship of these variables is expressed through the constitutive equation. Under suitable transformations, with a mechanics basis, the constitutive equation may be reinterpreted in general state equation forms.

Chapter 1 gave the fundamental ideas of state and control in a relatively informal manner. It stressed the choice of the variables from an engineering and physical motivational viewpoint. These basic ideas are extended here in generality and abstraction to model a wide spectrum of structures. Geometrical interpretations are attempted throughout, often by the use of representative spaces to describe the system. Illustrations are used to enable the presentation of the theory to be of a reasonably formal nature.

Section 2.2 introduces the necessary notations and terminology by giving precise meanings to the notions of state, control and response. The system model is then defined in section 2.3 in terms of particular mathematical relationships of these entities. In general, following the developments of Chapter 1, the constituent parts of the system model will consist of (i) the state equations—2.3.1, (ii) certain 'starting' information on the states—2.3.2, and (iii) the state-response description—2.3.3.

2.2 PRELIMINARY DEFINITIONS, PROPERTIES AND ASSUMPTIONS

Consider a spatial domain D, with boundary ∂D, defined in three-dimensional Euclidean space E^3, with spatial coordinate vector $y = (y_1, y_2, y_3)^T$. Let the time domain be T, an interval $[t^L, t^R]$ of the real line E^1.

The *state* of the model, defined for all $y \in D$, at any time instant $t \in T$, is denoted by the n-valued vector function $x(t, y)$ with coordinates $\{x_i(t, y); i = 1, \ldots, n\}$. For given values of t and y, the x_i may be conveniently regarded as the variables characterizing the internal behaviour or state of the system model. They are 'controlled' variables. For example, in a beam model, with static flexural deformations only considered, the state is specified by four variables—the deflection and its three successive derivatives (related to slope and the notions of moment and shear force, respectively). In certain circumstances, it is convenient to think of the set of all possible functions $\{x(t, y); t \in T, y \in D\}$ defined on $T \times D$ (the product space of T and D) as comprising the 'state function space', in which the x_i are coordinates. Other state spaces may equally well be defined.

Control is maintained on the model by the r-valued control vector function $u(t, y)$ with components $\{u_j(t, y); j = 1, \ldots, r\}$. u_j may be defined over all or part of the spatial domain D. For the same example, the control is provided by the choice of beam rigidity. With a similar intent for the introduction of the state function space defined above, the set of all possible functions $\{u(t, y); t \in T, y \in D\}$ defined on $T \times D$ may be thought of as a control function space.

The *response*, or outward behaviour variables $z(t, y)$ with components $\{z_k(t, y); k = 1, \ldots, m \leq n\}$ will be related to the state by suitable algebraic transformations. For the specific structural example at hand, deflection may be considered as the response, and this is also the first state coordinate. In this case, the relationship of state and output is a linear transformation of the general form.

$$z_k(t, y) = \sum_{i=1}^{n} a_{ki} x_i(t, y) \qquad k \leqslant n$$

where a_{ki} are constants.

As defined, u and x (and z) are continuous functions in level (that is, in control and state function spaces, respectively) and over the parameter sets t and y. The systems to be considered, in general, will be nonlinear in both the state and control. In a sense, the control (along with known end-state conditions—see section 1.3) forms an input to the model, while the response is an output form. The state represents the internal behaviour of the model; for structural models, a transformation is always known for any given model between state and response, and knowledge of the former defines the latter.

In subsequent discussions, for the range and behaviour of structural models treated, the literal distinction between the time domain (T) and the space domain (D) will be eliminated for mathematical convenience, although it is acknowledged that they are essentially different physically. To enable this, the parameter vector y will be enlarged to contain, in general, four components $\{y_i; i = 1, \ldots, 4\}$ where it is recognized that $y_4 \triangleq t$. Only during particular applications or illustrations will reference be made to time or space explicitly. Such reasoning allows a discussion of static and dynamic structural behaviour to proceed in the same format. The resulting four-dimensional Euclidean space of the parameters $\{y_i; i = 1, \ldots, 4\}$ will be denoted Y, ($Y \triangleq T \times D$), and the intervals of variation of y_i by $[y_i^L, y_i^R]$; that is $y_i \in [y_i^L, y_i^R]$, $i = 1, \ldots, 4$. (The superscript L, R notation implies a visualization of the coordinate space where, loosely, L stands for the 'left-hand' and R the 'right-hand' end points of this space.)

The above descriptions apply to **deterministic models**, that is, models with properties which are considered to be of known value and fully predictable. An alternative system model, the **stochastic** or **probabilistic model**, regards the model properties as random with given probability distributions (and, hence, not uniquely definable in advance) and which are used to calculate the probable response of the model; the behaviour is given to lie within certain probabilistic bounds. (The terms 'stochastic', 'probabilistic' and 'random' are used interchangeably.) Provided that the probability distributions are specified in advance, there are no prominent dissimilarities between deterministic and stochastic treatments.

A random field assumption: To extend the concepts of state and control to a probabilistic format, the state and control functions are endowed with an additional parameter set Ω (a sample space) such that $\{x(\omega, y); y \in Y, \omega \in \Omega\}$ now represents a random field. The control and output functions are defined equivalently. A random field is here taken to denote a family of random variables indexed by points in the parameter space $Y \subset E^4$ (although this space may correspond to an abstract space in the general theory of random fields—see *Notes*).

A random field may be regarded as the multidimensional equivalent of a stochastic process (random process or random function). A stochastic process is indexed by a single parameter, y say. For each y,

$x(\omega,\cdot)$ is defined on a sample space Ω and is a random vector. For each probability parameter $\omega \in \Omega$, $x(\cdot, y)$ is a function of y and is termed a realization (sample function) of the process.

It is assumed that the statistical characteristics of the random vectors (variables) are known. That is, the system is stochastic in the sense just defined. The most suitable way to characterize random vectors (variables) is by the notation $x(y)$ where the probability parameter is understood. It will generally be clear from the context whether deterministic or stochastic concepts are implied.

Notice that the deterministic state-modelling notions extend readily to the probabilistic case by endowing the state, control, output and model parameters with random field properties. Deterministic differential (difference) equations will be seen to have equivalent probabilistic counterparts, namely stochastic differential (difference) equations.

2.3 SYSTEM MODELS

2.3.1 The State Equations

2.3.1.1 INTRODUCTION

The state equations are an alternative expression of the constitutive relationship and show the dependence of the state on the control (in addition to other system model parameters). In the following, this dependence will be taken to be in the form of time and space differential operators and, in general, will be nonlinear. The choice of the constitutive relationship is based on the designer's comprehension of the structural action involved; (for example, shell action, plate action—that is, whether the designer considers the system will behave as a shell, plate or other structure).

The model will be defined in the four-dimensional space Y, or subspaces of Y, and expressed in state form. With the notes and assumptions of the foregoing section (2.2) the state equations will assume the form of vector partial differential equations defined over a space-time domain. Three standard forms are considered and, for purposes of distinction, will be arbitrarily labelled types I, II and III (sections 2.3.1.2, 2.3.1.3 and 2.3.1.4, respectively). They are the only standard distributed parameter forms that appear in the control literature, where their occurrence is often a specialized form of versions given here.

The choice and usage of these three forms in the present structures case requires explanation. Commencing with type III, it is emphasized that this type has only been included in the present treatment for completeness because, as mentioned above, it occurs in the control literature. It is shown that structures can be interpreted in this form, and its usage on occasions may be favourable computationally, but the form is not favoured by the writer as it lacks complete physical interpretation. The remaining discussion in the following two paragraphs on the choice of the state equation forms will, therefore, wholly centre on types I and II.

In deciding on the form of state equations, standard forms are sought and, in particular, standard first-order forms are sought. The first-order requirement foresees possible numerical solutions of the differential equations, solutions which are usually only valid for first-order equations. The first-order nature also follows from the notion of state; the state vector components for structures will invariably be related to the derivative of the adjacent state components. Thus, when the state components are differentiated, this will lead to an ordered hierarchy of first-order equations. Lastly, the first-order form allows any general n'th order equation to be reduced to a standard form, allowing a common description of all systems.

Thus, two fundamental first-order forms arise (with, obviously, intermediate combinations possible). In particular, state equations type I express the behaviour of the model in terms of the behaviour in the direction of a single independent parameter. State equations type II give equal emphasis to all the independent parameters. The two forms may be considered as alternatives for different modelling situations, the choice of usage being left to the applier. The equation types apply to any domain dimension equal to or below that described in section 2.3.1.2 and 2.3.1.3 for the respective type; their use is not restricted to any particular domain dimension within this range. Type III is specifically for a two-dimensional domain as noted in section 2.3.1.4. The equation type gives equal emphasis to both independent parameters but in a different sense to the two-dimensional form of type II. It is remarked in passing that various combinations of type I, II and III forms could conceivably be constructed, but their use would not be favoured owing to their lack of physical interpretation.

2.3.1.2 STATE EQUATIONS TYPE I

$$\partial x(y)/\partial y_4 = f[y, x(y), \ldots, \partial_l x(y), \ldots, u(y)] \tag{2.1}$$

where $y = (y_1, \ldots, y_4)^T$, $l = (l_1, l_2, l_3)$ and $\partial_l x$ is as defined in the 'notation'. f is defined over the domain $Y \subset E^4$; $f = (f_1, \ldots, f_n)^T$ and, in general, is a nonlinear vector-valued function of both the equation dependent variables x and u and the equation independent variables y.

The choice of derivatives with respect to y_4 appearing on the left-hand side is arbitrary. In fact, derivatives with respect to any y_i, $i = 1, 2, 3, 4$, are permissible on the left-hand side provided derivatives with respect to the same parameter do not occur on the right-hand side.

Equation (2.1) is an extension of the finite dimensional standard equation (1.1). (By the introduction of additional state variables for the state derivatives on the right-hand side of (2.1), equation (2.1) could be further reduced to a set of first-order equations, but then this extension would not apply.)

2.3.1.3 STATE EQUATIONS TYPE II

$$\partial x(y)/\partial y_i = f^i[y, x(y), \ldots, \partial_l x(y), \ldots, u(y)] \qquad (i = 1, 2, 3) \quad (2.2)$$

where $l = (l_h, l_k)$, $(h, k = 1, 2, 3;\ h, k \neq i)$ and $\partial_l x$ is as defined in the 'notation'. f^i, $i = 1, 2, 3$, are, in general, nonlinear vector-valued functions of the arguments shown and have to be such that they satisfy certain compatibility conditions; that is, every solution of one equation is a solution of the other equations.

Equations (2.2) are a special form of the Pfaffian system of equations. The vector y is taken to have only three components (y_1, y_2, y_3) here (compare with four for type I) as the model is primarily intended for system models described over a three-dimensional spatial domain.

In (2.2) the derivatives of state with respect to each of the independent variables y_i have been isolated on the left-hand side. Derivatives of state with respect to the remaining independent variables y_h, y_k $(h, k \neq i)$ may occur on the right-hand side. As for the type I equations, (2.2) reduce to the standard lumped parameter form (equation (1.1)) as a special case when y is one-dimensional.

2.3.1.4 STATE EQUATIONS TYPE III

$$\partial^2 x(y)/\partial y_1 \partial y_2 = f[y, x(y), \ldots, \partial_l x(y), \ldots, u(y)] \qquad (2.3)$$

where $y = (y_1, y_2)^T$, l is both l_1 and l_2 but never l_1 and l_2 together in the same term, $\partial_l x$ is as defined in the 'notation', and f is, in general, a nonlinear vector-valued function of the arguments shown.

The equations are applicable in descriptions over two-dimensional planar regions. The left-hand sides are now (compare with types I and II) second-order derivatives corresponding to the isolation of the mixed derivative terms from the remaining derivative terms. No mixed derivatives of state appear on the right-hand sides. The form, unlike (2.1) and (2.2), is not reducible to the lumped parameter version (equation (1.1)) in transferring to one-dimensional y, essentially because (2.3) highlights the mixed derivative terms which are absent in the lower dimension. There is a more general case than (2.3), namely, that which applies over a three-dimensional domain (mixed third-order derivatives occur on the left-hand sides), but its usefulness is doubtful essentially because of the occurrence of the higher derivatives.

2.3.1.5 A NOTE ON THE CONTROLS

In equations (2.1, 2, 3) the control appears only on the right-hand sides and is free of differential operators. Both requirements are for convenience in controlling the system. The second requirement in particular eliminates jumps in values of the state variables caused by jumps in the control variables (for example where a structural element changes geometry abruptly). The forms of (2.1, 2, 3) only permit finite changes in the states for controls of an impulse form. Also the occurrence of control derivatives produces an ambiguity in the design problem as knowledge of the control and its derivative at any location defines the control at any adjacent location. No design problem then exists at this last location.

2.3.1.6 METHODS OF REDUCTION

The form of equations (2.1, 2, 3) is consistent with the reduction of a high order, with respect to y_i ($i = 4$ for (2.1); $i = 1, 2, 3$ for (2.2); $i = 1, 2$ for (2.3)), partial differential equation to a set of first-order (second-order for III) differential equations. These are the so-called **state variable** or **state space formulations** of the system equations. Conventional structural thinking would tend to operate in the reverse manner to this, namely, to eliminate all but one of the behaviour variables (the response variable), yielding a single high-order equation governing the behaviour of the model. Any partial differential equation may be reduced to (2.1, 2, or 3) by introducing suitable (state) variables.

In the general mathematical theory of control, without regard to the physical meaning of the variables involved, suitable reduction procedures are well established for ordinary differential equations of order greater than one. The extension to partial differential equations is slightly more complicated owing to the additional cross-derivatives with respect to the several independent variables. As with the ordinary differential equation case, the many and various forms of possible reductions suggest a nonunique property of the reductions and the availability of various choices as a basis for the reduction. Any set of state and control variables may be chosen provided the set satisfies equation (2.1) (or (2.2) or (2.3) if these equation types are sought). This degree of freedom in choice of the method of reduction, as well as in the choice of equation form (that is, type I, II or III), however, does not vary the final result of manipulations of the equations. This may be demonstrated, for example, in the problem of optimization—see the illustrations in Part C.

Reduction algorithms leading to sets of equations of the form (2.1), (2.2) and (2.3) but satisfying them only in a mathematical sense (with the state and control variables generally lacking physical significance) are included in the *Appendix*.

If such reduction algorithms were the only ones possible, the use of control theory in modelling structures would undoubtedly be restrictive. Fortunately, this is not the case, and reduction procedures (logically based on the principles of mechanics) can be found which have variables and state equations of physical significance. These are illustrated now.

2.3.1.7 ILLUSTRATION OF THE PROPOSED REDUCTION PROCEDURES

To emphasize the type of reduction proposed consider as an illustration the shallow shell equations. For zero Poisson's ratio, the equations read

$$\frac{\partial}{\partial y_1}\left[D\left(\frac{\partial w_1}{\partial y_1} - w_3 z_{11}\right)\right] + \frac{\partial}{\partial y_2}\left[\frac{D}{2}\left(\frac{\partial w_1}{\partial y_2} + \frac{\partial w_2}{\partial y_1} - 2w_3 z_{12}\right)\right] + q_1 = 0$$

$$\frac{\partial}{\partial y_2}\left[D\left(\frac{\partial w_2}{\partial y_2} - w_3 z_{22}\right)\right] + \frac{\partial}{\partial y_1}\left[\frac{D}{2}\left(\frac{\partial w_1}{\partial y_2} + \frac{\partial w_2}{\partial y_1} - 2w_3 z_{12}\right)\right] + q_2 = 0$$

$$z_{11}\left[D\left(\frac{\partial w_1}{\partial y_1} - w_3 z_{11}\right)\right] + 2z_{12}\left[\frac{D}{2}\left(\frac{\partial w_1}{\partial y_2} + \frac{\partial w_2}{\partial y_1} - 2w_3 z_{12}\right)\right] \tag{a}$$

$$+ z_{22}\left[D\left(\frac{\partial w_2}{\partial y_2} - w_3 z_{22}\right)\right] + \frac{\partial^2}{\partial y_1^2}\left[-K\frac{\partial^2 w_3}{\partial y_1^2}\right] + 2\frac{\partial^2}{\partial y_1 \partial y_2}\left[-K\frac{\partial^2 w_3}{\partial y_1 \partial y_2}\right]$$

$$+ \frac{\partial^2}{\partial y_2^2}\left[-K\frac{\partial^2 w_3}{\partial y_2^2}\right] + q_3 = 0$$

where y_1, y_2, y_3 denote the coordinate axes (Cartesian). The middle surface of the shell is described by

$$z = z(y_1, y_2).$$

Derivatives of z with respect to the coordinates y_1 and y_2 are denoted by a subscript notation on z. (For example $z_{12} \triangleq \partial^2 z/\partial y_1 \partial y_2$.)

q_1, q_2, q_3 denote the components of the distributed surface load. w_1, w_2, w_3 denote the shell deformations. D and K are the extensional and bending stiffnesses of the shell.

It is remarked that intuitive arguments, similar to that outlined in Chapter 1, could be employed to give the same reduction results as detailed here. The following discussion, however, attempts to remove much of the qualitative nature of intuitive arguments by converting the reduction procedures into semi-mechanical routines.

Consider the reduction process involved in attaining equations of the form *type I* where the variables will be chosen to take on a physical meaning. The state and control variables chosen will first be listed along with the associated state equations and then the process used to obtain the state, control and state equations will be explained.

The state variables are chosen as

$$
\begin{aligned}
&x_1 \triangleq w_1 \qquad x_2 \triangleq D\left(\frac{\partial w_1}{\partial y_1} - w_3 z_{11}\right) \\
&x_3 \triangleq w_2 \qquad x_4 \triangleq \frac{D}{2}\left(\frac{\partial w_1}{\partial y_2} + \frac{\partial w_2}{\partial y_1} - 2w_3 z_{12}\right) \\
&x_5 \triangleq w_3 \qquad x_6 \triangleq \frac{\partial w_3}{\partial y_1} \qquad x_7 \triangleq K\frac{\partial^2 w_3}{\partial y_1^2} \\
&x_8 \triangleq \frac{\partial}{\partial y_1}\left(K\frac{\partial^2 w_3}{\partial y_1^2}\right) + 2\frac{\partial}{\partial y_2}\left(K\frac{\partial^2 w_3}{\partial y_1 \partial y_2}\right)
\end{aligned} \tag{b}
$$

and the controls $u_1 \triangleq D$, $u_2 \triangleq K$ (which are functionally related).

Neglecting sign conventions, x_1, x_3 and x_5 are identified as the deformations, x_2 as the in-plane normal force in the y_1 direction, x_4 as the in-plane shearing force, x_6, x_7 and x_8 as the slope, internal moment and 'transverse force' in the y_1 direction. (In fact x_8 is the familiar Kirchoff combination of twisting moment and out-of-plane shearing force.)

Differentiating the state vector $x = (x_1, \ldots, x_8)^{\mathrm{T}}$ with respect to y_1 yields the state equations

$$
\begin{bmatrix}
\dfrac{\partial x_1}{\partial y_1} \\[2ex]
\dfrac{\partial x_2}{\partial y_1} \\[2ex]
\dfrac{\partial x_3}{\partial y_1} \\[2ex]
\dfrac{\partial x_4}{\partial y_1} \\[2ex]
\dfrac{\partial x_5}{\partial y_1} \\[2ex]
\dfrac{\partial x_6}{\partial y_1} \\[2ex]
\dfrac{\partial x_7}{\partial y_1} \\[2ex]
\dfrac{\partial x_8}{\partial y_1}
\end{bmatrix}
=
\begin{bmatrix}
\dfrac{x_2}{u_1} + x_5 z_{11} \\[2ex]
-q_1 - \dfrac{\partial x_4}{\partial y_2} \\[2ex]
\dfrac{2x_4}{u_1} + 2x_5 z_{12} - \dfrac{\partial x_1}{\partial y_2} \\[2ex]
-q_2 - \dfrac{\partial}{\partial y_2}\left[u_1\left(\dfrac{\partial x_3}{\partial y_2} - x_5 z_{22}\right)\right] \\[2ex]
x_6 \\[2ex]
\dfrac{x_7}{u_2} \\[2ex]
x_8 - 2\dfrac{\partial}{\partial y_2}\left(u_2\dfrac{\partial x_6}{\partial y_2}\right) \\[2ex]
z_{11}x_2 + 2z_{12}x_4 + z_{22}\left[u_1\left(\dfrac{\partial x_3}{\partial y_2} - x_5 z_{22}\right)\right] + \dfrac{\partial^2}{\partial y_2^2}\left[-u_2\dfrac{\partial^2 x_5}{\partial y_2^2}\right] + q_3
\end{bmatrix} \tag{c}
$$

which for constant or finite dimensional controls are now in the standard form of type I.

The process of obtaining (b) and (c) followed the following generalized outline. (The outline will be seen to be a generalization to distributed parameter system models type I of the lumped parameter example given in Chapter 1.)

(i) The dependent variables in the original equations may be categorized as 'behaviour' variables and 'geometry' variables. The order of the original equations in the behaviour variables (irrespective of the order in the geometry variables) determines the number of states; for equations of total order n in the behaviour variables (with respect to some independent variable y_a), there result n state variables. The choice of the independent variable y_a is arbitrary. For the particular example, equations (a) are second-order in w_1 and w_2 and fourth-order in w_3 giving a total order of eight (with respect to either y_1 or y_2). Eight state variables result.

For definiteness in this example y_1 has been chosen as the independent variable. The equations (a) are however symmetrical with respect to both y_1 and y_2, and either could have been chosen. (In certain circumstances it will nevertheless be more favourable to choose a particular independent variable.)

(ii) The n-state variables are chosen such that each is related to a b'th derivative (with respect to y_a) of the behaviour variables. For q equations of total order n in behaviour variables, $b = 0, 1, \ldots, n_1 - 1$; $\ldots; b = 0, 1, \ldots, n_j - 1; \ldots; b = 0, 1, \ldots, n_q - 1$; where $\Sigma_1^q n_j = n$. That is, for each equation of order n_j in the behaviour variable, n_j states are introduced related to the 0'th order through $(n_j - 1)$'th order of this behaviour variable. The increasing order of the derivatives from 0 to $n_j - 1$ ensures that when the state variables are differentiated with respect to y_a, the first-order state equations (total order n_j) are equivalent to the original n_j'th order equation. For example, consider equation $(a)^3$. (Equations $(a)^1$ and $(a)^2$ follow similar arguments; the resulting states and state equations are additive to those obtained from $(a)^3$.) The states $x_5, \ldots, x_8$ were chosen related to the b'th derivative of w_3 (total order four with respect to y_1 in equation $(a)^3$) where b ranged from 0 to 3.

(iii) The detail of the state variables are adjusted to coincide with the definition of a meaningful quantity, while the resulting state equations should not only conform to the type I format but should also be equivalent to the original n_j'th order equation. The state equations should also be able to be interpreted in terms of equilibrium, compatibility and constitution at what would be the lower level of an equivalent multilevel model. Continuing with the example of equation $(a)^3$, the states $x_5, \ldots, x_8$

were adjusted in detail to take on the meanings of deflection, slope, internal moment and Kirchhoff 'transverse force' respectively, while the resulting state equations may be given the following interpretation: $(c)^5$ and $(c)^6$ represent compatibility and constitution combined, and $(c)^7$ and $(c)^8$ together represent equilibrium. Equations $(c)^{5\to 8}$ together are equivalent to the original fourth order equation $(a)^3$.

(iv) Control variables choose themselves. They represent the physical properties of the structure. In the present example, the controls were chosen as the extensional and bending stiffnesses.

To complete the discussion on equations (c), for the two in-plane portions, equilibrium is represented by the second and fourth equations, while the conditions of compatibility and constitution combined are contained in the first and third equations.

Similar reductions may be performed to yield equations *type II*. To illustrate the decomposition procedure involved and as a comparison with the decomposition just given for type I, consider the shell equations once more. Again it will prove convenient to list the states, controls and state equations and then to outline the process whereby these were obtained. The same notation x and u will be used for the state and control again, although equivalence with (b) is not implied.

The following state variables are introduced:

$$
\begin{aligned}
& x_1 \triangleq w_1 \qquad x_2 \triangleq w_2 \\
& x_3 \triangleq D\left(\frac{\partial w_1}{\partial y_1} - w_3 z_{11}\right) \qquad x_4 \triangleq \frac{D}{2}\left(\frac{\partial w_1}{\partial y_2} + \frac{\partial w_2}{\partial y_1} - 2w_3 z_{12}\right) \\
& x_5 \triangleq D\left(\frac{\partial w_2}{\partial y_2} - w_2 z_{22}\right) \\
& x_6 \triangleq w_3 \qquad x_7 \triangleq \frac{\partial w_3}{\partial y_1} \qquad x_8 \triangleq \frac{\partial w_3}{\partial y_2} \\
& x_9 \triangleq K\frac{\partial^2 w_3}{\partial y_1^2} \qquad x_{10} \triangleq K\frac{\partial^2 w_3}{\partial y_1 \partial y_2} \qquad x_{11} \triangleq K\frac{\partial^2 w_3}{\partial y_2^2} \\
& x_{12} \triangleq \frac{\partial}{\partial y_2}\left[K\frac{\partial^2 w_3}{\partial y_1^2}\right] \qquad x_{15} \triangleq \frac{\partial}{\partial y_1}\left[K\frac{\partial^2 w_3}{\partial y_2^2}\right] \\
& x_{13} \triangleq \frac{\partial}{\partial y_1}\left[K\frac{\partial^2 w_3}{\partial y_1^2}\right] + \frac{\partial}{\partial y_2}\left[K\frac{\partial^2 w_3}{\partial y_1 \partial y_2}\right] \\
& x_{14} \triangleq \frac{\partial}{\partial y_2}\left[K\frac{\partial^2 w_3}{\partial y_2^2}\right] + \frac{\partial}{\partial y_1}\left[K\frac{\partial^2 w_3}{\partial y_1 \partial y_2}\right].
\end{aligned}
\tag{d}
$$

The controls $u_1 \triangleq D$, $u_2 \triangleq K$ remain the same. Notice that for each derivative of w_i, $i = 1, 2, 3$ to the order α, there were introduced $\alpha + 1$ state variables, so that a pyramid effect results with (for example, considering w_3) the apex at $\alpha = 0$ (one state variable, namely x_6) and base at $\alpha = 3$ (four state variables, namely $x_{12}, \ldots, x_{15}$). The interpretation of the state variables is evident; in particular for the in-plane equations they are displacements, normal and shearing forces; for the out-of-plane equation they are displacement, slopes, internal direct and twisting moments, and internal shearing forces, all in the y_1 and y_2 directions where applicable. In addition two coupling state variables x_{12} and x_{15} appear. They have no accepted appellation but may be given physical meaning.

To ensure equation equivalence when the state variables are differentiated, certain auxiliary dependent variables are required. They may be treated as auxiliary controls although they may not be directly altered by the designer in the manner u_1 and u_2 can be. Set

$$u_3 \triangleq \frac{\partial}{\partial y_1}\left[D\left(\frac{\partial w_2}{\partial y_2} - w_3 z_{22}\right)\right] \qquad u_4 \triangleq \frac{\partial}{\partial y_2}\left[D\left(\frac{\partial w_1}{\partial y_1} - w_3 z_{11}\right)\right]$$

$$u_5 \triangleq \frac{\partial}{\partial y_1}\left\{\frac{\partial}{\partial y_2}\left[K\frac{\partial^2 w_3}{\partial y_1^2}\right]\right\} \qquad u_6 \triangleq \frac{\partial}{\partial y_2}\left\{\frac{\partial}{\partial y_2}\left[K\frac{\partial^2 w_3}{\partial y_1^2}\right]\right\}$$

$$u_7 \triangleq \frac{\partial}{\partial y_1}\left\{\frac{\partial}{\partial y_1}\left[K\frac{\partial^2 w_3}{\partial y_1^2}\right] + \frac{\partial}{\partial y_2}\left[K\frac{\partial^2 w_3}{\partial y_1 \partial y_2}\right]\right\}$$

$$u_8 \triangleq \frac{\partial}{\partial y_2}\left\{\frac{\partial}{\partial y_1}\left[K\frac{\partial^2 w_3}{\partial y_1^2}\right] + \frac{\partial}{\partial y_2}\left[K\frac{\partial^2 w_3}{\partial y_1 \partial y_2}\right]\right\} \tag{d$'$}$$

$$u_9 \triangleq \frac{\partial}{\partial y_1}\left\{\frac{\partial}{\partial y_2}\left[K\frac{\partial^2 w_3}{\partial y_1^2}\right] + \frac{\partial}{\partial y_1}\left[K\frac{\partial^2 w_3}{\partial y_1 \partial y_2}\right]\right\}$$

$$u_{10} \triangleq \frac{\partial}{\partial y_1}\left\{\frac{\partial}{\partial y_1}\left[K\frac{\partial^2 w_3}{\partial y_2^2}\right]\right\} \qquad u_{11} \triangleq \frac{\partial}{\partial y_2}\left\{\frac{\partial}{\partial y_1}\left[K\frac{\partial^2 w_3}{\partial y_2^2}\right]\right\}.$$

Differentiating the state variables with respect to y_1 and y_2 in turn, a set of first-order equations (the state equations) is obtained equivalent to the original shell equations.

$$
\begin{aligned}
&\frac{\partial x_1}{\partial y_1} = \frac{x_3}{u_1} + x_6 z_{11} && \frac{\partial x_1}{\partial y_2} = \frac{2x_4}{u_1} - \frac{\partial x_2}{\partial y_1} + 2x_6 z_{12} \\
&\frac{\partial x_2}{\partial y_1} = \frac{2x_4}{u_1} - \frac{\partial x_1}{\partial y_2} + 2x_6 z_{12} && \frac{\partial x_2}{\partial y_2} = \frac{x_5}{u_1} + x_6 z_{22} \\
&\frac{\partial x_3}{\partial y_1} = -q_1 - \frac{\partial x_4}{\partial y_2} && \frac{\partial x_3}{\partial y_2} = u_4 \\
&\frac{\partial x_4}{\partial y_1} = -q_2 - \frac{\partial x_5}{\partial y_2} && \frac{\partial x_4}{\partial y_2} = -q_1 - \frac{\partial x_3}{\partial y_1} \\
&\frac{\partial x_5}{\partial y_1} = u_3 && \frac{\partial x_5}{\partial y_2} = -q_2 - \frac{\partial x_4}{\partial y_1} \\
&\frac{\partial x_6}{\partial y_1} = x_7 && \frac{\partial x_6}{\partial y_2} = x_8 \\
&\frac{\partial x_7}{\partial y_1} = \frac{x_9}{u_2} && \frac{\partial x_7}{\partial y_2} = \frac{x_{10}}{u_2} \\
&\frac{\partial x_8}{\partial y_1} = \frac{x_{10}}{u_2} && \frac{\partial x_8}{\partial y_2} = \frac{x_{11}}{u_2} \qquad \text{(e)} \\
&\frac{\partial x_9}{\partial y_1} = x_{13} - \frac{\partial x_{10}}{\partial y_2} && \frac{\partial x_9}{\partial y_2} = x_{12} \\
&\frac{\partial x_{10}}{\partial y_1} = x_{14} - \frac{\partial x_{11}}{\partial y_2} && \frac{\partial x_{10}}{\partial y_2} = x_{13} - \frac{\partial x_9}{\partial y_1} \\
&\frac{\partial x_{11}}{\partial y_1} = x_{15} && \frac{\partial x_{11}}{\partial y_2} = x_{14} - \frac{\partial x_{10}}{\partial y_1} \\
&\frac{\partial x_{12}}{\partial y_1} = u_5 && \frac{\partial x_{12}}{\partial y_2} = u_6 \\
&\frac{\partial x_{13}}{\partial y_1} = u_7 && \frac{\partial x_{13}}{\partial y_2} = u_8 \\
&\frac{\partial x_{14}}{\partial y_1} = u_9 && \frac{\partial x_{14}}{\partial y_2} = z_{11}x_3 + 2z_{12}x_4 + z_{22}x_5 + q_3 - u_7 \\
&\frac{\partial x_{15}}{\partial y_1} = u_{10} && \frac{\partial x_{15}}{\partial y_2} = u_{11}
\end{aligned}
$$

The meaning of these equations is apparent. For the in-plane equations, the first and second equations (with respect to both derivatives) are compatibility and constitution together. The third and fourth (with respect to y_1) and the fourth and fifth (with respect to y_2) equations are equilibrium. For the out-of-plane equations, the sixth to eighth (with respect to both derivatives) in appropriate combinations are compatibility and constitution combined. The ninth and tenth equations referring to derivatives with respect to y_1 (or equivalently the tenth and eleventh equations referring to the derivatives with respect to y_2) are equilibrium. The remaining equations for both in-plane and out-of-plane ensure consistency with the original two second-order and one fourth-order equations.

These equations are now in the standard form of type II. The general process of obtaining (e), (d) and (d)$'$ will now be outlined. (The process is a generalization to distributed parameter system models type II of the lumped parameter example of Chapter 1.)

(i) For the original system equations of total order cn in the behaviour variables (with respect to the independent variables y_k, $k = 1, \ldots, c$; $c \leq 3$), irrespective of the order in the geometry variables, cn state variables are introduced. For the shell equations (a), w_1 and w_2 are to the second order and w_3 to the fourth order with respect to both y_1 and y_2. That is, sixteen state variables result.

(ii) The cn state variables are chosen related to increasing derivatives with respect to all independent variables. The process of obtaining these state variables is similar to that outlined for type I with the extension here to derivatives over all the independent variables and not just one independent variable (as in type I). For example consider (a)^3, the state vector has one component related to the 0'th order of w_3 (namely x_6), two components related to the first order (x_7 and x_8), three components to the second order (x_9, x_{10} and x_{11}), and so on. Notice in this last mentioned case the mixed y_1y_2 derivative was introduced to complete the three second order derivatives. When the same process is repeated on (a)^1, there results a state (x_1) to the 0'th order in w_1 and two states (x_3 and x_4) to the first order. For (a)^2, the state to the 0'th order in w_2 is x_2, and to the first order are x_4 and x_5. Notice that x_4 is common to the reduction of (a)^1 and (a)^2 and hence the total number of states for (a) was reduced from sixteen to fifteen.

(iii) The detail of the state variables is adjusted as for the type I reduction with the same qualifications but here extended to the directions of all independent variables. For (a)^3, the states may be interpreted as deflection, slope, moments and shearing forces. (Two variables, x_{12} and x_{15} do not however fulfill the requirement of having accepted appellations although they may be given physical meaning. Their presence ensures that the state equations are equivalent to the original system equations.) Similar interpretations may be given to the in-plane portions of (a).

(iv) Auxiliary çontrols are introduced as the derivatives (with respect to all the independent variables) of the states with the highest order derivatives. For an equation of order cn_j in a behaviour variable (with respect to all y_k, $k = 1, \ldots, c$; $c \leq 3$), there will be n_j states of the highest order $n_j - 1$. Thus $cn_j - 1$ auxiliary controls are introduced, being derivatives of these n_j states with respect to all y_k, $k = 1, \ldots, c$. The remaining derivative of the state (that is the difference between cn_j, the total number of possible derivatives of state, and $cn_j - 1$, the number of auxiliary controls) becomes the original system equation (but now using the newly introduced state and control notation). The choice of the state that receives this individual treatment is arbitrary, provided on differentiation it leads to the system equation. The presence of the auxiliary controls ensures equivalence of the original system equation and the state equations. They occupy the base ($\alpha = 4$) of the pyramid previously mentioned. These ideas are perhaps easier to see in the illustration. Consider $(a)^3$ (total order in w_3 is eight with respect to y_1 and y_2). The highest order derivative states are $x_{12}, \ldots, x_{15}$ and are all third order in w_3. Therefore $8 - 1$ auxiliary controls $u_5, \ldots, u_{11}$ were introduced and all are fourth order in w_3. The remaining derivative of state, namely $\partial x_{14}/\partial y_2$ was set equal to the system equation $(a)^3$ and became $(e)^{14}$-second equation.

(v) The conventional controls choose themselves. They represent the physical properties. For the example they were the extensional and bending stiffnesses.

In the illustration at hand, a reduction to equations type II avoided the choice (as was necessary for type I) of the independent variable required in the differentiation on the left-hand side by having separate derivatives of both y_1 and y_2 on the left-hand side. For these symmetrical equations, such a reduction may be the more favourable over type I. It is seen that the results are applicable for variable thickness shells. Also the twisting term in the out-of-plane contribution $(a)^3$ to equations (a) splits neatly between derivatives with respect to y_1 and y_2, and the Kirchhoff 'transverse force' becomes the more usual out-of-plane shearing force.

Generally any partial differential equation defined over a three dimensional spatial region may be reduced to the type II form, albeit with an increase in the number of dependent variables. This large increase in the number of variables (and the consequent rise in the number of equations that have to be handled, although admittedly of low order) appears to be the main objection to the type II form. Associated with this is a certain repetition of information (in the form of common equations) within the state equation representation. The use of auxiliary control variables also does not appeal but this time in a physical rather than a mathematical sense. Its advantages appear to lie in the treatment of structures whose behaviour is similar (though not necessarily the same) in the independent variable directions. For asymmetrical equations and for economy in computations, the type I representation would be sought.

Consider the same illustration, but now interpreted in the standard form of *type III*. This equation type relies on the symmetry of the structure (yet in a different manner to type II) by emphasizing common cross derivatives. It is anticipated from inspection of the composition of the in-plane shearing term and the out-of-plane twisting term occurring in the shell equations (a) that the type III representation will be better suited to the out-of-plane portion compared with the in-plane portion. This statement will be amplified following the illustration. Consider the new states

$$\begin{aligned} x_1 &\triangleq w_1 \qquad & x_2 &\triangleq w_2 \\ x_3 &\triangleq w_3 \qquad & x_4 &\triangleq K\frac{\partial^2 w_3}{\partial y_1 \partial y_2} \end{aligned} \tag{f}$$

with controls of $u_1 \triangleq D$, $u_2 \triangleq K$ as before. The states clearly represent the deformations in each of the coordinate directions and the twisting moment.

Taking the cross derivatives of the states $x_1, \ldots, x_4$ with respect to y_1 and y_2 results in the state equations;

$$\begin{bmatrix} \dfrac{\partial^2 x_1}{\partial y_1 \partial y_2} \\[2ex] \dfrac{\partial^2 x_2}{\partial y_1 \partial y_2} \\[2ex] \dfrac{\partial^2 x_3}{\partial y_1 \partial y_2} \\[2ex] \dfrac{\partial^2 x_4}{\partial y_1 \partial y_2} \\ \\ \\ \\ \end{bmatrix} = \begin{bmatrix} -\dfrac{2}{u_1}\left\{q_2 + \dfrac{\partial}{\partial y_2}\left[u_1\left(\dfrac{\partial x_2}{\partial y_2} - x_3 z_{22}\right)\right]\right\} - \dfrac{\partial}{\partial y_1}\left(\dfrac{\partial x_2}{\partial y_1} - 2x_3 z_{12}\right) \\[2ex] -\dfrac{2}{u_1}\left\{q_1 + \dfrac{\partial}{\partial y_1}\left[u_1\left(\dfrac{\partial x_1}{\partial y_1} - x_3 z_{11}\right)\right]\right\} - \dfrac{\partial}{\partial y_2}\left(\dfrac{\partial x_1}{\partial y_2} - 2x_3 z_{12}\right) \\[2ex] \dfrac{x_4}{u_2} \\[2ex] \dfrac{1}{2}\left\{q_3 + \dfrac{\partial^2}{\partial y_1^2}\left(-u_2\dfrac{\partial^2 x_3}{\partial y_1^2}\right) + \dfrac{\partial^2}{\partial y_2^2}\left(-u_2\dfrac{\partial^2 x_3}{\partial y_2^2}\right)\right. \\ \quad + z_{11}u_1\left(\dfrac{\partial x_1}{\partial y_1} - x_3 z_{11}\right) + z_{12}u_1\left(\dfrac{\partial x_1}{\partial y_2} + \dfrac{\partial x_2}{\partial y_1} - 2x_3 z_{12}\right) \\ \quad \left. + z_{22}u_1\left(\dfrac{\partial x_2}{\partial y_2} - x_3 z_{22}\right)\right\} \end{bmatrix} \tag{g}$$

The main criticism of the form of (g) is that it does not contain enough information as it only highlights the cross derivative terms appearing in the original high order equations (a). It is remarked that to obtain the first and second state equations it had to be assumed that the control u_1 was constant (in order to obtain mixed state derivative terms free of control derivative terms which are to an odd order) whereas the third and fourth equations are for general u_1 and u_2 (as they contain mixed state derivative terms directly). The total set of equations is only of a type III form for constant controls. A general breakdown to a type III form is impossible where the highest order of any dependent variable is odd as occurred in the in-plane equations for D above.

Briefly, the outline to the above reduction is as follows. The similarities with the above reduction outlines for types I and II will be apparent and will not be emphasized.

(i) For a system equation of order $2p$ in its mixed derivatives of the behaviour variables, irrespective of the order in the geometry variables, p state variables are introduced. For the example (a), $p = 1$ in $(a)^1$ and $(a)^2$ and $p = 2$ in $(a)^3$, leading to four state variables in total.

(ii) The states are chosen related to the cross derivatives of the behaviour variable with the first state variable of 0'th order and the last of order $(2p - 2)$. The state variables thus differ by order 2 in their derivatives such that when the mixed derivatives of state are taken, there results an ordered hierarchy of state equations. For the example, considering $(a)^3$, the first state variable x_3 is 0'th order in w_3, the last state variable x_4 is second order in w_3.

(iii) The detail of the states is modified to agree in form with a meaningful quantity, keeping in mind that the resulting state equations are required to be equivalent to the original system equations. For this equation type, as compared with I and II, it appears that no clearly defined constitution—compatibility—equilibrium breakdown is possible. Considering the example, the states x_1, x_2, x_3 and x_4 may clearly be interpreted as deformations and twisting moment.

(iv) The controls choose themselves. They represent the physical properties of the structure. In the example they are the extensional and bending stiffnesses.

2.3.1.8 GENERAL COMMENTS

Notice that by choosing the state variables and equations to satisfy physical motives in the above example, the type I representation has been restricted to applications involving constant or finite dimensional controls and the type III representation has been restricted to constant controls (principally in order that derivatives of the control do not appear on the right-hand sides). In structures where such cases occur, and completely general controls are still required, it will be found necessary to choose state variables and state equations without total physical significance.

A reduction of the same shell equations to a state-control form of the types I, II and III satisfying the mathematics only, could be carried out according to the algorithms in the Appendix, section 2.4. For type I, in addition to the unusual meaning of several of the variables and state equations, there would result eleven state equations (compared with eight above). Eleven is the sum of the orders of the y_1 derivatives in w_i, $i = 1, 2, 3$ (eight), D (one) and K (two). In general for a constitutive equation n'th order in a behaviour variable and r'th order in a geometry variable, there will result $(n + r)$ first order state equations. For a reduction to a state-control form of the equations type II, satisfying the mathematics only, there would result fifty state equations (compared with thirty above). Again the increase in the number of equations may be attributed to the terms which are derivatives of the geometry variable. For equations type III with all derivatives fully expanded, there would result an additional state variable (and hence an additional state equation) for the out-of-plane portion while the in-plane portion contains derivatives in one variable whose highest order is odd and clearly cannot be reduced to the even derivative form required by a type III format.

Between the two reduction schemes outlined (namely one motivated by giving meaning to the variables and equations concerned (illustrated with reference to the shallow shell equations above)—the other satisfying the mathematics alone without regard to meaning (the algorithms of the Appendix)) there exist various schemes with combinations of qualities borrowed from these two schools of approach. These will not be outlined here, but instead various alternative reduction schemes with associated discussions may be found in the design example sections of Part C.

The two distinct reduction proposals would appear to be the fundamental reduction schemes leading to the lowest and highest number of state equations respectively. Conglomerate schemes borrowing ideas from both have an intermediate number. The validity of any reduction scheme can only be verified by showing the equivalence of the low order state equations with the original high order equation. The requirement of meaningful choices of state and control according to physical arguments can apparently be put to one side in formulating any reduction scheme.

One final note on the nonuniqueness of a set of state variables is required. It is apparent that within each equation type (I, II or III) a set of state variables may be associated with a given high order system model equation in many ways (for a given set of controls). The most desirable is the choice motivated by giving meaning to variables involved, leading to equations of equilibrium, compatibility and constitution. However, for any set of state variables $x_1, x_2, \ldots, x_n$ satisfying the definition of state, and for a given model and set of controls, it is possible to construct another set of state variables as functions of $x_1, x_2, \ldots, x_n$. Formally, a new set of state variables may be written

$$x_i^* = X_i(x) \qquad i = 1, 2, \ldots, n$$

provided there exists a unique (nonsingular) transformation between the set of values x^* and x. This is tantamount to changing the coordinate system in the state space. As anticipated the resulting state equations are altered; this may or may not be desirable from a computational viewpoint.

The convenience of using the state variable form is apparent. Apart from the appropriateness physically of the state variables to the description of the internal composition of the model in certain cases, the resulting set of equations reduces to a form tractable to machine computation, while with the use of matrix and vector notation, the mathematics becomes very elegant indeed. The standard form ((2.1), (2.2) or (2.3)) is appealing with regard to the preparation of standard solving routines, while their first order property (second order for type III) is far more suitable to solution techniques than higher order equations. All equations are amenable to a reduction to the standard form of either (2.1), (2.2) or (2.3) (and in certain cases to all three) by a suitable choice of new (state) variables, facilitating a general discussion for all systems. Simultaneous equations are additive. The size of the state vector and state equations are increased accordingly (that is the sum of the state equations corresponding to each individual high order equation).

Recalling the lumped parameter reduction procedure introduced in Chapter 1 it is noted that state variables could be chosen as meaningful quantities while the resulting state equations were applicable for general (variable) controls. The extension of these traits to distributed parameter reduction procedures was only possible for the type II models. For type I and III models, only one of these traits could be satisfied at a time. The inference to draw from this is that it may be preferable to discretize distributed parameter models, before starting computations, in all but one independent variable direction such that the designer is then working with a lumped parameter form (see Chapter 1). (With discretization comes the additional gain of simplified computations. In particular, lumped parameter system designs are an order of magnitude less difficult than distributed parameter system design.) For system model manipulations (such as much analysis, identification, estimation and other procedures) and for the modelling of structures with constant controls, the distributed parameter form could be used directly while preserving physical meaning of all variables and equations.

2.3.1.9 PROBABILISTIC EQUIVALENT

The state at any y (spatial or temporal coordinate) in stochastic models is regarded as the information that uniquely determines the probability distribution of the state at any other $y = y'$ (Chapter 1). It is evident therefore that the state, as defined for example in the lumped parameter case,

$$\mathrm{d}x(y)/\mathrm{d}y = f[x(y), u(y), y] \tag{1.1}$$

represents a stochastic process 'without after effect', that is a Markov process. The Markovian property is directly attributable to the way in which the concept of state has been defined. Markov processes are the probabilistic equivalent of the deterministic principles of (classical) mechanics—this property is sometimes referred to as the generalized causality principle; for evolutionary processes, the future may be predicted from a knowledge of the present alone.

By definition, a stochastic process $\{x(y); y \in Y\}$ is a (real, vector valued) Markov process if for every finite set of values $y^0 < y^1 < \ldots < y^{k-1} < y^k$ in Y

$$\begin{aligned} P\{x(y^k) < \xi^k \mid x(y^i) = \xi^i, i = 0, 1, \ldots, k-1\} \\ = P\{x(y^k) < \xi^k \mid x(y^{k-1}) = \xi^{k-1}\}. \end{aligned}$$

The term on the right-hand side of this equation is referred to as the 'transition probability distribution function' or simply the 'transition function'. It does not depend on values of x previous to y^{k-1}. A Markov process is completely defined by specifying the absolute probability distribution $F(x^0)$ and the transition probability distribution.

Note that the stochastic processes representing the state may not in general be Markov. The probabilistic form of the state has been defined in this manner in analogy with the deterministic definition of the state. Markov processes imply a form of dependency between states at successive y values but not total dependency as may be anticipated in structural applications. The Markov assumption has been introduced in order to obtain solutions. It represents a compromise with the complete stochastic treatment where a solution is almost certainly unattainable. The theory of Markov processes is quite well delineated and this theory may be freely used to simplify the calculations in the stochastic case.

Discrete stochastic systems. Discretizing the parameter set $Y \subset E^1$ such that $\{y^i; i = 0, 1, \ldots, N\} \in Y$, allows a 'finite dimensional distribution' representation of the stochastic process. That is, the stochastic process $\{x(y, \omega);\ y \in Y,\ \omega \in \Omega\}$ may be characterized by the joint distribution or joint density function (the notation $x^\alpha \equiv x(\alpha)$)

$$F(x^0, \ldots, x^N) \quad \text{or} \quad p(x^0, \ldots, x^N) \qquad \forall \{y^i\} \in y$$

respectively (Kolmogorov 1956), where x is the conventional state column vector $(x_1, \ldots, x_n)^{\mathrm{T}}$. Equivalent distributions apply for other vectors.

The probability space will always be considered continuous and hence the density function will always exist. (This is not to be taken as a restriction on the approach, which is equally capable of handling discrete distributions, but rather delineates the scope of following sections. The extension to the treatment of discrete probability distributions will be apparent.)

Processes such as these, that is with a continuous probability space and discrete parameter set, may be referred to as 'random sequences' (the corresponding realization being referred to as a 'sample sequence'). The terminology 'stochastic process' is commonly saved for the case of continuous probability space, continuous parameter set (the corresponding realization being a 'sample function').

State equations with this discrete character are naturally referred to as stochastic difference equations. Stochastic difference equations may be regarded in a like manner to their deterministic equivalents; for a given control, the solution of either may be regarded as an algorithm defining (the joint probability distribution of) x^i recursively from the previous value x^{i-1}. Under the assumptions made above for the concept of state, these processes $\{x^i;\ i = 0, 1, \ldots, N\}$ are Markov processes with a finite number of states. (See Doob 1953, Wong 1971 and others.)

For a Markov process, the joint density function may be written

$$\begin{aligned} p(x^0, \ldots, x^N) &= p(x^N \mid x^0, \ldots, x^{N-1})p(x^0, \ldots, x^{N-1}) \\ &= p(x^N \mid x^{N-1})p(x^0, \ldots, x^{N-1}) \end{aligned}$$

Repeating the procedure, the density function reduces to

$$p(x^0, \ldots, x^N) = p(x^0) \prod_{i=1}^{N} p(x^i \mid x^{i-1}).$$

The conditional function $p(x^i \mid x^{i-1})$ is referred to as the 'transition probability density' and denotes the probability that the system which had state x^{i-1} at y^{i-1} will for $y^i > y^{i-1}$ have a state x^i.

2.3.2 End-State Conditions

To completely define the state throughout the model, certain 'starting' values of the state are required. These values are conventionally termed boundary and terminal conditions (here collectively referred to as end-state conditions) and may be expressed as conditions of state specified at the left and/or right interval limits (y_i^{L} and y_i^{R} respectively) of the independent variables $\{y_i;\ i = 1, \ldots\}$. The state at y_i^{L} and y_i^{R} will be required to belong to a given set of states S^{L} and S^{R} respectively. (The term 'end' is used in a 'left' and 'right' sense and not in an evolutionary sense, while the terms 'left' and 'right' imply an orientation of the coordinate space relative to the reader.)

Structural problems will generally be described with end-state sets S^{L} and S^{R} prescribed respectively by

(i) At y_i^{L}, $i = 1, \ldots, 4$; the intersection of p surfaces whose equations are

$$S_\alpha^{\mathrm{L}}(x, \ldots, \partial_l x, \ldots) = 0 \qquad \begin{matrix} \alpha = 1, 2, \ldots, p \\ 0 \le p \le n \end{matrix} \tag{2.4a}$$

(ii) At y_i^{R}, $i = 1, \ldots, 4$; the intersection of q surfaces whose equations are

$$S_\beta^{\mathrm{R}}(x, \ldots, \partial_l x, \ldots) = 0 \qquad \begin{matrix} \beta = 1, 2, \ldots, q \\ 0 \le q \le n \end{matrix} \tag{2.4b}$$

where for a well defined problem, $p + q = n$ (that is, the total number of end-state conditions equals the number of state equations). In (2.4), l is determined by the state equation type (that is I, II or III) (for example, in I, $l = (l_j, l_k, l_h)$; $j, k, h\ (\neq i) = 1, \ldots, 4$) and $\partial_l x$ is defined in the 'notation'.

As an illustration, consider the boundary conditions along the free edge $y_1 = a$ of a shell. For zero Poisson's ratio they read

$$\begin{aligned}
&\left.-\frac{\partial}{\partial y_1}\left(K\frac{\partial^2 w_3(y_1, y_2)}{\partial y_1^2}\right) - 2\frac{\partial}{\partial y_2}\left(K\frac{\partial^2 w_3(y_1, y_2)}{\partial y_1 \partial y_2}\right)\right|_{y_1 = a} = 0 \\
&\left.-K\frac{\partial^2 w_3(y_1, y_2)}{\partial y_1^2}\right|_{y_1 = a} = 0 \\
&D\left[\frac{\partial w_1(y_1, y_2)}{\partial y_1} - w_3 z_{11}\right]_{y_1 = a} = 0 \\
&\frac{D}{2}\left[\frac{\partial w_1(y_1, y_2)}{\partial y_2} + \frac{\partial w_2(y_1, y_2)}{\partial y_1} - 2w_3 z_{12}\right]_{y_1 = a} = 0
\end{aligned} \tag{h}$$

representing conditions of zero transverse shearing force (the Kirchhoff condition), zero bending moment, zero normal in-plane force and zero in-plane shearing force.

For state equations type I, setting the controls $u_1 \triangleq D$, $u_2 \triangleq K$ and the states as in equations (b), then these end conditions become

$$\left.-x_8\right|_{y_1=a} = 0, \qquad \left.-x_7\right|_{y_1=a} = 0$$
$$\left.x_2\right|_{y_1=a} = 0, \qquad \left.x_4\right|_{y_1=a} = 0 \tag{i}$$

respectively. For state equations type II, with the same controls but now with the states as in equation (d), the same end conditions become

$$\left.-x_8 - \frac{\partial x_{10}}{\partial y_2}\right|_{y_1=a} = 0, \qquad \left.-x_9\right|_{y_1=a} = 0$$
$$\left.x_3\right|_{y_1=a} = 0 \qquad \left.x_4\right|_{y_1=a} = 0. \tag{j}$$

Similarly (but here for constant u_1, u_2) for state equations type III using (f), then

$$\left.-\frac{\partial^3 x_3}{\partial y_1^3} - 2\frac{\partial x_4}{\partial y_2}\right|_{y_1=a} = 0, \qquad \left.-\frac{\partial^2 x_3}{\partial y_1^2}\right|_{y_1=a} = 0$$
$$\left.\frac{\partial x_1}{\partial y_1} - x_3 z_{11}\right|_{y_1=a} = 0 \qquad \left.\frac{\partial x_1}{\partial y_2} + \frac{\partial x_2}{\partial y_1} - 2x_3 z_{12}\right|_{y_1=a} = 0. \tag{k}$$

In dynamic problems over the time interval, S^{L} and S^{R} represent initial and final (or collectively, terminal) conditions on the state. Note that the inconsistency of specifying the final state without ensuring the controllability of the model or whether that state is attainable, should be guarded against.

The above formulation for (2.4a, b) includes the case of end-state constraints. The question of state constraints is dealt with in Part B.

Random end-state conditions. For random state variables the end-state conditions will be given in terms of certain probabilistic characteristics of these variables—for example, probability densities: $p[x(y^{\mathrm{L}})]$ is the probability density function of the state at y^{L} such that $p[x(y^{\mathrm{L}})]\,\mathrm{d}x(y^{\mathrm{L}})$ is the probability that the state $x(y^{\mathrm{L}})$ is contained within the elemental volume $\mathrm{d}x(y^{\mathrm{L}})$ $(= \mathrm{d}x_1(y^{\mathrm{L}}) \ldots \mathrm{d}x_n(y^{\mathrm{L}}))$ about $x(y^{\mathrm{L}})$.

Deterministic end-state conditions may be considered as special cases of the random specification. For example the probability density function becomes the Dirac delta function; for $x(y^{\mathrm{L}}) = c$, a fixed vector of constants, then $p[x_i(y^{\mathrm{L}})] = \delta(x_i(y^{\mathrm{L}}) - c_i)$, $i = 1, \ldots, n$.

2.3.3 Response Transformation

The response will be related to the state through an algebraic equation of the form

$$z(y) = h[x(y), u(y), y] \tag{2.5}$$

where $h = (h_1, \ldots, h_m)^T$ in general is a nonlinear vector-valued function of the arguments shown. Equation (2.5) includes the case where the state and response bear a one-to-one relationship.

2.3.4 Comment

It will be apparent that the state equations given by (2.1) (or 2.2 or 2.3) and the end-state conditions (2.4) (together with an appropriate response transformation), represent a set of equations where the number of unknowns $(n + r)$ exceeds the number of equations (n) as the r controls are still unspecified.

For given controls the equations may be solved for the unknown states. This is the familiar *analysis* problem. By comparison the *synthesis* problem makes no *a priori* assumptions as to the form of the control. In general for a specified performance (state) there will not exist a unique solution and a means is required of directly selecting a control such that the system model not only performs as specified but is optimal in some sense. A performance (or design) index (or optimality criterion) provides the basis for a unique and at the same time meaningful solution. A value or rating of the index corresponds with each feasible solution (control) and from which the optimum solution may be chosen.

As control theory establishes the relationships under which a system model may be controlled, optimal control theory establishes a particular control according to a given criterion. It is the subject of optimal control (in a structures sense) which is taken up later.

A note on terminology. In the following presentation the terminology 'system model type I (or II or III)' will refer to a system model with a control-state description of type I (or II or III) together with appropriate end-state conditions and response transformation. The end-state conditions and response transformation will often be omitted in the discussion of the model but it is emphasized that their specification in a suitable form is implied. This will facilitate subsequent developments of the modelling procedures. It also will be found semantically convenient in the following chapters to use the terminology 'system model', 'system' and 'model' synonymously although a distinction between the abstract mathematical model and the real physical system is always intended. The model is only ever a representation of the system.

2.4 APPENDIX: ALTERNATIVE REDUCTIONS OF THE SYSTEM EQUATION

Three algorithms are given for the reduction of a general partial differential equation to the form of system type I (equation 2.1), type II (equation 2.2), and type III (equation 2.3). At the outset it is emphasized that the resulting sets of equations satisfy the mathematical definitions of state and control but will often lack physical meaning. These mechanical means of system equation reduction are offered as alternatives to the reduction schemes proposed earlier. Their use is illustrated in Part C.

System Type I: Consider a general equation in independent variables $\{y_p; p = 1, \dots, 4\}$ and dependent variables $\{v_j; j = 1, \dots, s\}$,

$$F[y_1, \dots, y_4, \dots, v_j, \dots, \partial_l v_j, \dots] = 0 \qquad (j = 1, \dots, s) \quad (2A\text{-}1)$$

where $l = (l_1, \dots, l_4)$. F is a generalized function of the arguments shown.

Assume that the highest order derivatives of v_j with respect to y_4 have order mj and that (without loss of generality) the highest order derivative in y_4 of all the v_i occurs in v_s. Then solving for this derivative (that is $\partial^{ms} v_j / \partial y_4^{ms}$), introduce the auxiliary dependent (state) variables x_i according to;

$$x_1 \triangleq v_1, x_2 \triangleq \frac{\partial v_1}{\partial y_4}, \dots, x_{m1} \triangleq \frac{\partial^{m1-1} v_1}{\partial y_4^{m1-1}},$$

$$x_{m1+1} \triangleq v_2, x_{m1+2} \triangleq \frac{\partial v_2}{\partial y_4}, \dots, x_{m1+m2} \triangleq \frac{\partial^{m2-1} v_2}{\partial y_4^{m2-1}},$$

$$\cdots\cdots\cdots\cdots$$

$$x_{\left[\sum_1^{s-1} mj\right]+1} \triangleq v_s, x_{\left[\sum_1^{s-1} mj\right]+2} \triangleq \frac{\partial v_s}{\partial y_4}, \dots, x_{\left[\sum_1^{s} mj\right]} \triangleq \frac{\partial^{ms-1} v_s}{\partial y_4^{ms-1}}$$

and controls

$$u_1 \triangleq \frac{\partial^{m1} v_1}{\partial y_4^{m1}}, u_2 \triangleq \frac{\partial^{m2} v_2}{\partial y_4^{m2}}, \dots, u_{s-1} \triangleq \frac{\partial^{m(s-1)} v_{(s-1)}}{\partial y_4^{m(s-1)}}.$$

Differentiating the state variables $\{x_i;\ i = 1, \dots, \Sigma_1^s mj = n\}$ with respect to y_4 yields the state equations of system type I—equation (2.1). Notice that derivatives with respect to y_4 on the left-hand side are arbitrary and in fact any $y_1, \dots, y_4$ could have been chosen; the reduction procedure remains the same. The highest derivatives of v_j with respect to y_4 in the above case for $j = 1, \ldots, (s-1)$ are chosen as control variables $\{u_k;\ k = 1, \ldots, (s-1) = r\}$. This satisfies the mathematical definition of control. The properties of the system will determine the choice of these variables. The reduction procedure extends readily to the case where (2A-1) are sets of simultaneous equations; the resulting state equations are suitably enlarged.

Notice that conventional controls (geometry terms) are interpreted as state variables. The controls in this case are the derivatives of the geometry terms with respect to y_4. A general property of the reduction algorithm is that the control occurs linearly in the resulting state equations. That is, this form of the reduction is likely to lead to design cases which are formulated in a singular control sense. Hence to avoid singular control formulations it will require a criterion nonlinear in the control and this may not be the case. Notice the reduction scheme of section 2.3 rarely, if ever, leads to state equations linear in the control. (The final optimization solutions will in fact be the same no matter which reduction scheme is employed. It is the awkwardness of singular control formulations which may occur in one case and which do not appeal.)

System Type II: Consider a general equation in two independent variables y_1 and y_2 and dependent variables $\{v_j; j = 1, \ldots, s\}$

$$F[y_1, y_2, \ldots, v_j, \ldots, \partial_l v_j, \ldots] = 0 \qquad (j = 1, \ldots, s) \tag{2A-2}$$

where $l = (l_1, l_2)$. F is a generalized function of the arguments shown.

For each dependent variable v_j, assume that the highest derivative is of order mj and that (2A-2) can be solved for one of the highest derivatives, for example $\partial^{mj} v_j / \partial y_2^{mj}$.

Introduce, for each v_j, state variables according to

$$x^j_1 \triangleq v_j,$$

$$x^j_2 \triangleq \frac{\partial v_j}{\partial y_1}, \qquad x^j_3 \triangleq \frac{\partial v_j}{\partial y_2},$$

$$x^j_4 \triangleq \frac{\partial^2 v_j}{\partial y_1^2}, \qquad x^j_5 \triangleq \frac{\partial^2 v_j}{\partial y_1 \partial y_2}, \qquad x^j_6 \triangleq \frac{\partial^2 v_j}{\partial y_2^2},$$

$$\cdots\cdots\cdots\cdots$$

$$x^j_{\frac{mj(mj-1)}{2}+1} \triangleq \frac{\partial^{mj-1} v_j}{\partial y_1^{mj-1}}, \quad x^j_{\frac{mj(mj-1)}{2}+2} \triangleq \frac{\partial^{mj-1} v_j}{\partial y_1^{mj-2} \partial y_2}, \ldots,$$

$$x^j_{\frac{mj(mj+1)}{2}-1} \triangleq \frac{\partial^{mj-1} v_j}{\partial y_1 \partial y_2^{mj-2}}, \quad x^j_{\frac{mj(mj+1)}{2}} \triangleq \frac{\partial^{mj-1} v_j}{\partial y_2^{mj-1}}$$

and control variables according to

$$u^j_1 \triangleq \frac{\partial^{mj} v_j}{\partial y_1^{mj}},\ u^j_2 \triangleq \frac{\partial^{mj} v_j}{\partial y_1^{mj-1} \partial y_2}, \ldots, u^j_{mj} \triangleq \frac{\partial^{mj} v_j}{\partial y_1 \partial y_2^{mj-1}}.$$

The superscript j on the states and controls indicates they are associated with $v_j, j = 1, \ldots, s$.

Differentiating the states with respect to y_1 and y_2 gives state equations of type II.

System Type III: Consider the general partial differential equation

$$F[y_1, y_2, \ldots, v_j, \ldots, \partial_l v_j, \ldots] = 0 \qquad (j = 1, \ldots, s) \quad \text{(2A-3)}$$

defined over the $y_1 y_2$-plane, where $l = (l_1, l_2)$ and $\{v_j; j = 1, \ldots, s\}$ are equation dependent variables.

It is assumed that the highest order mixed derivatives of v_j with respect to y_1 and y_2 have order $2(mj)$ (clearly an even number) and that the highest order mixed derivative of all the v_j occurs in v_s and can be solved for. It is remarked that a system type III representation is inapplicable where the highest order (straight) derivative of any v_j is odd.

Introduce state variables according to

$$x_1 \triangleq v_1, x_2 \triangleq \frac{\partial^2 v_1}{\partial y_1 \partial y_2}, \ldots, x_{m1} \triangleq \frac{\partial^{2m1-2} v_1}{\partial y_1^{m1-1} \partial y_2^{m1-1}},$$

$$x_{m1+1} \triangleq v_2, x_{m1+2} \triangleq \frac{\partial^2 v_2}{\partial y_1 \partial y_2}, \ldots, x_{m1+m2} \triangleq \frac{\partial^{2m2-2} v_2}{\partial y_1^{m2-1} \partial y_2^{m2-1}},$$

$$\cdots\cdots\cdots\cdots$$

$$x_{\left[\sum_1^{s-1} mj\right]+1} \triangleq v_s, x_{\left[\sum_1^{s-1} mj\right]+2} \triangleq \frac{\partial^2 v_s}{\partial y_1 \partial y_2}, \ldots, x_{\left[\sum_1^{s} mj\right]} \triangleq \frac{\partial^{2ms-2} v_s}{\partial y_1^{ms-1} \partial y_2^{ms-1}}$$

and controls

$$u_1 \triangleq \frac{\partial^{2m1} v_1}{\partial y_1^{m1} \partial y_2^{m1}},\ u_2 \triangleq \frac{\partial^{2m2} v_2}{\partial y_1^{m2} \partial y_2^{m2}}, \ldots, u_{(s-1)} \triangleq \frac{\partial^{2m(s-1)} v_{(s-1)}}{\partial y_1^{m(s-1)} \partial y_2^{m(s-1)}}.$$

Taking the mixed $y_1 y_2$ derivative of the state gives a system of type III form—equation (2.3). Analogous comments apply to the above reduction as were made for the reduction to type I systems just considered.

2.5 NOTES, COMMENTS AND BIBLIOGRAPHY

Where the bound theorems of plasticity are invoked, the relevant model is an equilibrium or compatibility equation and is not the higher constitutive equation. This situation produces certain anomalies.

For the definition of state spaces other than that above see for example Balakrishnan (1965) and Greenberg (1971).

The above deterministic—stochastic classification of models is the one commonly accepted in systems theories. See for example Tsypkin (1971) and Bellman (1961).

For random field theory, see Wong (1971). For stochastic processes see Doob (1953), and for Markov processes see for example Doob, Bharucha-Reid (1960), Kolmogorov (1956), and Wong.

For a discussion on the three model types see Carmichael and Goh (1977). State equations type I may be found in Wang and Tung (1964) and Sirazetdinov (1964) among others. Courant and Hilbert (1962) give the further reduction of type I equations. State equations type II may be found in Lurie (1963) and Butkovskii *et al.* (1968) among others. For comments on the compatibility requirements for equation (2.2) see Ames (1965). Mention is made of Pfaffian systems in Lurie (1963) and Haack and Wendland (1972). State equations type III may be found in A. I. Egorov (1963, 1964) and Butkovskii (1969) among others.

For the reduction of ordinary differential equations to first order form see Pontryagin (1962). Some ideas on the reduction of partial differential equations is given in Courant and Hilbert (1962). Elgerd (1967) discusses various choices of state variables for a given system.

Comments on the form of equations (2.1), (2.2), and (2.3) can be found in Carmichael (1977b).

The shallow shell equations are given in Flugge (1973). See also Flugge and Timoshenko and Woinowsky-Krieger (1959) for notes on the Kirchhoff shearing force and boundary conditions.

Comments on ideas related to changing the coordinate system in the state space may found in Lanczos (1949) and Synge (1960).

See Porter (1969), for example, for the form of the response equation.

Wang and Tung (1964) give a special case of the type I reduction outlined in the Appendix above. The type II reduction is due to Armand (1972) based on Lurie (1963).

Chapter 3

Model Decomposition

3.1 INTRODUCTION

Decomposition of the system model may be considered along four lines although obvious overlapping occurs:

(a) According to the organization or construction of the model equations. Decomposition typically corresponds to equation partitioning. Examples include the partitioning of masses in a dynamic lumped parameter system representation or of nodes in a frame stiffness or flexibility representation.

(b) According to an hierarchy. There is frequently an order of magnitude change and hence a change in units on going from the system to the subsystem (as opposed to maintaining the same units for the system and subsystems for the other decomposition types). An example is a framed structure which may be decomposed into members which in turn may be decomposed into elements. This form of decomposition allows for the ready inclusion of nonlinear system behaviour and highlights the subsystem interaction of equilibrium and compatibility.

(c) According to the nature or type of control. Each subsystem has a model formulation of a different character to the other subsystems, such as for example, choosing slabs, beams and columns as the subsystems in a general building structure.

(d) Related to the independent variable interval, where the subsystems correspond with subintervals. Typical applications include the treatment of discontinuities in the state or model as occur for example at internal supports in continuous beams where the point of discontinuity represents the junction of the subsystems.

Each of these decomposition types is discussed in the following. Also, notes are given on systems that are physically staged or may be conceptually staged; alternatively such systems may be thought of as being composed of subsystems or parts serially connected. Some extensions to parallel connections are possible. There is a close relationship between staged systems and (d). Overlapping may occur between the various decomposition types as, for example, using substructure techniques of matrix structural analysis which fit (a), (b) and (c) and the staged system ideas.

The ideas on decomposition serve to highlight the modelling aspects of systems while they lead on to the multilevel optimization techniques in Chapter 11. When the decomposition is used in conjunction with optimization techniques (Chapter 11), the integrated optimization problem for the system is decomposed into subproblems with coupling. The means of handling this coupling constitute the distinction between the available multilevel optimization techniques.

The above decomposition types follow a *vertical* (or between levels (b))/*horizontal* (or within a level (a, c and d)), classification. Vertical decomposition implies an hierarchical multilevel system where the lower level subsystems and subsystem interaction may be isolated. Subsystem units and form will generally be different to that of the higher level system. Examples of vertical decomposition in the following relate to framed structures and the beam equation. For the framed structure, the subsystems in a two level hierarchy are the members with the subsystem interaction being equilibrium and compatibility at the member junctions. For the beam, the subsystems are infinitesimal elements or cross sections with equilibrium and compatibility between elements being the subsystem interaction. Typically equilibrium and compatibility relationships express subsystem interaction for vertical decomposition.

Horizontal decomposition implies that the subsystems or constituent parts are at the same level as the system, the decomposition occurring through the removal of interaction terms. Subsystem units and form will typically be similar to that of the system. Examples used later to illustrate this are a two degree of freedom system decomposed into two single degree of freedom systems; the fourth order beam equation decomposed into two groups (each of second order) representing a 'compatibility subsystem' and an 'equilibrium subsystem'; a framed structure where the node equations are uncoupled from each other; and a two span continuous beam where the spans are chosen as the subsystems. Equilibrium and compatibility may no longer be the subsystem interactions and the constituent subsystems need not have physical meaning.

The decomposition arguments advanced in the following are developed for two level formulations, the extension to many levels being straightforward. For the many levels case, horizontal and vertical decomposition may be mixed. The related optimization techniques developed in Chapter 11 are applicable for both horizontally and vertically decomposed models.

3.2 VERTICAL DECOMPOSITION

3.2.1 Decomposition According to Hierarchy

To illustrate vertical decomposition two examples, relating to framed structures and the beam equation, are used.

In essence, the vertical decomposition process involves two aspects

(a) The segregation of levels, and

(b) The recognition of the interaction between subsystems (lower level(s)) and the uncoupling of the subsystems at the lower level(s).

Framed structures. Consider a general flexibility or stiffness model (constitutive relationship) for a planar frame

$$R = K\Delta$$

where R is the structure nodal loading vector, Δ is the structure nodal displacement vector and K is the structure stiffness matrix.

For illustration purposes consider a two level hierarchy where the subsystems are the component members of the structure (system). The relevant model (constitutive relationship) at the subsystem level is

$$\begin{bmatrix} p \\ V \\ M_a \\ M_b \end{bmatrix}_i = \begin{bmatrix} EA/L & & & \\ & 12EI/L^3 & -6EI/L^2 & -6EI/L^2 \\ & -6EI/L^2 & 4EI/L & 2EI/L \\ & -6EI/L^2 & 2EI/L & 4EI/L \end{bmatrix}_i \begin{bmatrix} u \\ v \\ \phi_a \\ \phi_b \end{bmatrix}_i$$

or

$$P_i = k_i U_i$$

where E, A, I and L are the member elastic modulus, cross sectional area, moment of inertia and length respectively. P, k and U are the member end forces, stiffness matrix and member end displacements respectively.

For all N members

$$\begin{bmatrix} P_1 \\ P_2 \\ \vdots \\ P_N \end{bmatrix} = \begin{bmatrix} k_1 & & & \\ & k_2 & & \\ & & \ddots & \\ & & & k_N \end{bmatrix} \begin{bmatrix} U_1 \\ U_2 \\ \vdots \\ U_N \end{bmatrix}$$

or

$$F = k\delta.$$

Subsystem interaction is expressed through compatibility and equilibrium at nodes or junctions of the members. Compatibility reads

$$\delta = A_{*}\Delta$$

where A_{*} is the displacement transformation matrix. Equilibrium reads

$$R = A_{*}^{\mathrm{T}}F.$$

Obviously the subsystem models combine through their interaction relationships (compatibility and equilibrium) to produce the system model, where

$$K = A_{*}^{\mathrm{T}}kA_{*}$$

In decomposing a structural system, the reverse procedure would be followed, namely starting with the system model and ending with the subsystem models and the subsystem interaction. Note that the subsystem models are uncoupled, the coupling being provided by the subsystem interaction.

The beam equation. In first order form, the beam equation may be written

$$\begin{bmatrix} \dfrac{\mathrm{d}w}{\mathrm{d}y} = \theta \\ \dfrac{\mathrm{d}\theta}{\mathrm{d}y} = \dfrac{M}{EI} \\ \dfrac{\mathrm{d}M}{\mathrm{d}y} = S \\ \dfrac{\mathrm{d}S}{\mathrm{d}y} = q \end{bmatrix}$$

where w is the beam displacement, θ the slope, M the internal bending moment, S the internal shearing force and q is an applied distributed load.

This is equation (c) of Chapter 1 with conventional structures notation replacing the state variable and control variable notation.

For flexural behaviour the relevant model at the subsystem (infinitesimal element or cross section) level is the moment–curvature relationship

$$M(y)/E(y)I(y) = 1/r(y)$$

where $1/r$ is the curvature.

Subsystem interaction is expressed through element equilibrium and compatibility. Equilibrium is

$$dM/dy = S \qquad dS/dy = q.$$

Compatibility is

$$1/r = d^2w/dy^2$$

or in first order form

$$dw/dy = \theta \qquad d\theta/dy = 1/r.$$

It is seen that the subsystem models are uncoupled with the coupling or interaction provided by equilibrium and compatibility. Here the number of subsystems is infinite. Elements of finite size and finite in number may be obtained by using a finite difference approximation to the above derivatives.

3.3 HORIZONTAL DECOMPOSITION

3.3.1 Decomposition According to the Construction of the Model

3.3.1.1 EXAMPLES

Three illustrations are used to illustrate this form of decomposition. Conventional structures notation is used. These are then shown to belong to standard approaches existing in the control literature. These standard approaches are given for the four main models of interest, namely algebraic models, ordinary differential equation models, partial differential equation models and difference equation models.

Structural dynamics. For the two degree of freedom system ('far-coupled' assuming flexible girders) shown in Fig. 3.1, the equations of motion (undamped case) are

$$M_1\ddot{w}_1 + k_1w_1 - k_2(w_2 - w_1) = F_1(t)$$
$$M_2\ddot{w}_2 + k_2(w_2 - w_1) + k_3w_2 = F_2(t)$$

or in the matrix form

$$\begin{bmatrix} M_1\ddot{w}_1 \\ M_2\ddot{w}_2 \end{bmatrix} + \begin{bmatrix} k_1 - k_2 & -k_2 \\ -k_2 & k_2 + k_3 \end{bmatrix} \begin{bmatrix} w_1 \\ w_2 \end{bmatrix} = \begin{bmatrix} F_1(t) \\ F_2(t) \end{bmatrix}$$

or in first order state equation form

$$\dot{w}_1 = v_1$$
$$\dot{v}_1 = 1/M_1[F_1 - k_1w_1 + k_2(w_2 - w_1)]$$
$$\dot{w}_2 = v_2$$
$$\dot{v}_2 = 1/M_2[F_2 - k_2(w_2 - w_1) - k_3w_2]$$

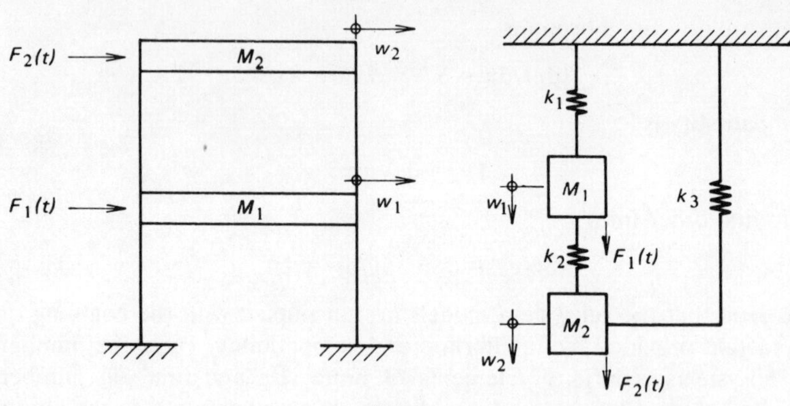

Fig. 3.1

Superposed dots denote differentiation with respect to time. v_1 and v_2 are velocities of M_1 and M_2 respectively.

The system model (equations of motion, constitutive relationship) may be conveniently broken into two subsystem models, corresponding to the behaviour of each of the two masses. Coupling is through the $k_2(w_2 - w_1)$ term which is reflected in the off-diagonal terms in the matrix form.

In general for a system having N masses and N degrees of freedom, the equations of motion in second order form are

$$M\ddot{w} + kw = F(t)$$

where M is a diagonal $N \times N$ matrix, $w = (w_1, w_2, \ldots, w_N)^T$, k is an $N \times N$ matrix stiffness coefficient matrix, and $F = (F_1, F_2, \ldots, F_N)^T$. The off diagonal terms in the k matrix provide the coupling between subsystems. In first order form

$$\dot{x} = \Phi x + \text{forcing function contribution}$$

where $x = (w_1, v_1, \ldots, w_N, v_N)^T$ is the state vector and Φ is a matrix (transition matrix, fundamental matrix, principal matrix).

A framed structure. Consider the frame and loading shown in Fig. 3.2. The structure stiffness equations read, considering bending effects only,

$$\begin{bmatrix} M_2 \\ M_3 \\ 0 \end{bmatrix} = \begin{bmatrix} 8EI/L & 2EI/L & -6EI/L^2 \\ & 8EI/L & -6EI/L^2 \\ \text{symmetric} & & 24EI/L^3 \end{bmatrix} \begin{bmatrix} \theta_2 \\ \theta_3 \\ \delta \end{bmatrix}$$

where θ_2, θ_3, and δ are the structure rotations at nodes 2 and 3, and horizontal displacement respectively, M_2 and M_3 are the 'fixed end' moments for member 2–3, E is the material modulus, I is the member moment of inertia, and L is the member length.

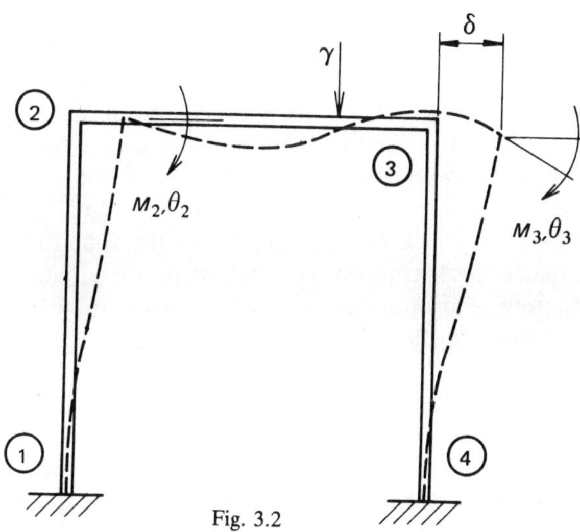

Fig. 3.2

The most convenient way of decomposing this model in a horizontal sense is to isolate the equations corresponding to the rotations and the displacement from each other. Several choices of interaction are possible.

For a vertical decomposition, the uncoupled subsystem models are

$$\begin{bmatrix} M_{12} \\ M_{21} \\ M_{23} \\ M_{32} \\ M_{34} \\ M_{43} \end{bmatrix} = \begin{bmatrix} 4EI/I & 2EI/L & & & & \\ & 4EI/L & & & & \\ & & 4EI/L & 2EI/L & & \\ & & & 4EI/L & & \\ & & & & 4EI/L & 2EI/L \\ \text{symmetric} & & & & & 4EI/L \end{bmatrix} \begin{bmatrix} \phi_{12} \\ \phi_{21} \\ \phi_{23} \\ \phi_{32} \\ \phi_{34} \\ \phi_{43} \end{bmatrix}$$

with interaction

$$\begin{bmatrix} \phi_{12} \\ \phi_{21} \\ \phi_{23} \\ \phi_{32} \\ \phi_{34} \\ \phi_{43} \end{bmatrix} = \begin{bmatrix} 0 & 0 & -1/L \\ 1 & 0 & -1/L \\ 1 & 0 & 0 \\ 0 & 1 & 0 \\ 0 & 1 & -1/L \\ 0 & 0 & -1/L \end{bmatrix} \begin{bmatrix} \theta_2 \\ \theta_3 \\ \delta \end{bmatrix}$$

$$\begin{bmatrix} M_2 \\ M_3 \\ 0 \end{bmatrix} = \begin{bmatrix} 0 & 1 & 1 & 0 & 0 & 0 \\ 0 & 0 & 0 & 1 & 1 & 0 \\ -1/L & -1/L & 0 & 0 & -1/L & -1/L \end{bmatrix} \begin{bmatrix} M_{12} \\ M_{21} \\ M_{23} \\ M_{32} \\ M_{34} \\ M_{43} \end{bmatrix}$$

where the M's and ϕ's are the member end moments and rotations respectively.

The beam equation. For the previously given beam equation or its discrete equivalent, horizontal decomposition may be performed in several ways. The two obvious decompositions are (a) to break the four first order equations into four parts, but this gives considerable interaction between parts, or (b) to break the four first order equations into two parts, each comprising two first order equations. Compatibility type equations and equilibrium type equations may be recognized with interaction through the term M.

3.3.1.2 FORMAL CONTROL THEORY DESCRIPTION

The ideas expressed in the preceding examples can be shown to belong to standard control theory techniques of horizontal decomposition. Consider algebraic, differential and difference equation models in turn.

Algebraic (non-difference) equation models. Consider a system (composed of N subsystems or constituent parts) given by

$$F(x, u) = 0 \tag{3.1}$$

where $F = (F^{1\mathrm{T}}, \ldots, F^{N\mathrm{T}})^{\mathrm{T}}$, $x = (x^{1\mathrm{T}}, \ldots, x^{N\mathrm{T}})^{\mathrm{T}}$, and $u = (u^{1\mathrm{T}}, \ldots, u^{N\mathrm{T}})^{\mathrm{T}}$ and F^i, x^i and u^i may be vector quantities, and the superscript relates to the relevant subsystem.

The subsystems may be modelled as

$$F^i(x^i, u^i, \pi^i) = 0 \tag{3.2}$$

and the interaction or coupling between subsystems as

$$\pi^i = \gamma^i(x^j, u^j) \qquad j = 1, \ldots, N; j \neq i. \tag{3.3}$$

Here π^i are the interconnection variables that relate subsystem i to the remaining $(N - 1)$ subsystems, and γ^i is a general function of the arguments shown.

For the frame structure example, one approach is to set

$$\begin{aligned} &\pi^1 \triangleq \delta \\ &\pi_1^2 \triangleq EI, \quad \pi_2^2 \triangleq \theta_2, \quad \pi_3^2 \triangleq \theta_3. \end{aligned}$$

This gives the system model as

$$\begin{aligned} M_2 &= 8EI\theta_2/L + 2EI\theta_3/L - 6EI\pi^1/L^2 \\ M_3 &= 2EI\theta_2/L + 8EI\theta_3/L - 6EI\pi^1/L^2 \end{aligned}$$

and

$$0 = -6\pi_1^2\pi_2^2/L^2 - 6\pi_1^2\pi_3^2/L^2 + 24\pi_1^2\delta/L$$

which are two uncoupled sets of equations.

Ordinary differential equation models. Consider an n'th order system

$$dx(y)/dy = f[x(y), u(y), y]. \tag{3.4}$$

The system may be decomposed into N subsystems or constituent parts, each of dimension n^i such that

$$\sum_{i=1}^{N} n^i = n \tag{3.5}$$

$$\frac{dx^i(y)}{dy} = f^i[x^i(y), \pi^i(y), u^i(y), y]. \tag{3.6}$$

The interconnection between subsystems is provided by

$$\pi^i(y) = \gamma^i(x^j, u^j) \qquad j = 1, \ldots, N; \quad j \neq i. \tag{3.7}$$

Note that x^i, u^i, π^i, f^i, and γ^i may all be vector quantities.

For the beam equation

$$\begin{aligned} dx_1/dy &= x_2 \\ dx_2/dy &= x_3/u \\ dx_3/dy &= x_4 \\ dx_4/dy &= q \end{aligned}$$

two possible decompositions are

(a) to let $\pi^1 \triangleq x_2$, $\pi^2 \triangleq x_3$, and $\pi^3 \triangleq x_4$ giving four subsystems

$$\begin{aligned} dx_1/dy &= \pi^1 \\ dx_2/dy &= \pi^2/u \\ dx_3/dy &= \pi^3 \\ dx_4/dy &= q \end{aligned}$$

(b) to let $\pi^1 \triangleq x_3$, giving two subsystems

$$\begin{aligned} dx_1/dy &= x_2 & \qquad dx_3/dy &= x_4 \\ dx_2/dy &= \pi^1/u & \qquad dx_4/dy &= q \end{aligned}$$

The subsystems are of an equilibrium type and a compatibility type. In Chapter 11 it is shown that solutions for the associated optimization problem can be constructed from solutions that satisfy equilibrium and solutions that satisfy compatibility.

For the two degree of freedom system, setting $x_1 \triangleq w_1$, $x_2 \triangleq \dot{w}_1$, $x_3 \triangleq w_2$, $x_4 \triangleq \dot{w}_2$, $u_1 \triangleq k_1$, $u_2 \triangleq k_2$, and $u_3 \triangleq k_3$, and assuming M_1 and M_2

are constant

$$\begin{aligned}
\dot{x}_1 &= x_2 \\
\dot{x}_2 &= 1/M_1[F_1 - u_1 x_1 - u_2(x_3 - x_1)] \\
\dot{x}_3 &= x_4 \\
\dot{x}_4 &= 1/M_2[F_2 - u_2(x_3 - x_1) - u_3 x_3].
\end{aligned}$$

The system may be decomposed by setting

$$\pi_1^1 \triangleq x_3, \qquad \pi_2^1 \triangleq u_2, \qquad \pi^2 \triangleq x_1$$

to give two subsystems associated with mass 1 and mass 2 respectively

$$\begin{aligned}
\dot{x}_1 &= x_2 \\
\dot{x}_2 &= 1/M_1[F_1 - u_1 x_1 - \pi_2^1(\pi_1^1 - x_1)]
\end{aligned}$$

and

$$\begin{aligned}
\dot{x}_3 &= x_4 \\
\dot{x}_4 &= 1/M_2[F_2 - u_2(x_3 - \pi^2) - u_3 x_3].
\end{aligned}$$

Difference equation models may be decomposed in an entirely analogous fashion to the ordinary differential equation models. *Partial differential equation models* are most conveniently treated by discretization first to give difference or ordinary differential equation models.

3.3.2 Decomposition of the Independent Variable Interval

For a system model

$$\mathrm{d}x(y)/\mathrm{d}y = f[x, u, y] \qquad y \in [y^{\mathrm{L}}, y^{\mathrm{R}}] \tag{3.8}$$

with given state boundary conditions at y^{L} and y^{R}, assume that at some known conditions of the form

$$\psi[x(y'), y'] = 0 \tag{3.9}$$

there exists a discontinuity in the model or in the state. A convenient way to handle this problem is to decompose the interval into two subintervals from y^{L} to y' and from y' to y^{R}. For the first subinternal

$$\mathrm{d}x^1/\mathrm{d}y = f^1[x^1, u^1, y] \tag{3.10}$$

and for the second subinterval

$$\mathrm{d}x^2/\mathrm{d}y = f^2[x^2, u^2, y] \tag{3.11}$$

where x^1 and x^2 and y' and y'^{+} are related by

$$\begin{aligned}
y' - y'^{+} &= 0 \\
h[x^1(y'), y'] - x^2(y'^{+}) &= 0.
\end{aligned} \tag{3.12}$$

Consider symmetric two span continuous beam as an example with the centre support located at y'. There

$$x_1(y') = 0$$
$$x_2(y') = 0$$

which are of the form (3.9), and

$$x_1^1(y') - x_1^2(y'^+) = 0$$
$$-x_2^1(y') - x_2^2(y'^+) = 0$$
$$x_3^1(y') - x_3^2(y'^+) = 0$$
$$-x_4^1(y') - x_4^2(y'^+) = 0$$

which are of the form (3.12).

3.3.3 Decomposition According to the Nature of the Control

Generally such decompositions can be made to fit the other mentioned decomposition forms. The subsystems typically have different mathematical formulations.

3.4 STAGED SYSTEMS

Where the structure is essentially 'undirectional', for example a transmission tower, a cantilever, . . . , the structure may be regarded as being physically staged. For example a tall building may be regarded as staged according to storey heights if the structure is given a 'direction' from its base to the top or vice versa. Transfer matrix ideas are important here. A structure may also be staged conceptually even if no apparent physical staging is present. For example, members in a truss may be numbered and the staging taken to follow the numbering system.

Consider as an example the discrete version of the beam equation (replacing the derivatives by finite difference approximations),

$$x_1(k+1) = x_1(k) + \Delta x_2(k)$$
$$x_2(k+1) = x_2(k) + \Delta x_3(k)/u(k)$$
$$x_3(k+1) = x_3(k) + \Delta x_4(k)$$
$$x_4(k+1) = x_4(k) + \Delta q(k)$$

where Δ represents the discretization interval size. In general form

$$x(k+1) = f[x(k), u(k), k]. \tag{3.13}$$

That is the beam may be regarded as being divided into elements of size Δ. Each element represents a stage.

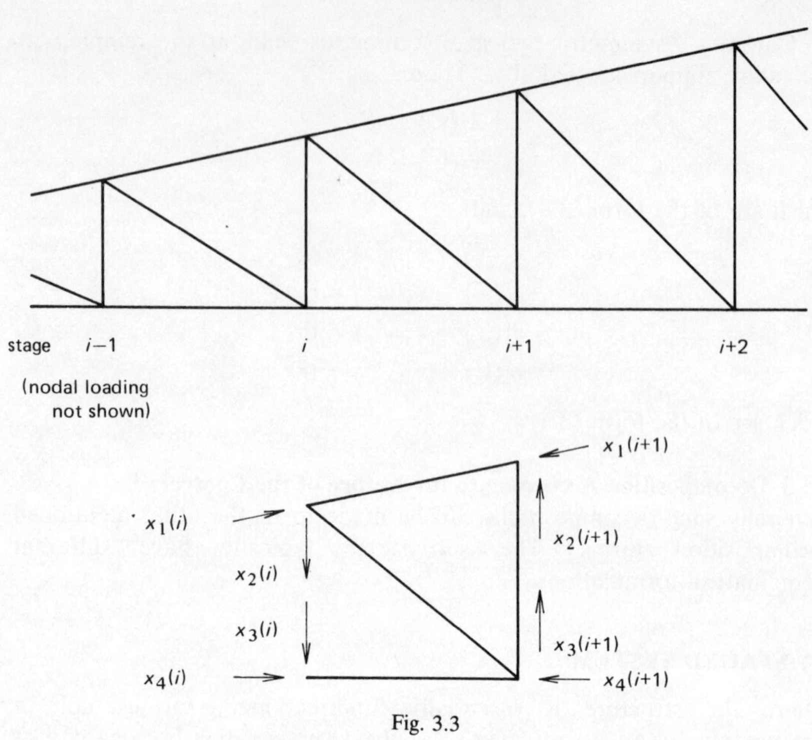

Fig. 3.3

Consider as a second example the truss shown in Fig. 3.3. The truss may be partitioned into stages representing substructures. Each substructure is coupled to the adjacent substructures. The state variables denoted $x = (x_1, x_2, x_3, x_4)^T$ are shown in the figure and represent the interacting forces between substructures. The controls for any stage are the geometric and material properties of the relevant substructure.

3.5 NOTES, COMMENTS AND BIBLIOGRAPHY

[3.1] See for example the seminal work of Mesarovic *et al*. (1970) and Mesarovic (1973) for the distinction between vertical and horizontal decomposition. The presentation uses abstract set theory notation.

The classification of the various decomposition types follows Schoeffler (1971b). See also Mahmoud (1977a).

Substructure analysis is well treated in Przemieniecki (1968).

Decomposition type ideas have been used in the structural optimization literature by Kirsch (1975), Kirsch and Moses (1979), Kirsch *et al*. (1972), Vanderplaats and Moses (1972), Baker *et al*. (1978) and Arora and Govril (1977).

Other notes on decomposition, staging and related topics can be found in Chapter 11.

[3.2] See Clyde (1970a) and Carmichael and Clyde (1975).

For a completely general theory for structures it will require a partitioning of the state vector into generalized forces and generalized displacements. A correspondence with existing structural practice would then be evident.

[3.3] Beliveau (1977) gives the relation between the second order and first order structural dynamics models. Generally for computational purposes the second order form is preferred, but for generality in derivations and discussions the first order form is preferred.

For algebraic models see Bauman (1968a) and the references of Mahmoud (1977a).

Note that the given horizontal decomposition for the frame in general is not possible if members are chosen as the subsystems as in general there will be more or less equations comprising the structure constitutive relationship than there are members. Choosing the nodes as the constituent parts or subsystems is reminiscent of the 'method of joints' for analyzing statically determinate trusses. It is also a valid method of analyzing structures using graph theory where either members or joints may be taken as the nodes of a linear graph. In choosing the member nodes as the subsystems, nodal equilibrium and compatibility become the subsystem model with the constitutive equations for the members becoming interaction. For linear graph modelling of structures see Fenves and Branin (1963), Fenves (1966a), Fenves and Gonzalez-Caro (1971) and Spillers (1972).

1.2 The horizontal decomposition ideas for ordinary differential equations follow Smith and Sage (1973a) and Guinzy and Sage (1973).

The decomposition of difference equations is given in Fry and Sage (1973). Wismer (1969, 1971b, 1973) discretizes partial differential equations before decomposing.

2 In the control literature this is referred to as trajectory decomposition (Bauman 1968a, 1968b, 1971).

[3.4] For transfer matrices see Pestel and Leckie (1963) and Livesley (1964).

Examples of physical staging can be seen in Palmer (1973) and references of Palmer. Conceptual staging can be seen in Kalaba (1962) and Khachaturian and Haider (1966). For staging in trusses see Singaraj and Rao (1972, 1975).

For comments on staged systems see Ray and Szekely (1973).

Part B

Design

Chapter 4

Design in a Systems Sense

4.1 GENERAL

An examination of the total structural design process may be profitably undertaken using the approach of 'systems engineering' with its methodology based essentially on generalizations of real case histories. Established structural design procedures are seen to be iterative in nature. The iterations arise from the analysis-based mode of attack on the design problem and are not inherent in design. By suitably defining the design problem, it is shown that much of the iterative process of established structural design procedures may be eliminated if emphasis is placed on a synthetic approach. Generally a structure will be synthesized in an optimal sense, with the optimization being performed in terms of a criterion derived from imposed (often subjective) value statements. Using the modelling procedures of the previous sections, it is shown that the optimum design problem is now within the realm of the well delineated body of theory and techniques of optimal control systems. In this sense the design problem is a single-level or multilevel, single-goal problem. Extensions to multiple goal problems are considered.

4.2 THE DESIGN PROCESS

The logic of the evolution of a design may be conveniently interpreted in the six stages of problem definition, value system definition, system generation, system evaluation, selection and action. The order of attack is as critical as the development of a rational system model and strongly influences the final design. By providing such a construction from which to work, each stage may be given a correct perspective. Feedback may occur within stages in an effort to refine the problem at any of the six stages, while a certain merging or overlapping may be noticeable between successive stages. A systematic approach to the hierarchy of stages in the design process will generate clear thinking at each stage

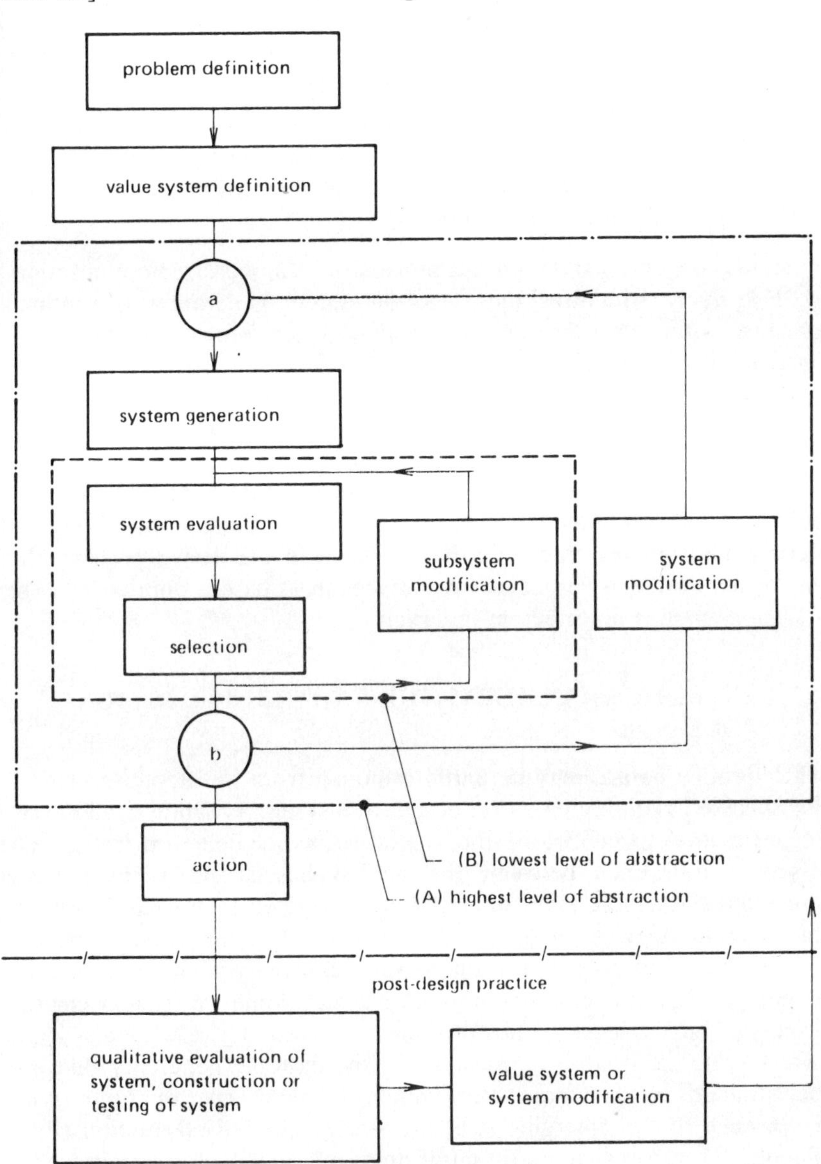

Fig. 4.1 Structural design process

and lend objectivity to a procedure which would otherwise be considered qualitative or intuitive.

Expressed in systems terms, the conventional notion of 'structural design', being a phase of the total design process, may be viewed as a closed loop operation of iterative modification and feedback to the analysis stage (designated by the full lines in Fig. 4.1). The terminal points of the loop cycle are based, respectively;

(a) *initial*, upon a postulated system extrapolated from experience or based on an idea (third stage of the total design process), and

(b) *final*, upon satisfaction of a prearranged performance specification (fifth stage of the total design process).

In short, conventional design is a process of trial and error optimization.

For many structures the stage of system generation is routinely obvious with the subsystem interrelations predefined by mechanics. Systems are commonly divided into lower level subsystems ('subsystem delineation') to produce a tractable model and a tractable design subproblem, although certain inconsistencies in the modelling procedure will be noticeable. In particular there exists an interdependence of each level, requiring knowledge at a higher level when designing a lower level subsystem. No isolated systems exist. The introduction of a series of design subproblems creates further iteration in the design process (that is further to that produced by an analysis-based approach). This iteration again is not inherent in design.

4.3 SYNTHETIC TRANSFORMATIONS WITHIN THE DESIGN PROCESS

The iterative nature may be partly removed from the design process, if for specified requirements of a design, the system is synthesized *directly* to meet the specification, the operative word being 'directly'. The essential difference between the analysis-based and synthesis-based procedures is at the level of abstraction adopted in the computations. (The terminology 'level of abstraction' is used in the sense relating to the quantity of *a priori* data assumed.) Analysis-based techniques impose a total system configuration *ab initio*, while the system emerges from *any* given level of abstraction as a natural consequence of the direct synthetic treatment. Presumably the extreme generality that may be attained in the direct case would involve little or no *a priori* knowledge of the emerging structure—refer level of abstraction (A) in Fig. 4.1. However, for a solution of practical significance, certain leading properties of the system configuration are best assumed—the corresponding level of abstraction is intermediate between levels (A) and (B) in Fig. 4.1. The choice of abstraction level on which the designer chooses to work would be a balance between his engineering judgements and desired computation load. A synthesis-type treatment can only proceed where certain of the system properties remain free and adjustable. It is apparent that a synthesis-type format to design is the fundamental and at the same time more rational approach.

4.4 THE THEORY OF OPTIMAL CONTROL SYSTEMS

Generally one desires to synthesize a system which is optimal in a certain sense; a design criterion or index, resulting from an imposed value statement, is implied. Optimum system design is of central concern in optimum control theory which exploits the synthetic nature of the problem. It is the philosophy of this theory that will be found most useful in the structural design problem. The philosophy rests on very broad grounds, typical of techniques in systems theory, only conversing in the entities state and control (and sometimes response), which take on very definite meanings in the design problem.

In simple terms, synthesis is thus equivalent to choosing the controls throughout the structure; optimal synthesis or optimal control selects the controls so as to extremize some design criterion. In addition supplementary design constraints are also usually present. It is the theory of control that is concerned with the mathematical formulation of laws for the control of systems. These comments are amplified in later chapters following the introduction of the necessary terminology (Chapter 5).

Optimal control theory in other engineering branches has elevated the 'art' of design to a status approaching a systematic and exact 'science'. This has occurred despite the everpresent yet necessary 'engineering judgements', which recognize the existence in all designs of certain intangible quantities that defy precise mathematical statements. This theory offers the same advantages to structural design.

4.5 NOTES, COMMENTS AND BIBLIOGRAPHY

[4.1] The term 'systems engineering' is used in the sense of Hall (1962) as distinct from a systems theory (for example Klir 1969) or a control systems theory (for example Fel'dbaum 1965).

Comments on the 'systems approach' to the design problem as mentioned in the Preface may be found in Hall (1962), Hare (1967) and Jenkins (1969).

[4.2] For the logic of design see Hall (1962). See also Khachaturian (1968), Clyde (1970a) and Majid (1974).

Very lucid discussions on the philosophy of design may be found in Gregory (1963), Pister (1972), and Porter (1969).

Au (1966) discusses structural design as a game. The papers of Traum and Zalewski (1968) and Fenves (1966b) are also of interest. A game theoretic approach is given by Banichuk (1973, 1975, 1976).

Hall (1962) mentions 'subsystems delineation'. The inconsistencies in the modelling procedure have been noted by Clyde (1970a).

[4.3] See also Brotchie (1967) and Rozvany (1966a).

The usual technical papers on synthetic type approaches relate to a *design tool* and not *design itself*. That is, they assume a design concept has already been selected and that an appropriate mathematical model for the class of structure exists. Hence this is towards the lower level of abstraction.

Properties of the structure which are given or assumed are sometimes termed 'preassigned parameters' or simply 'parameters'. These quantities together with the control (design) variables, will completely define a design. They are invariant in the design process. For example where the layout of a truss is assumed and it is only required to determine the cross section properties, then the member lengths, node locations and support conditions might be referred to as parameters. Cross section properties are the control (design) variables.

In general the more parameters known (that is, the lower the level of abstraction) the easier the design problem.

Note the concept of a 'parameter study' means a 'control (design) variable study' in the present terminology. Parameters are regarded as fixed entities in any problem.

References to structural synthesis (direct design) are Francis (1953, 1955), Schmidt (1958), Lin (1961, 1963), Brotchie (1962, 1963, 1964) and Van der Neut (1949) among others. Hillerborg's work on reinforced concrete slabs is related. See also the work reported in Majid (1974).

References where optimization ideas are used to determine the feedback in an iterative analysis approach include Hughes and Mistree (1975, 1977) and Hughes *et al*. (1977). See also Kavlie and Powell (1971) and Kirsch and Rubinstein (1972).

Background to the design problem. The fervour of research in the field of *system optimization* in recent years has yielded a theory with a certain amount of maturity. Certainly realistic problems are now tractable using the concepts and techniques offered by 'modern' control theory.

Historically, the aerospace, electrical, chemical and mechanical engineering disciplines have promoted the development of this more substantial theory in an attempt to satisfy more stringent design specifications and operating conditions. The merging of ideas in these disciplines under a general control systems theory has stimulated the recent research impetus through drawing upon the results and experience in these separate branches of engineering. Modern control theory, in these disciplines, has supplanted design tools that were largely graphical or qualitative in character and a design process of a trial and error nature. It is now firmly entrenched in these disciplines as a result of its proven utility in design. The introduction of the digital computer may be partly credited with this change in design philosophy.

The related (and largely subsumed) field of *structural optimization*, however, has tended in many cases to proceed along established structural design avenues, with the result that progress has been slow and the level of realism of many problems tractable has been all too low. Nevertheless, the field has received heightened interest in recent professional journals. A review of the field may mention the *surveys* of Wasiutynski and Brandt (1963), Barnett (1966), Gerard (1966), Kowalik (1966), Rozvany (1966a), Schmit (1969a, 1969b), Sheu and Prager (1968), Pierson (1972a), Olhoff (1976), Niordson and Pedersen (1973), McIntosh (1974), and Venkayya (1978) among others; the *monographs* of Cox (1965), Owen (1965), Rozvany (1976), Hemp (1973), Spillers (1975a), Majid (1974), Distefano (1974a), Gallagher and Zienkiewicz (1973), Fox (1971), Spunt (1971), Prager (1974), Schmit (1974), Sawczuk and Mroz (1975), Rozvany and Hill (1976), Save and Massonet (1972), AGARD-CP-36-70, AGARD-AG-149-71, and AGARD-CP-123, and a recent AIAA film (1972) on the subject. See also Dym (1974b), Venkayya and Khot (1974), Cohn (1968), Cyras (1975), Cohn and Maier (1977) and Haug (1977). Certainly publications in the field have been very profuse, and while the 'state of the art' reviews above concentrate much of the essential literature, they are far from exhaustive.

Individual contributions to the structural optimization literature are cited in the following chapters.

Analogies between structural optimization problems and problems in optimal control (and also multistage decision theory) have recently been employed to give an extended range of optimization solution techniques. However in some cases there appears to be no realization of the significance of their analogies (in terms of modelling of their structure and the components of the design problem) apart from a direct application of mathematical techniques to the optimum problem.

The earliest established analogies appear as essential steps in the transition to a more systematized and formalized control approach. It should be emphasized that the solution techniques used in control are solely extensions to established mathematical extremization processes available prior to the advancement of systems concepts. Hence the adoption of control's solution techniques in structural applications appears natural in the evolution of structural optimization. However, it is the conceptual framework of control theory which offers the power to the approach.

Chapter 5

The Optimal Control Problem

5.1 INTRODUCTION

The problem of developing an optimal system is one of finding an admissible control such that the system functions according to the design objective. A more formal statement will be given later. The design objective or criterion is expressed analytically as a functional or function with, in general, both state and control variable arguments. Certain physical, operational and engineering constraints may be present, restricting the control choice. This choice may also be simplified if the search is confined to certain classes of systems (for example shell action, plate action). The problem is thus one of choosing the system control such that the system operates in some best way, while observing the constraints present. An extremization of the criterion is implied.

The formulation of an optimal control problem requires the following components.

(i) A model of the system to be controlled (refer Part A). This is the constitutive equation (together where applicable with end-state conditions and response transformation) ideally expressed in one of the standard forms detailed in Part A. It characterizes the system and enables the effect of alternative controls on the system to be predicted.

(ii) The constraints upon the design (section 5.2). Constraints limit the range of permissible solutions and fix many of the system properties.

(iii) The demands presented to the system in the form of a design goal (objective, criterion or index) (section 5.3). The criterion is derived from a design value statement. To evaluate possible alternative solutions, a scalar index is introduced. The problem is to determine the control that gives the least or greatest value of this index.

Solution controls are said to be *feasible* if they satisfy the system model and are within the permissible bounds as defined by the constraints. Where a range of feasible solutions exists the problem is considered *well posed*. The design goal provides the criterion by which the optimal control is chosen from the set of feasible controls in order that the constraints are satisfied in the best manner.

Using a state and control foundation, superficially different design problems may be shown to share a common mathematical basis, leading to common solution techniques (Part C).

The following outline of the optimal control problem is primarily for the single level, single criterion case. Comments on the multicriteria case are given following the initial single level, single criterion presentation but the formal development of multicriteria (Chapter 10) and multilevel (Chapter 11) problems is saved for their respective chapters.

The outline is given for the general optimal control problem corresponding to the single level state models of Chapter 2. Specializing to discrete systems and algebraic systems follows straightforwardly.

5.2 DESIGN CONSTRAINTS

5.2.1 Introduction

Constraints influence the design solution characteristics by isolating admissible solutions from all possible solutions, and give meaning to the choice of the optimal system. Constraints may be defined on certain subsets, boundaries or throughout the Y domain and will be given in the form of inequalities or equalities.

In a sense the previous system equations may be regarded as (differential) equality constraints over the total Y domain. The system is constrained to belong to the class of systems whose constitutive relationships are of this form. Terminal and boundary conditions may be likewise treated as equality constraints at $t^{L,R}$ and on ∂D respectively.

Constraints typically restrict the freedom of location of the state and control variables in their respective function spaces. The range of possible values that the states and controls may assume is reduced to a set of *admissible* values. (The idea of admissibility will be later extended to include allowable classes of functions.)

The following three articles categorize the constraints according to whether they relate to the control (section 5.2.2), state (section 5.2.3) or combined control and state (section 5.2.4). A further article (section 5.2.5) on reliability constraints has been included because of the present popularity of the subject in the structures literature, although it can be shown that it falls within the previous constraint categories.

5.2.2 Constraints on the Control

Geometric, material and related physical properties, functional and aesthetic considerations of the design restrict the choice of the control vector u to lie within a set or region U in the space of the control.

$$u(y) \in U \qquad \forall y \in Y \tag{5.1}$$

The admissible region U may vary with the parameters $\{y_i; i = 1, \ldots\}$.

$$U = U(y)$$

Controls satisfying the above requirement are termed admissible controls. Of particular interest will be constraints such that

$$U \triangleq \{u; h_j^{(1)}[y, u(y)] \leq 0, j = 1, 2, \ldots, m^{(1)}\}$$
$$m^{(1)} \leq r \quad \text{for equality constraints} \tag{5.2}$$

where $h_j^{(1)}$ are prescribed functions of the arguments shown. The sense of the inequality is taken as less than or equal to zero without loss of generality.

As an illustration, physical limitations may restrict the rigidity, u_i, of structural members $\{i;\ i = 1, \ldots, r\}$, for all y, in which case the constraint assumes the form

$$0 \leq u_i \leq a_i \qquad i = 1, \ldots, r$$

or

$$(u_i - a_i) \leq 0, \qquad -u_i \leq 0$$

where the a_i are prescribed. The admissible region U in this case is a closed, bounded and convex set. In finite dimensions it may be geometrically interpreted as an r-dimensional polyhedron.

5.2.3 Constraints on the State

Similar bounds on the coordinates $x_1, \ldots, x_n$ of the state vector may be expressed;

$$x(y) \in X \qquad \forall y \in Y \tag{5.3}$$

where

$$X = X(y).$$

The state is constrained to lie within the set or region X defined in the state space. The admissible region will usually take the form

$$X \triangleq \{x; h_k^{(2)}[y, x(y), \ldots, \partial_l x(y), \ldots] \leq 0, k = 1, 2, \ldots\} \tag{5.4}$$

where $l = (l_1, \ldots)$ and $h_k^{(2)}$ are prescribed functions of the arguments shown.

State constraints represent imposed limitations on the system behaviour over space and time. The most obvious examples would be limitations on the structure displacements and rotations, internal moments and shearing forces, and include the notion of 'limit states' as a special case.

In general the state will be required to satisfy certain end conditions (equality constraints) at the left and/or right interval limits of the independent variables $\{y_i; i = 1, \ldots\}$. These are commonly termed state boundary and terminal conditions (Chapter 2).

5.2.4 Mixed State and Control Constraints

Frequently constraints imposed on designs are not expressions of either x or u alone. Rather, functions of both the state and control may be restricted to some admissible region V say, defined on the state-control product space. Analogous to the previous constraint formalisms, of most concern will be admissible regions

$$V \triangleq \{(x, u); h_i^{(3)}[y, x(y), \ldots, \partial_l x(y), \ldots, u(y)] \leq 0, i = 1, 2, \ldots, m^{(3)}\}$$
$$m^{(3)} \leq r \quad \text{for equality constraints} \qquad (5.5)$$

where the ordered pair $(x, u) \in V$, $V = V(y)$, $h_i^{(3)}$ are functions of the given arguments, and $l = (l_1, \ldots)$.

Many existing approaches to optimum structural design classify their design constraints according to whether they are 'geometric' or 'behavioural'. The classification terms suggest that the equivalent constraints would generally be grouped under the present 'control' and 'state' constraints respectively. Often no distinction is made in existing design approaches for constraints which are combinations of the two types of constraints (that is geometric-behavioural), possibly because the associated design techniques are not strongly influenced by classification in a design model. Techniques to be outlined in Part C however reflect, and in fact are determined by, the form of any constraints present.

Where the system is stochastic, (5.1) to (5.5) may be replaced by expressions giving the mathematical expectations of the constraint. For example (5.5) becomes

$$E\{h_i^{(3)}[y, x(y), \ldots, \partial_l x(y), \ldots, u(y)]\} \leq 0 \qquad i = 1, 2, \ldots, m^{(3)}. \quad (5.6)$$

5.2.5 Reliability Constraint

The requirement that a structure function without 'failure' is fundamental. 'Failure' is implied in the sense of exceeding a certain limit state, corresponding, for example, to measures of unserviceability or instability.

For stochastic systems, a scalar-valued constraint, the system reliability, is employed to ensure the successful functioning of the system. The equivalent constraint for deterministic systems is embodied in the concept of 'factor of safety'.

Reliability constraints can be shown to be mixed state-control constraints or state-only constraints. Reliability as a design criterion is considered in the following section.

5.3 DESIGN OPTIMALITY CRITERIA

Optimality criteria provide the means of quantitatively assessing alternative designs. The design solutions are only optimal in the sense of the criteria which follow from the design problem statements, although computational tractability reasons may warrant introducing alternative, simpler criteria. The latter criteria obviously lead to suboptimal designs with respect to the original criteria.

Optimality implies an extremization requirement on some measure J, the *optimality criterion*. In general this measure will be a functional of both state and control functions and will be a scalar quantity

$$\hat{J} \triangleq \text{ext}\, J(x, u, y) \qquad \forall y \in Y. \tag{5.7}$$

The criterion J may be thought of as assigning a unique real number to each admissible solution. The optimum $\hat{J}$ is chosen from the many feasible values of J. Alternatively J may be considered as a function in which the controls play the role of the independent variables. The criterion derives from an imposed value system, the correct identification of which remains essential for a meaningful design. Only its mathematical formulation is included here. Quantitative measures must replace qualitative (in subjective value systems) for the mathematical problem to exist.

Suboptimal control assumes an additional role to that mentioned in the opening paragraph of this section. In particular the implementation of the optimal control may be infeasible for engineering, economic or other reasons (that is other constraints not allowed for in the mathematics of the design problem). Knowing the optimal control enables the implementation of a suboptimal form with a full understanding of the consequences of such action. In this sense the optimal control serves as a design standard by which alternative controls may be evaluated.

Without loss of generality, minimization will be implied in all optimization studies. It will be appreciated that any problem in maximization may be conveniently treated as a problem in minimization by means of a suitable negative transformation: $\max(-J) = -\min(J)$.

Two analytically tractable parts of a criterion, covering a broad class of problems may be recognized. (These are essentially generalizations of the same quantities extremized in the classical calculus of variations. In particular note the correspondence with the Bolza problem.) Various design indices may be obtained by specializing, or applying suitable mathematical transformations to either. Non-analytic criteria are not considered initially. The two distinguishable parts are:

(i) A generalized *domain criterion* in which J is a scalar quantity obtained by integrating over the domain of the independent variables. In notation consistent with the system modelling of Chapter 2,

$$J = \int_Y G[y, x(y), \ldots, \partial_l x(y), \ldots, u(y)] \, \mathrm{d}Y \tag{5.8}$$

where $l = (l_1, \ldots)$. The integrand G is a prescribed scalar function of the arguments shown. $Y \subset E^\infty$, $\alpha = 1, \ldots$ with coordinate vector $y = (y_1, \ldots)^\mathrm{T}$.

(ii) An *end criterion* expressing a general function of the states at the right and/or left interval limits of the independent variables $\{y_i; i = 1, \ldots\}$. For example, a so-called 'final criterion' is a function of the states at the right limit of the time interval $[t^\mathrm{L}, t^\mathrm{R}]$. Reverting to the original distinction between the time domain (T) and the space domain (D), then

$$J = \int_D g[x(y, t)] \bigg|_{t=t^\mathrm{R}} \mathrm{d}D \tag{5.9}$$

where g is a scalar function of the states shown. Also, for example, a criterion defined on a closed boundary curve ∂D,

$$J = \oint_{\partial D} g'[x(\sigma)] \, \mathrm{d}\sigma \tag{5.10}$$

where σ is a measure of arc length.

The domain criterion receives sufficient usage in structural applications to warrant its own treatment, although it can be transformed into an end criterion. This is illustrated in the following example. It is remarked that a very general criterion contains both domain and end criterion parts and hence, for this case, a separate treatment of each part is required.

As an example the domain criterion presented in (i) may be transformed into an end criterion by suitably augmenting the state space. In, for example, a type I format, by introducing an additional state coordinate $x_0(y)$, where

$$\frac{\mathrm{d}x_0(y)}{\mathrm{d}y_4} = f_0 = \int_D G[y, x(y), \ldots, \partial_l x(y), \ldots, u(y)] \, \mathrm{d}D$$

with $x_0(y_1, y_2, y_3, y_4^\mathrm{L}) = 0$, then minimizing the domain criterion over the domain $Y = T \times D$ is equivalent to minimizing $x_0(y_1, y_2, y_3, y_4^R)$. It is seen that this is a special case of (ii). Hence derivations based on the end criterion in (ii) will apply to the domain criterion in (i) combined with an augmented state space. This result is used in the derivation of certain design optimality conditions given in Part C.

Probabilistic systems. For random values of its arguments, the general criterion J of this section is now a random quantity, and hence an unsuitable measure. A suitable deterministic measure, over which the minimization may be carried out, is the expected value or first moment (in a probabilistic sense) of J, $E\{J\}$,where $E\{\cdot\}$ denotes the expectation operation. The expectation operation may be visualized as taking the average of the criterion evaluated for each of the possible values of its arguments.

In general, this expected value of the random measure J, is used as the system criterion. However, in certain applications a measure or index of reliability may be relevant; that is extremizing the index may relate to minimizing the probability of the structure exceeding (both positive and negative senses implied together or singly) a particular limit state, or maximizing the probability of non-exceedance in order that the system attains a maximum level of reliability. This is a non-analytic criterion. Notice that this is a different situation to the one in which a system is designed for a given reliability (the probability of the state exceeding a given limit state is prescribed). Reliability in this context is a constraint (section 5.2).

Comment. Several criteria (resulting from multiple requirements on a design) expressed for the one problem in general lead to different points in solution (control variable) space. In general the points do not coincide and hence the existence of more than one criterion simultaneously is inadmissible for a meaningful problem. Auxiliary conditions, equivalent to constraints, may however, coexist with the optimality criterion. Adaptations of Lagrangian multiplier and weighting function concepts may also be employed for a solution. Alternatively trade-offs or adjustments may be made between the several design requirements. See Chapter 10.

5.4 THE OPTIMIZATION PROBLEM

5.4.1 A Statement of the Problem

Using a state-control basis for the modelling of the components of the design problem, superficially different problems can be shown to share a common mathematical association. (The common conceptual basis has always existed.) A statement of the design problem and its solution may then be treated in unified modes.

The difficulty has existed in elaborating the last two sections, of achieving a formulation which is of sufficiently broad generality yet not so general as to prohibit the development of effective solution procedures. For the level of generality of the modelling and of the previous two sections, the design problem may be stated as follows.

Deterministic. The simplest deterministic problem may be formulated as: to find the control $\hat{u}(y)$ which minimizes the criterion functional (parts (i) and (ii)), for a system behaving according to equation (2.1) (or (2.2) or (2.3)) over a given domain Y, with end-state conditions (2.4). $\hat{u}$ is termed the optimal control.

Stochastic. The equivalent stochastic problem chooses the control to minimize the expected value of J subject to a system equation, which is now a stochastic differential equation, and end-state conditions, which now have probabilistic characteristics. The extension, in principle, from the deterministic case is quite straightforward.

Provided the probability characteristics of the variables are known and given the basic Markovian assumption, it is apparent that there are no prominent dissimilarities in the deterministic and stochastic formulations. The solutions should also be similar. Stochastic solutions will only permit optimality on the average whereas deterministic solutions will be optimal for each case; this difference, however, evolves from the idea of probability rather than different formulations.

The problem outlined in the deterministic case is one of functional minimization while the problem class is of a generalized Bolza type (for multiple integrals and with side constraints) encountered in the calculus of variations. Where part (ii) of the criterion is identically zero in the Bolza problem, it is the problem of Lagrange. Where part (i) is identically zero in the Bolza problem, it is the problem of Mayer. The various problem forms are interchangeable by suitably defining new variables.

Complications are added by the prescription of constraints on the admissible state and control regions—that is equations (5.1) to (5.5). For lumped parameter systems, the extension or generalization of the calculus of variations to account for bounded controls is due to Pontryagin. More formally the extension is known as Pontryagin's (minimum, maximum) principle.

Extensions of the principle to general nonlinear distributed parameter systems are available for system model types I, II, and III. The necessary conditions for optimality in general constitute a set of partial differential equations nonlinear in both the state and control variables and of the boundary value type (end conditions are split), the solution of which may present certain complications. Mathematical tools available to handle nonlinear partial differential equations are at the present stage most inadequate.

Necessary optimality conditions for the problem with constraints on the state have also been obtained for the lumped parameter case.

An alternative approach to the control optimization problem and one which extends readily to the stochastic case is Bellman's dynamic programming based on Bellman's principle of optimality. Here the conditions to be solved for optimality assume the form of a recurrence relation with the optimal control resulting as a by-product of the solution process. There are, however, certain computation limitations which restrict the scope of application of the conditions. Dynamic programming is found most useful in the stochastic case.

Alternative solution procedures involve discretization of the time or space variables. Complete discretization gives a mathematical programming problem.

All solution procedures have some limitation, the area of application dictating the procedure adopted in any given case.

5.4.2 Modifications to the General Problem

The above problem components and verbal descriptions require only slight modification to suit system models other than outlined in Chapter 2 and for which the above components apply.

For the design problem corresponding to ordinary differential equation models the (in general) four-dimensional domain Y reduces to one dimension. The same solution techniques apply though obviously much simplified.

For the design problem corresponding to difference equation models the indexing parameter (independent variable) y is replaced by a stage counter k. Integrals become finite summations. Continuous-y solution procedures become discrete-y solution procedures, namely the discrete maximum principle and discrete dynamic programming. Mathematical programming applies directly.

For the design problem corresponding to algebraic (non-difference) equation models the independent variable y is dropped. The criterion becomes a (scalar, nonlinear) function of the state and control variables. Mathematical programming and dynamic programming techniques may be used for solution.

5.5 STANDARD PROBLEMS

5.5.1 General

Subsequent chapters deal with several standard problems and for ease of reference these are catalogued here. Note that the relevant literature describes many related forms to those given but the following versions have been adopted. Reference may then be made in subsequent chapters to the particular problem without continuous repetition of the problem statement. Variations to the standard problems such as by the incorporation of certain constraints or changes in boundary conditions are noted in subsequent chapters where relevant.

5.5.2 Problems (OD); Ordinary Differential Equation Models

(a) Problem (OD1). Consider a system modelled according to the standard lumped parameter form

$$\mathrm{d}x(y)/\mathrm{d}y = f[x(y), u(y), y] \qquad y \in [y^{\mathrm{L}}, y^{\mathrm{R}}]$$

where $x(y) = (x_1, \ldots, x_n)^{\mathrm{T}}$ is the state vector
$u(y) = (u_1, \ldots, u_r)^{\mathrm{T}}$ is the control vector
y is the independent variable of time or space
$f = (f_1, \ldots, f_n)^{\mathrm{T}}$ is a nonlinear vector function

with the boundary conditions

$$M^1[x(y^{\mathrm{L}}), y^{\mathrm{L}}] = 0$$
$$M^2[x(y^{\mathrm{R}}), y^{\mathrm{R}}] = 0$$

where M^1 and M^2 are p and q dimensional vectors respectively. The optimality criterion is

$$\min J = \int_{y^{\mathrm{L}}}^{y^{\mathrm{R}}} G[x(y), u(y), y]\,\mathrm{d}y + g[x(y), y]\Bigg|_{y=y^{\mathrm{L}}}^{y=y^{\mathrm{R}}}$$

where G and g are scalar single-valued functions of their respective arguments.

In the time domain, this problem is frequently referred to as a *trajectory optimization problem*, or in the calculus of variations as a *Bolza problem* with the state equations as equality constraints. y^{R} may be free or specified; in some cases y^{R} may be infinite.

$\hat{u}$ is termed the optimal control, $\hat{u}(y)$ the optimal policy and where applicable $u(x(y))$ is termed the control law.

(b) Problem (OD2). For the special linear-quadratic problem the state equations and criterion are modified to become

$$\mathrm{d}x(y)/\mathrm{d}y = A(y)x(y) + B(y)u(y)$$

where $A(y)$ is an $n \times n$ matrix
$B(y)$ is an $n \times r$ matrix

$$\min J = [\tfrac{1}{2}x^{\mathrm{T}}(y)g_{xx}x(y) + g_x x(y)]_{y=y_{\mathrm{L}}}^{y=y_{\mathrm{R}}}$$
$$+ \int_{y_{\mathrm{L}}}^{y_{\mathrm{R}}} \{\tfrac{1}{2}[x^{\mathrm{T}}(y)G_{xx}(y)x(y) + x^{\mathrm{T}}(y)G_{xu}(y)u(y)$$
$$+ u^{\mathrm{T}}(y)G_{ux}(y)x(y) + u^{\mathrm{T}}(y)G_{uu}(y)u(y)]$$
$$+ G_u(y)u(y) + G_x(y)x(y)\}\,\mathrm{d}y$$

where G_{xx}, G_{uu} and g_{xx} are symmetric weighting matrices of size $n \times n$, $r \times r$ and $n \times n$ respectively.

G_{ux} is an $r \times n$ matrix
G_{xu} is an $n \times r$ matrix
G_u is a $1 \times r$ vector
G_x is a $1 \times n$ vector
g_x is a $1 \times n$ vector.

Subscripts x and u are mnemonics only and do not denote derivatives. The problem is sometimes known as the *linear regulator problem*.

5.5.3 Problems (D); Difference Equation Models

(a) Problem (D1).

$$x(k+1) = F[x(k), u(k), k] \qquad k = 0, \ldots, N-1.$$

$F = (F_1, \ldots, F_n)^{\mathrm{T}}$ is a nonlinear vector function. Boundary conditions and criterion are

$$M^1[x(0), 0] = 0$$
$$M^2[x(N), N] = 0$$

$$\min J = g[x(k)]\Big|_{k=0}^{k=N} + \sum_{k=0}^{N-1} G[x(k), u(k), k]$$

G, g are scalar single-valued functions of their respective arguments.

N may be free or specified. In some cases N may be regarded as being infinite.

$$x(k) = (x_1, \ldots, x_n)^{\mathrm{T}} \text{ is the state at stage } k$$
$$u(k) = (u_1, \ldots, u_r)^{\mathrm{T}} \text{ is the control at stage } k.$$

For given u and boundary conditions, x is completely defined by the state equations.

The problem then is to determine an admissible sequence $u(k)$, $k = 0, \ldots, N-1$ satisfying the system equations and boundary conditions and minimizing J. $\hat{u}(k)$, $k = 0, \ldots, N-1$ is termed the optimal sequence or policy.

(b) Problem (D2). For the linear-quadratic case

$$x(k+1) = A(k)x(k) + B(k)u(k)$$

$A(k)$ $n \times n$ matrix
$B(k)$ $n \times r$ matrix

$$\begin{aligned} \min J = {} & [x^{\mathrm{T}}(k) g_{xx} x(k) + g_x x(k)]_{k=0}^{k=N} \\ & + \sum_{k=0}^{N-1} x^{\mathrm{T}}(k) G_{xx}(k) x(k) + x^{\mathrm{T}}(k) G_{xu}(k) u(k) \\ & + u^{\mathrm{T}}(k) G_{ux}(k) x(k) + u^{\mathrm{T}}(k) G_{uu}(k) u(k) \\ & + G_x(k) x(k) + G_u(k) u(k) \end{aligned}$$

G_{xx} $n \times n$ matrix, symmetric
G_{xu} $n \times r$ matrix
G_{ux} $r \times n$ matrix
G_{uu} $r \times r$ matrix, symmetric
G_x $1 \times n$ vector
G_u $1 \times r$ vector
g_{xx} $n \times n$ matrix, symmetric
g_x $1 \times n$ vector

Boundary conditions remain the same.

Note that the symbols A, B, g, G, J have been used in both the (OD) and (D) problems because they have similar meanings. However, they are not the same.

5.5.4 Problems (P); Partial Differential Equations Models

(a) Problem (PI); System Model Type I. Consider a general distributed parameter system described by the system of partial differential equations

$$\partial x_i / \partial y_4 = f_i[y, x, \ldots, \partial_l x, \ldots, u] \qquad i = 1, \ldots, n \tag{a}$$

where $l = (l_1, l_2, l_3)$ and $\partial_l x$ is as defined in the notation. $x(y) = (x_1, \ldots, x_n)^{\mathrm{T}}$ denotes the state and $u(y) = (u_1, \ldots, u_r)^{\mathrm{T}}$ the control at any $y = (y_1, \ldots, y_4)^{\mathrm{T}}$; $y \in [y_i^{\mathrm{L}}, y_i^{\mathrm{R}}]$, $i = 1, \ldots, 4$.

The values that the control u may take will be assumed to be restricted to a region U in the space of controls with coordinates $u_1, \ldots, u_r$.

$$u(y) \in U \tag{b}$$

The control functions will be assumed to have piecewise continuous properties. Admissible controls will then belong to U and be piecewise continuous.

Boundary conditions are of the form

$$\begin{aligned} &\partial_{(l-1)}x_i \quad \text{given at} \quad y_k^{\mathrm{L}}, y_k^{\mathrm{R}} \qquad k = 1, 2, 3 \\ &x_i \quad \text{given at} \quad y_4^{\mathrm{L}}, y_4^{\mathrm{R}} \end{aligned} \tag{c}$$

where $\partial_{(l-1)}x$ denotes derivatives of the type $\partial_l x$ as defined in the notation but to the overall power (L − 1) in the numerator and with the power of either y_1, y_2 or y_3 reduced by one in the denominator. The form of the boundary conditions bears a direct relationship to the $\partial_l x$ differential terms appearing on the right-hand side of the system equations. It is assumed that the boundary conditions in association with (a) define the state for a given control. Conditions (c) are intended to imply 'split' conditions at y_i^{L} and y_i^{R} where this occurs. The values taken by i in (c) are determined by the conditions of any given problem.

The control is to be selected from all the admissible controls so that the functional

$$J = \int_Y G[y, x, \ldots, \partial_l x, \ldots, u] \, \mathrm{d}y \tag{d}$$

takes on a minimum value. In (d), $Y \subset E^4$ has coordinates $y = (y_1, \ldots, y_4)^{\mathrm{T}}$.

End state criteria for example of the form

$$\int_{\mathbf{Y}} g[y, x] \Big|_{y_4^{\mathrm{R}}} \, \mathrm{d}\mathbf{y}$$

may also be considered. Here $Y = \mathbf{Y} \times Y_4$.

(b) Problem (PII); System Model Type II. Consider a system described over a closed region Y in the $y_1 y_2 y_3$ space with piecewise smooth boundary surfaces ∂Y^{a} and ∂Y^{b}.

The system equations are

$$\partial x / \partial y_i = f^i[y, x, \ldots, \partial_l x, \ldots, u] \qquad i = 1, 2, 3 \tag{a}$$

where $l = (l_h, l_k)$ $(h, k = 1, 2, 3;\ h, k \neq i)$ and $\partial_l x$ is as defined in the notation. $x(y) = (x_1, \ldots, x_n)^{\mathrm{T}}$ denotes the state and $u(y) = (u_1, \ldots, u_r)^{\mathrm{T}}$ the control at any $y \in Y$, $y = (y_1, y_2, y_3)^{\mathrm{T}}$. f^i, $i = 1, 2, 3$ are in general nonlinear vector-valued functions of the arguments shown and have to be such that they satisfy certain compatibility conditions.

The set of available controls will not usually be arbitrary but will be constrained to some admissible region U. A control $u(y)$ will be said to be admissible if

$$u(y) \in U(u) \qquad \forall y \in Y \tag{b}$$

and $u(y)$ is piecewise continuous in Y.

State boundary conditions will be specified on ∂Y^{a} and ∂Y^{b} of the form

$$\partial_{(l-1)}x_j \text{ given} \tag{c}$$

and bear a direct relationship to the $\partial_l x$ terms appearing on the right-hand side of the system equations. (This follows from the choice of state variables.) The values taken by j in the boundary conditions are determined by the conditions of any given problem.

It is assumed that the state may be found uniquely from (a) and (c) for any given admissible control.

Alternative controls will be taken to be evaluated according to the optimality criterion

$$\min J = \int_Y G[y, x, \ldots, \partial_l x, \ldots, u] \,\mathrm{d}y. \tag{d}$$

Boundary criterion terms of the form

$$\left.\int_{\partial Y^{b}} g[x] \,\mathrm{d}y_1 \,\mathrm{d}y_3 \right|_{y_2^{b}}$$

and similarly for the boundaries $\partial Y^{b} \mid y_1^{b}$ and $\partial Y^{b} \mid y_3^{b}$ and ∂Y^{a} may also be appended.

(c) Problem (PIII); System Model Type III. Let y denote a two dimensional coordinate vector, $y = (y_1, y_2)^{\mathrm{T}}$ and Y a region in the $y_1 y_2$ plane with piecewise continuous boundary curves ∂Y^{a} (inner) and ∂Y^{b} (outer). The symbol σ will be taken as an arc length of a curve.

For a state vector $x(y) = (x_1, \ldots, x_n)^{\mathrm{T}}$ and control vector $u(y) = (u_1, \ldots, u_r)^{\mathrm{T}}$ defined for all $y \in Y$, consider a system in the region Y described by the set of partial differential equations

$$\partial^2 x / \partial y_1 \partial y_2 = f[x, \ldots, \partial_l x, \ldots, u, y] \tag{a}$$

where $l = l_1$ or l_2 but never (l_1, l_2) together; $\partial_l x$ is as defined in the notation. (This is a special case where $L = l_1$ or l_2 directly.) $f = (f_1, \ldots, f_n)^{\mathrm{T}}$ is in general a nonlinear vector function of the arguments shown.

Boundary conditions on x will be given of the form

$$x_i(\sigma), \ldots, \partial_{l-1} x_i(\sigma) \tag{b}$$

implying lower order derivatives to the state derivatives appearing on the right-hand side of (a). These will be distributed between ∂Y^{a} and

∂Y^b and even over portions of ∂Y^a and ∂Y^b. That is, split boundary conditions are implied. The values taken by i in (b) are determined by the conditions of any given problem.

The controls will be taken to be piecewise continuous functions of the coordinates y_1 and y_2; it is assumed that discontinuities may occur along some isolated closed smooth lines Σ_0 which may be reduced to the boundary curves ∂Y^a or ∂Y^b by continuous deformations.

The control is assumed to be within some permissible region U.

The problem considered here is one of finding the control $u(y)$ which minimizes the criterion

$$J = \iint_Y G(x, \ldots, \partial_l x, \ldots, u, y_1, y_2)\, dy_1\, dy_2 + \oint_{\partial Y^a} g_a(x, \sigma)\, d\sigma + \oint_{\partial Y^b} g_b(x, \sigma)\, d\sigma$$

where G, g_a and g_b are scalar functions of their given arguments.

This problem may be specialized such that the region Y is a rectangular region.

Consider a system defined over a rectangular domain defined by the limits $[y_j^L, y_j^R]$, $j = 1, 2$. The system is modelled according to a type III form with end-state conditions

$$x_i(y_1, y_2), \ldots, \partial_{l-1} x_i(y_1, y_2) \quad \text{specified at} \quad y_j^L, y_j^R; \qquad j = 1, 2$$

($l = l_1$ on y_1^L, y_1^R boundaries, $l = l_2$ on y_2^L, y_2^R boundaries; split boundary conditions are implied), and criterion

$$J = \iint_Y G[x, \ldots, \partial_l x, \ldots, u, y_1, y_2]\, dy_1\, dy_2 + \int_{y_1} g_1(x, y_1)\, dy_1 \Big|_{y_2^L}^{y_2^R} + \int_{y_2} g_2(x, y_2)\, dy_2 \Big|_{y_1^L}^{y_1^R}.$$

5.5.5 Problems (A); Algebraic (Non-Difference) Equation Models

(a) Problem (A1). Consider the three problem components, namely a system model, constraints and a criterion respectively, of the form

$$F(x, u) = 0$$

$$u \in U, \quad x \in X, \quad \text{and} \quad (x, u) \in V$$

$$\min J = G(x, u)$$

where $x = (x_1, \ldots, x_n)^T$ is the state vector, $u = (u_1, \ldots, u_r)^T$ is the control vector and F and G are respectively, vector and scalar functions of the arguments shown. U, X and V are the permissible regions of the constraints.

(b) Problem (A2). It is convenient to make no distinction between the state and control variables and between equality constraints and the system model. Thus setting $x = (x^{\mathrm{T}}, u^{\mathrm{T}})^{\mathrm{T}}$, problem (A1) becomes

$$\min J = G(x) \quad \text{subject to} \quad h_j(x) \leq 0.$$

For convenience the dimension of x will be retained as n. Each equality constraint, without loss of generality, has been replaced by two inequality constraints ($\geqslant 0$ and $\leqslant 0$) with the inequality constraints all being written as 'less than or equal to', also without loss of generality. (Multiplying throughout a constraint by -1 reverses an inequality sign.) h_j are scalar nonlinear functions of some or all of the x_i variables. Problem (A2) is sometimes referred to as a *parameter optimization problem* or *static problem*.

An alternative representation of problem (A2) is

$$\min\{G(x) \mid x \in R\}$$

where R is the feasible domain of x satisfying the constraints

$$R = \{x \mid h_j(x) \leq 0, \forall j\}.$$

Problem (A3). The linear version is

$$\min J = c^{\mathrm{T}}x \quad \text{subject to} \quad Ax + b \leq 0$$

where A is an $m \times n$ matrix of constants
b is an m dimensional vector of constants
c is an n dimensional vector of constants

5.6 AN OUTLINE

Having given a basis for the modelling of structures in Part A and the components of the design problem in Part B, the remainder of the work is concerned with the various solution techniques and the idiosyncrasies of deterministic optimization. It is shown that as a direct consequence of the common modelling basis proposed for structures, combined with the design philosophy of control systems theory, rules may be derived for the design problem in terms of common characteristic properties. Such rules enable the collection of structural design problems under a generalized approach. The difficulty in such general design endeavours is that the design problem formulation should be sufficiently broad so as to retain the necessary generality, yet narrow enough to permit effective solution. The form of the design results presented subsequently is reasonably general and is applicable to a wide spectrum of problems, yet further generalization is possible. Illustrations of the theory are given throughout, and these also serve to highlight the basic modelling and design problem components of Parts A and B.

The content of the ensuing chapters is briefly as follows.

Chapter 6 Mathematical Programming. Mathematical programming describes a group of techniques yielding the solution of problem (A). The group includes linear programming and special and general forms of nonlinear programming, devised to handle the various linear and nonlinear mathematical forms that the design problem components may take. Numerous applications of these techniques have been reported in the structural optimization literature. The treatment of mathematical programming in this chapter is developed through conventional calculus, linear programming and then the nonlinear forms. The chapter is presented first in the series of chapters on optimization techniques as it is conceptually the simplest yet contains most of the essential ideas on optimization.

Chapter 7 Dynamic Programming. In contrast to mathematical programming which results in solution algorithms, dynamic programming is an approach to an optimization problem. Systems with a series or staged form are particularly amenable to dynamic programming concepts. The approach can be applied to all the previously mentioned standard problems, typically ending in a recurrence relation having to be solved for optimality. It is logically equivalent to Pontryagin's principle and the calculus of variations described in the next chapter.

Chapter 8 Pontryagin's Principle; Variational Calculus. For problems (OD), (D) and (P), optimization based on Pontryagin's principle or variational calculus results in a set of necessary conditions that have to be satisfied for optimality. The necessary conditions for optimality in general constitute a set of differential or difference equations of the boundary value type. Although leading to the same result, Pontryagin's principle is found to be more suited to posing and solving engineering problems than the classical calculus of variations.

Chapter 9 Singular Control. Chapter 9 examines structural design problem formulations which are candidate singular optimal control problems; that is where, for example, the necessary conditions for optimality of Pontryagin's principle are satisfied in a trivial sense and supplementary conditions have to be examined to determine optimality. The occurrence of singular control problems in problems of structural optimization generally has only recently been observed. A discussion on singular control theory is given and its application on structural design problems is demonstrated.

Chapter 10 Multicriteria Optimization. The idea of an optimum solution for the single criterion problem gives way to the concept of Pareto optimality for multicriteria problems. A Pareto optimum solution is one in which no decrease is possible in any of the criteria without simultaneously increasing at least one of the other criteria. Various schemes are discussed for generating Pareto optimal solutions. The best or preferred solution is chosen from the set of Pareto optimal solutions through the specification of some additional value judgement by the designer. The results given in this chapter and the following chapter (on multilevel optimization) are generally applicable for all the standard problems.

Chapter 11 Multilevel Optimization. As multilevel systems theory treats the decomposition of systems into subsystems together with interaction, so there exist optimization methodologies that handle the case where problems are decomposed to subproblems. The central feature of the methodologies is the manner in which the solutions to the subproblems are coordinated in order that the solution of the original single level problem is obtained. The various multilevel schemes are iterative in nature transferring between the subproblems and an overall coordinating level. The subproblems may be solved by any of the techniques in Chapters 6, 7 or 8 that best suits the subproblem formulation.

Chapter 12 Lyapunov Theory in Design. For the particular structural optimization problem where stability with respect to time is required, the results of Lyapunov's second method may be adapted to give the solution. Obviously the approach lacks the generality of the previous optimization methodologies but is useful for this specialized problem.

Chapter 13 Energy and 'Optimality Criteria' Based Design. For completeness and because energy and 'optimality criteria' based approaches occupy a substantial portion of the structural optimization literature, the approaches are reviewed and then their equivalence with the results of the methodologies of the preceding chapters is shown. By showing this equivalence it is emphasized that the usefulness or efficiency of the energy/'optimality criteria' techniques is not questioned for the specialized problems on which they are formulated. However the control approach enables new interpretations of the established formulations and results of the energy/'optimality criteria' approaches.

5.7 NOTES, COMMENTS AND BIBLIOGRAPHY

[5.1] Alternative terminology for criterion is objective function, performance index, merit function, payoff function, figure of merit, goal, cost function, optimality criterion, design index, target function and others.

The components of the optimization problem are well delineated by Fel'dbaum (1965).

[5.2] The role of constraints in design has been outlined by Lee (1964), Bellman (1957) and Fel'dbaum (1965), among others.

An extended definition of U having state arguments in addition to the parameters y_i has been considered by Berkovitz (1961) but its usage is uncertain in the structures case.

For the 'geometric'/'behavioural' classification, see Rozvany (1966a), Sheu and Prager (1968) and Fox (1971) among others.

For limit state ideas see Comite Europeen du Beton (C.E.B.) (1964) and Rowe (1970). For reliability see Julian (1957), Freudenthal *et al.* (1966), Borges and Castanheta (1968), Pugsley (1966), Carmichael (1975) and Carmichael and Clyde (1976).

Another type of constraint which arises in some problems is that of the discrete-valued control variable. In such cases the control variable is not to be selected from a continuous range of values but is permitted to take on only one of a discrete set of values. For example, manufacturers catalogues only list certain sizes of rolled steel sections rather than a continuous range.

Multipurpose design or structures with multiple loading conditions increase the number of equality constraints (the system model for the various purposes or loadings) on the problem. See Karihaloo (1979a, b, c, d), Karihaloo and Parbery (1979a, b) and Karihaloo and Wood (1979). A solution is only optimal with respect to the particular design components for which it was found, but the solution may be made more acceptable by considering several purposes or loadings.

[5.3] For a discussion on transformations between various criteria see for example Tou (1964) among others. In most transformations, the dimensionality of the state vector is enlarged.

The reliability index (nonanalytic) is treated at length by Gnedenko *et al.* (1969) and Tsypkin (1971).

For comments on the meaning of several criteria for the one problem see for example Fel'dbaum (1965). See also Zadeh (1958) for nonscalar-valued criteria and Kalman (1964) on the question of optimality.

Care should be exercised in the choice of a criterion. For example in static structures, the fully utilized (fully stressed) design is not always the least weight and the least weight design is not always the least cost.

Graphically in the control variable space, the criterion may be drawn as sets of surfaces (level surfaces of $J(u)$). The locus of all points satisfying $J(u)$ = constant forms a surface, and for each value of the constant there corresponds a different member of a family of surfaces. The terminology isocost, isoprofit, isoweight or similar is used to describe these surfaces.

[5.4] For discussion of the various calculus of variations forms see Tou (1964), Bliss (1946) and Bolza (1931, 1961) among others.

For Pontryagin's principle see Pontryagin *et al.* (1962), Lee and Markus (1967), Leitmann (1966), Rozonoer (1959). See Bryson and Ho (1969) and Sage (1968) for minimum principle versions.

For the state constrained problem see Pontryagin *et al.* (1962), Berkovitz (1961, 1962) and Chang (1962) for example.

For dynamic programming see Bellman (1957, 1961), Bellman and Dreyfus (1962).

For the discrete maximum principle see Sage and White (1977).

It is noted that the earliest works in control on lumped parameter systems were variational in character, essentially being extensions of the classical calculus of variations. The original work in distributed parameter systems, as may have been anticipated, also employed variational arguments. Notable is the pioneering work of Butkovskii and Lerner (1960, 1961) and Butkovskii (1961, 1962, 1969). However, they considered only systems modelled by integral equations and, unless a transformation is known between differential equations and integral equations, the work is inapplicable to the present system cases. For general nonlinear systems, a transformation is usually not available. Later contributions on systems described by integral equations (primarily linear) are by Khatri and Goodson (1966) and Wang (1964) among others. However, the integral equation form will not be developed further here for the reason given above. Systems described by integro-differential equations (for example, Wittler and Shen 1969) will also not be discussed. Only differential distributed parameter systems will be considered further. For related background reading, reference should be made to the very complete surveys of Robinson (1971) and Butkovskii *et al.* (1968) while Wang (1968) gives an extensive bibliography.

[5.5] For problem (OD1), the special case of $G = 1$ and $g = 0$ and where y = time, that is where

$$J = \int_{t_0}^{t_f} \mathrm{d}t = (t_f - t_0)$$

is termed the time optimal problem. Here t_f and t_0 denote final and initial times respectively.

Athans and Falb (1966) discuss other special cases such as the minimum energy problem and the minimum effort problem.

Time may be interpreted as an additional state coordinate x_{n+1} with the corresponding state equation

$$\mathrm{d}x_{n+1}/\mathrm{d}t = f_{n+1} = 1.$$

For $x_{n+1}(t = 0) = 0$, then $x_{n+1} = t$.

M^1 and M^2 are sometimes referred to as initial and terminal manifolds when the independent variable is time.

Part C

Deterministic Optimization

Chapter 6

Mathematical Programming

6.1 INTRODUCTION

Mathematical programming describes a group of techniques for solving problems (A), that is for systems modelled according to algebraic relations. By various discretization schemes the problems (OD) and (P) can be made to fit an (A) form. Problems (D) are already algebraic and require no modification. Thus mathematical programming is of considerable importance in optimization. It is also conceptually elementary and has therefore attracted by far the most attention of all the optimization techniques in the structures literature.

For the general nonlinear programming problem (A2) of

$$\min J = G(x) \quad \text{subject to} \quad h_j(x) \leqslant 0 \qquad j = 1, \ldots, m \qquad \text{(A2)}$$

one attempts to find the vector $\hat{x}$ that minimizes J under the constraint conditions imposed. Values of x satisfying the constraints are termed *feasible*. (A2) has a wide range of solution techniques. Variously these may be cast according to the problem components or according to the characteristics of the technique. Commonly, a classification of *direct techniques* (for example elimination techniques, search techniques) or *indirect techniques* (for example gradient techniques, second order techniques) is used, the distinction depending on whether they operate directly on the function J being minimized or whether they use the necessary (Kuhn–Tucker) conditions for optimality. The Kuhn–Tucker conditions are generalizations of the calculus of maxima and minima to include inequality constraints.

Where (A2) takes on special forms, special techniques are available for its solution. The techniques exploit the relevant special form of the problem. In particular where J is a quadratic function and h_j are linear, then a *quadratic programming* algorithm may be used. Where J and h_j are separable functions, a *separable programming* algorithm may be used. Where J and h_j are polynomials *geometric programming* is applicable.

Each special technique offers advantages over the previously mentioned general nonlinear programming solution techniques or algorithms. *Integer programming* applies to the case where the variables may only take on discrete values in comparison to the other problems.

Where J and h_j are linear functions, the most efficient of the solution techniques, *linear programming*, is applicable—problem (A3). Frequently it is advantageous to convert a nonlinear problem into a sequence of linear problems (cutting plane method) for solution. Linear programming is the most popular of all the mathematical programming techniques. In comparison with general nonlinear programming where local and global extrema cause difficulties, linear programming guarantees a globally optimum solution. Nonuniqueness of the solution may still, however, occur.

The approach taken in this chapter is to first review some basic elementary concepts on maxima, minima, points of inflection and stationary values from the calculus. These are then generalized to include constraints (Kuhn–Tucker conditions) (section 6.2). Then the various special programming techniques (section 6.3) and general (unconstrained and constrained) nonlinear programming (section 6.4) are discussed and illustrated with structural examples. Comments on the application of mathematical programming to optimal control problems (OD, P, and D) (section 6.5) follow.

As noted in section 5.5 it is convenient in discussing the theory of mathematical programming to eliminate the distinction between state variables and control variables and to treat both as a general vector $x = (x^{\mathrm{T}}, u^{\mathrm{T}})^{\mathrm{T}}$. A similar device will be found useful also when discussing the calculus of variations later. In all other work however, a strict adherence to a control/state distinction is required.

It is also convenient to interpret the system model as an equality constraint. An equality constraint may be replaced by two inequality constraints ($\geqslant 0$ and $\leqslant 0$). Thus without loss of generality problem (A2) follows from (A1). The mathematical programming problem then has only two components, namely a criterion J and constraints h_j. Note that in all other work a strict distinction between a system model and the design constraints will be required and will be adhered to. Both the usage of x in place of x and u and the interpretation of the model as an equality constraint can lead to a laziness in the formulation of the design problem if the designer is unaware of optimization techniques other than mathematical programming.

The reasons are two-fold for presenting this chapter first in the optimization techniques; firstly, because of its conceptual simplicity thereby enabling a grasp of the notation and terminology in the easiest way and secondly because of its general applicability to most optimization problems.

6.2 THE CALCULUS; KUHN–TUCKER CONDITIONS

6.2.1 The Unconstrained Problem

The calculus gives the conditions for finding extrema (maxima or minima) of functions. For the unconstrained case and assuming G has first and second partial derivatives everywhere, a *necessary condition for an extremum* is

$$\partial G/\partial x = 0. \tag{6.1}$$

Values of x satisfying (6.1) are termed *stationary points. Necessary conditions for a minimum* are (6.1) together with

$$\partial^2 G/\partial x^2 \geqslant 0. \tag{6.2}$$

That is the *Hessian matrix* (symmetric) must be positive semidefinite. For strict inequality in (6.2) there result *sufficient conditions for a minimum.* Where the Hessian matrix equals zero for a stationary point, such a point is called a *singular point* and additional information is required to establish whether or not it is a minimum. All the above refers to *local or relative minima*. The *global or absolute minimum* may be found from an examination of all the local minima and the values of G at the interval limits of x (Fig. 6.1). More information about the extrema of the function G can be obtained if G is known to be convex or concave or unimodal or not unimodal (Fig. 6.2).

(Techniques which use the necessary conditions (6.1) and (6.2) in

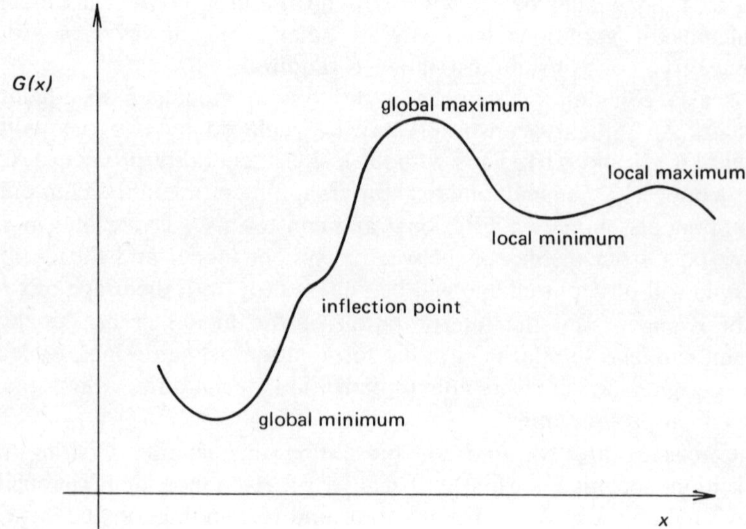

Fig. 6.1 Stationary points—single variable case

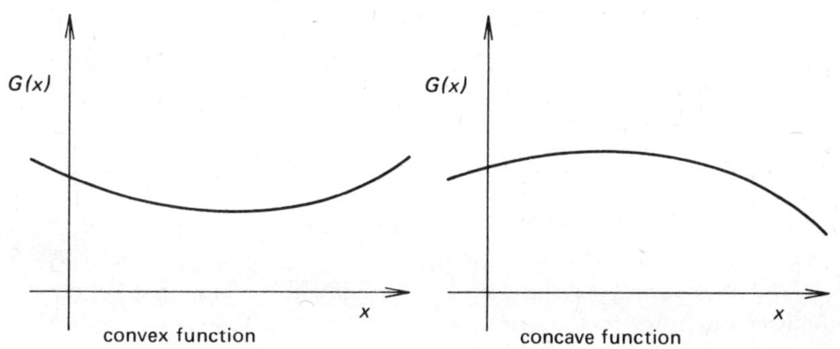

Fig. 6.2 Single variable case

some way to locate an extremum are referred to as *indirect methods* in contrast to *direct methods* which locate an extremum by comparison of function values at various points. Both methods lead to prescribed routines or algorithms for finding extrema. In the indirect methods, (6.1) may be used as equations to solve directly or as a test for stationary points. All the existing nonlinear programming algorithms yield essentially local optima. Convergence to a global optimum usually requires some prior knowledge of the form of the criterion.)

6.2.2 Equality Constraints: Lagrange Multipliers

A more general problem is the one with equality constraints, namely

$$\min J = G(x) \quad \text{subject to} \quad h_j(x) = 0 \qquad j = 1, \ldots, m < n \tag{6.3}$$

G and h_j are assumed to be not linear (see section 6.3). Such a problem may be solved by eliminating m of the variables through the use of the equality constraints and the problem is then unconstrained. An alternative and usually easier way is by the use of *Lagrange multipliers*.

Form a *Lagrangian* L by adjoining the equality constraints to the criterion through m Lagrange 'undetermined multipliers'.

$$L(x, \lambda) \triangleq G(x) + \sum_{j=1}^{m} \lambda_j h_j(x). \tag{6.4}$$

Necessary conditions for a stationary value are

$$\begin{aligned} \partial L/\partial x_i &= 0 \qquad i = 1, \ldots, n \\ \partial L/\partial \lambda_j \quad (= h_j) &= 0 \qquad j = 1, \ldots, m \end{aligned} \tag{6.5}$$

These are $m + n$ equations in $m + n$ unknowns λ and x.

Example: Consider the design of a cylindrical pressure vessel of maximum volume but with a constraint that the area of surface metal used be a constant. Assume a constant thickness of metal. The problem is

$$\max V = \pi R^2 H \quad \text{subject to} \quad 2\pi R^2 + 2\pi RH = \alpha$$

where R and H are cylinder radius and length respectively, and α is a given surface area and is a constant.

Two approaches to the problem are possible. The first adjoins the equality constraint to the criterion by means of a Lagrange multiplier to form a Lagrangian,

$$L = \pi R^2 H + \lambda[2\pi R^2 + 2\pi RH - \alpha].$$

Necessary conditions for a stationary value are (6.5)

$$\partial L/\partial H = 0 = \pi R^2 + \lambda 2\pi R$$
$$\partial L/\partial R = 0 = 2\pi RH + \lambda[4\pi R + 2\pi H]$$
$$\partial L/\partial \lambda = 0 = 2\pi R^2 + 2\pi RH - \alpha.$$

These represent three equations in three unknowns, R, H, and λ. Note that the last equation is the original equality constraint. Solving,

$$R = (\alpha/6\pi)^{1/2}, \qquad H = (2\alpha/3\pi)^{1/2}, \qquad \lambda = -(\alpha/24\pi)^{1/2}.$$

The second approach uses the equality constraint to solve for one of the variables, H say

$$H = (\alpha - 2\pi R^2)/2\pi R.$$

This is then substituted into the criterion, giving an unconstrained problem of

$$\max V = \alpha R/2 - \pi R^3.$$

A necessary condition for a stationary value is (6.1)

$$\mathrm{d}V/\mathrm{d}R = 0 = \alpha/2 - 3\pi R^2$$

giving the same result as before for R. Backsubstituting in the equality constraint gives the result for H also as before.

6.2.3 Inequality Constraints; the Kuhn–Tucker Conditions; Duality

Consider now the still more general problem of

$$\min J = G(x) \quad \text{subject to} \quad h_j(x) \leq 0 \qquad j = 1, \ldots, m \tag{6.6}$$

If a Lagrangian is again formed, then necessary conditions for stationarity are

$$\frac{\partial L}{\partial x} = \frac{\partial G}{\partial x} + \lambda^{\mathrm{T}} \frac{\partial h}{\partial x} = 0 \quad \text{where} \quad \lambda_j \begin{cases} \geqslant 0 \text{ for } h_j(x) = 0 \\ = 0 \text{ for } h_j(x) < 0. \end{cases} \tag{6.7}$$

This is the essence of the Kuhn–Tucker theorem in nonlinear programming with qualifications and formalities removed. λ in the above context is often referred to as a generalized Lagrange multiplier (Fig. 6.3).

The Kuhn–Tucker conditions are used in nonlinear programming techniques to test a point for relative minimum properties or their basis is used to find a point which decreases the value of the criterion.

The concept of duality is important in mathematical programming and it is convenient to discuss it here. For the *primal problem*

$$\min\{G(x) \mid h_j(x) \leqslant 0, j = 1, \ldots, m; x_i \geqslant 0, i, \ldots, n\}$$

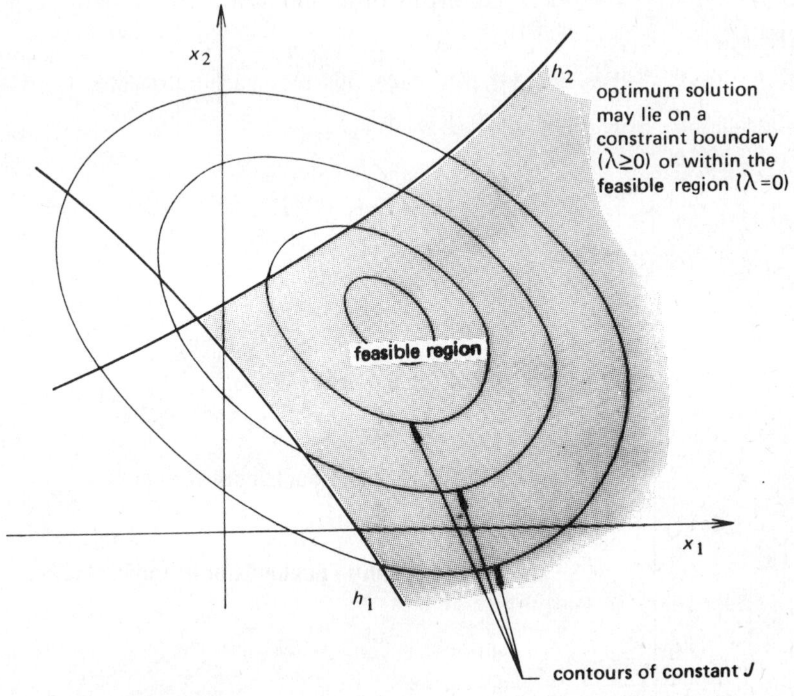

Fig. 6.3 Illustration of Nonlinear Programming—Two Variable Case

there exists a corresponding *dual* problem

$$\max\{L(x, \lambda) \mid \partial L(x, \lambda)/\partial x_i = 0, i = 1, \ldots, n; \lambda_j \geq 0, j = 1, \ldots, m\}$$

where $L(x, \lambda)$ is the Lagrange function defined in (6.4).

Certain bounding relationships exist between the primal and dual problems.

Frequently the dual is easier to solve than the primal and under certain conditions the optima of both problems coincide. Following from the Kuhn–Tucker theorem the Langrangian has a saddle point at the optimum

$$L(x, \hat{\lambda}) \leq L(\hat{x}, \hat{\lambda}) \leq L(\hat{x}, \lambda) \tag{6.8}$$

6.3 SPECIAL PROGRAMMING FORMS

6.3.1 Linear Programming

A linear programming problem is one in which both the criterion and the constraints are linear functions of x (problem (A3))

$$\min J = c^{\mathrm{T}}x \quad \text{subject to} \quad Ax + b \leq 0 \tag{A3}$$

where x is an n vector, b is an m vector, $m > n$. (Usually constraints involving a restriction on the sign of the variables—nonnegativity

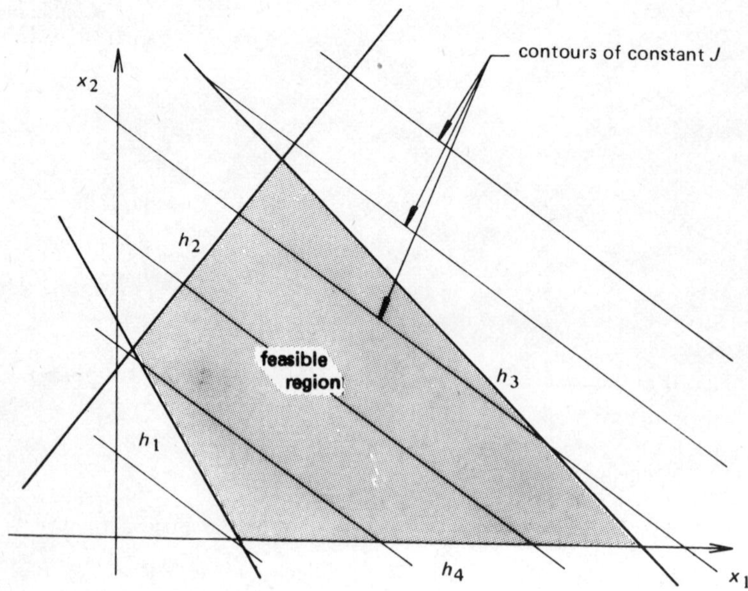

Fig. 6.4 Illustration of Linear Programming—Two Variable Case

constraints—are also given but are written separately to the above constraints) (Fig. 6.4).

Assuming a minimum exists then clearly this must lie at a constraint (a boundary of the feasible region). The fundamental result of linear programming follows provided certain conditions are met. In particular if A is of rank n and c^{T} has no collinear relationship with A then the minimum occurs at the intersection of n of the constraints. The way to a numerical solution algorithm (called the *simplex method* and variations on this method) follows. In particular n of the constraints, treated as equalities, are isolated at a time. Their solution if nonoptimal implies replacing one of the n constraints with another out of the remaining $m - n$ constraints so as to improve the value of the criterion. This process is repeated until no improvement in the value of the criterion is obtained and is a *finite* number of operations. Geometrically the optimum solution can be shown to occur on a constraint or at a vertex of the feasible region. The feasible region will be convex implying a globally optimum solution.

Because of the power of the linear programming solution, many nonlinear problems are given a linear framework (see the following example).

Duality in the linear programming problem assumes a neat form. In particular for the primal problem

$$\max\{c^{\mathrm{T}}x \mid Ax \leqslant b;\, x_i \geqslant 0,\, i = 1, \ldots, n\}$$

the dual is

$$\min\{b^{\mathrm{T}}\lambda \mid A^{\mathrm{T}}\lambda \geqslant c^{\mathrm{T}};\, \lambda_j \geqslant 0,\, j = 1, \ldots, m\}.$$

The primal is in n variables and m constraints while the dual is in m variables and n constraints. Where the i'th constraint is an equality then the i'th dual variable will be unrestricted in sign and vice versa.

Example: For the rigid plastic design of frames and continuous beams, where the primal problem is in terms of static variables, the dual problem will be in terms of kinematic variables.

6.3.2 Example: Lower Bound Design of Reinforced Concrete Slabs

The equilibrium equation which the field of state variables (internal moments) must satisfy in order to invoke the lower bound principle is

$$\frac{\partial^2 M_x}{\partial x^2} + \frac{\partial^2 M_y}{\partial y^2} - 2\,\frac{\partial^2 M_{xy}}{\partial x\,\partial y} = -\lambda q \qquad \text{(a)}$$

where λ is a multiplier applied to the working load $q(x, y)$ in order to obtain the desired design ultimate load. For a given ultimate load λq to be resisted, the cost of the design is some function of the moment capacities (control variables) provided, assuming a uniform slab thickness. For a minimum cost solution

$$\min C = \iint_A (M^x + M^y - \bar{M}^x - \bar{M}^y)\, dx\, dy \tag{b}$$

where the control variables M^x, M^y (positive moment capacities) and $\bar{M}^x$, $\bar{M}^y$ (negative moment capacities) are constrained by the above equilibrium relationship and their relationship with the state variables expressed in the yield criterion inequalities

$$\begin{aligned} M_{xy}^2 - (M^x - M_x)(M^y - M_y) &\leq 0 \\ M_{xy}^2 - (-\bar{M}^x + M_x)(-\bar{M}^y + M_y) &\leq 0 \\ M_x - M^x &\leq 0 \\ M_y - M^y &\leq 0 \\ -M_x + \bar{M}^x &\leq 0 \\ -M_y + \bar{M}^y &\leq 0. \end{aligned} \tag{c}$$

To apply linear programming, the constraints and the criterion require linearization. Firstly the derivatives in the equilibrium equation may be replaced by their finite difference equivalents. At any discretization point (i, j) the equilibrium equation is

$$\begin{aligned} &(M_x)_{i-1,j} - 2(M_x)_{i,j} + (M_x)_{i+1,j} + \\ &(M_y)_{i,j-1} - 2(M_y)_{i,j} + (M_y)_{i,j+1} + \\ &\tfrac{1}{2}(M_{xy})_{i-1,j-1} - \tfrac{1}{2}(M_{xy})_{i+1,j-1} - \tfrac{1}{2}(M_{xy})_{i+1,j-1} + \tfrac{1}{2}(M_{xy})_{i+1,j+1} \\ &+ \Delta^2(q)_{i,j}\lambda = 0 \end{aligned} \tag{d}$$

where Δ is the discretization interval. Boundary conditions may be similarly expressed.

The integral criterion may be replaced by a finite summation over the discretization points

$$\min C = \Delta^2 \sum_i \sum_j M_{i,j}^x + M_{i,j}^y - \bar{M}_{i,j}^x - \bar{M}_{i,j}^y \tag{e}$$

The linearized approximation to the yield criterion given by

Wolfensberger (1964) may be used and is of the form

$$\begin{aligned} |M_{xy}| + M_x - M^x &\leq 0 \\ |M_{xy}| + M_y - M^y &\leq 0 \\ |M_{xy}| - M_x + \bar{M}^x &\leq 0 \\ |M_{xy}| - M_y + \bar{M}^y &\leq 0. \end{aligned} \qquad \text{(f)}$$

This represents eight intersecting planes. The comparison with the nonlinear version is given in Fig. 6.5. The linearized yield surface lies within or on the nonlinear yield surface. This yield criterion may be defined for all discretization points. The linear programming problem is thus composed of the linear criterion (e) and linear constraints (d) and (f) in terms of the variables M_x, M_y, M_{xy}, M^x, M^y, $\bar{M}^x$ and $\bar{M}^y$ at all the discretization points.

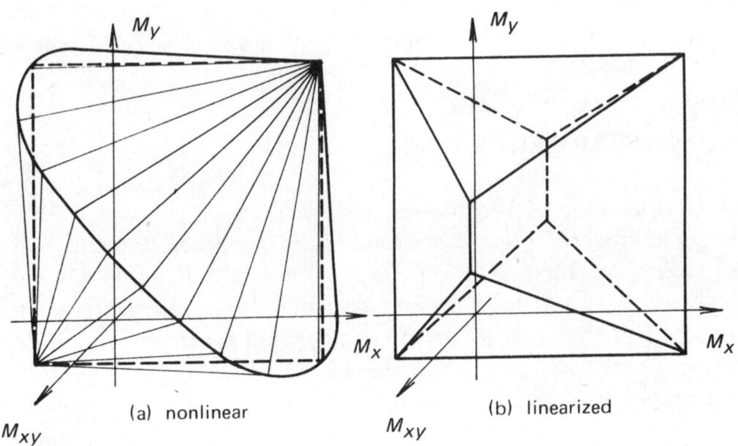

Fig. 6.5 Yield surfaces for reinforced concrete slabs

6.3.3 Geometric and Integer Programming

Geometric programming is distinct from the other mathematical programming techniques in that it is based on a geometric inequality. Geometric programming is concerned with finding the minimum of a polynomial subject to polynomial constraints of the form

$$\min J = \sum_{k=1}^{q} c_k \prod_{i=1}^{n} x_i^{a_{ki}}$$

$$\text{subject to} \quad \sum_{k=1}^{p} d_k \prod_{i=1}^{n} x_i^{b_{ki}} \leq 0 \qquad j = 1, \ldots, m \qquad \text{(A4)}$$

where c_k, d_k are coefficients, $k = 1, \ldots$
a_{ki}, b_{ki} are real numbers, $i = 1, \ldots, n$.

The above 'primal' problem may then be replaced by its 'dual' which is generally easier to solve. The solution of the dual problem equals the solution of the primal. A basic feature of geometric programming is that the optimal value of J may be found without first solving for the x_i.

Frequently the variables describing the optimization problem can only take on integer values, for example rolled steel sections only come in discrete sizes. In such a situation, assuming a continuous range of values may produce large errors.

The term 'integer programming' is often used for a linear programming problem where the variables can take on integer values only (*integer linear programming*) as this is where most research has been directed. Where some of the variables only are restricted to integer values, the problem type is referred to as *mixed integer programming*. Solution algorithms can be based on a cut method, branch and bound, implicit enumeration and others.

6.4 NONLINEAR PROGRAMMING

6.4.1 Classification of Techniques

A large number of algorithms have been proposed for the nonlinear programming problem solution. Each technique has its own advantages and disadvantages, there being no one algorithm suitable for all purposes. The choice of a particular algorithm for any situation depends on the problem formulation and the user.

Several classifications of the algorithms are possible whether according to the problem components or according to the characteristics of the solution technique. In the first category (and the one adopted below) the technique may be classified according to whether it is unconstrained or has equality and/or inequality constraints; discrete (integer) or continuous. In the second category the technique may be classified according to how it uses or doesn't use derivatives, the size of the step in the iterations, the starting point, whether it is direct or indirect, gradient or gradient free etc.

Unconstrained Problems

Techniques using derivatives. In finding the stationary values of $G(x)$ techniques have been proposed which use first and second order derivatives, both analytical and numerical.

The most commonly known methods using first order derivatives are the *gradient* or *steepest descent* methods (alternatively *steepest ascent* or hill climbing methods for a maximization problem) which involve iterations of improving estimates of coming closer to satisfying the stationary conditions (6.1). The improved value of x at the $(k + 1)$th iteration is given by

$$x^{k+1} = x^k + \Delta x^k = x^k + \lambda^k S^k \tag{6.9}$$

where S^k is a vector in direction Δx^k
λ^k is a scalar.

By proceeding in the direction of steepest descent

$$x^{k+1} = x^k - \lambda^k \nabla G(x^k) \tag{6.10}$$

where

$$\nabla G(x^k) \triangleq \left(\frac{\partial G(x^k)}{\partial x_1}, \ldots, \frac{\partial G(x^k)}{\partial x_n}\right)^{\mathrm{T}} \quad \text{is the gradient.} \tag{6.11}$$

The choice of λ determines the iteration step size leading to the various steepest descent procedures. Equation (6.10) is applied repeatedly until a stationary point is reached and where the components of $\nabla G(x^k)$ are equal to zero. Various iteration stopping rules are available. Examination of the Hessian matrix, if available, is necessary to distinguish the type of stationary point.

Techniques which use second derivatives in essence make a quadratic approximation to $G(x)$ rather than a linear approximation as in the gradient methods. For example in *Newton's method*.

$$\Delta x^k = -(\nabla^2 G(x^k))^{-1} \nabla G(x^k) \tag{6.12}$$

where $(\nabla^2 G(x^k))^{-1}$ is the inverse of the Hessian matrix. This implies that both the step and direction are specified. Various modifications have been proposed relating to the Hessian matrix and to the second partial derivatives by, for example, *Greenstadt* and *Marquardt* among others.

Frequently the best of the first order derivative techniques (for far away from the minimum) and the second order derivative techniques (for near the minimum) are combined in one algorithm.

Quadratic criteria of n variables can be minimized in n steps if the steps are taken in what are termed *conjugate directions*. The order in which the directions are used is not important. Frequently quadratic approximations can be made to nonlinear functions. The property of *conjugacy* is analogous to orthogonality. Algorithms using conjugate directions are those of *Fletcher and Reeves, Partan* (parallel tangents) *methods*, and *Zoutendijk's method* among others.

Variable metric (quasi-Newton, large step gradient) methods use only first order derivatives and approximate the Hessian matrix. Conjugate directions may or may not be employed. Generally they are of the form

$$x^{k+1} = x^k - \lambda^k \eta(x^k) \nabla G(x^k) \tag{6.13}$$

where $\eta(x^k)$ is a direction matrix and is an approximation to the inverse of the Hessian matrix.

For the steepest descent method $\eta^k = I$. For Newton's method $\eta^k = -(\nabla^2 G(x^k))^{-1}$.

Various choices of η^k exist leading to the algorithms of *Broyden*, *Davidon–Fletcher–Powell, Pearson, Fletcher, Greenstadt and Goldfarb* and *Goldstein and Price* as well as the *projected-Newton* and *Hessian matrix approximation* methods.

Search methods (no derivatives). Where it is inconvenient or impossible to evaluate derivatives as input to the problem, search methods find application although generally their convergence properties are not as good as for techniques using derivative information. Search methods essentially involve function evaluations and comparison. Various solution strategies have been proposed such as the *direct search* of Hooke and Jeeves, *polyhedron search* of Nelder and Mead, *simplex search* of Spendley, Hext and Himsworth, the methods of Rosenbrock, of Davies, Swann and Campey, Powell's method and *random search* methods.

Constrained Problems

Generally the inclusion of constraints makes the optimization problem harder to solve. For this reason transformations via penalty functions have been adopted converting the constrained problem to an unconstrained problem. Alternatively linear approximations may be used repeatedly to solve the nonlinear problem. A third approach to solving constrained problems uses a 'flexible tolerance' concept.

Linear approximation methods by and large involve the total linearization of the problem or linearization only of the constraints, though several other philosophies have been adopted. Total linearization enables the advantages of linear programming to be used in conjunction with an iterative solution algorithm. Taylors series may be used to linearize the relevant function about some x^k. For the problem

$$\begin{aligned} &\min G(x) \\ &\text{subject to} \quad h_i^1(x) = 0 \qquad i = 1, \ldots, m \\ &\qquad\qquad\quad h_i^2(x) \geq 0 \qquad i = m+1, \ldots, p \end{aligned} \tag{A5}$$

a first order Taylor's series approximation at x^k is

$$\begin{aligned} &\min G(x^k) + \nabla^T G(x^k)(x - x^k) \\ &\text{subject to} \quad h_i^1(x^k) + \nabla^T h_i^1(x^k)(x - x^k) = 0 \qquad i = 1, \ldots, m \\ &\qquad\qquad h_i^2(x^k) + \nabla^T h_i^2(x^k)(x - x^k) \geq 0 \qquad i = m+1, \ldots, p \end{aligned} \tag{A6}$$

which is a linear programming problem.

A quadratic approximation to the criterion has also been proposed, reducing the problem to a quadratic programming problem. Various combinations of 'unconstrained problem' techniques and linearization also exist. Related methods are the *projection methods* such as Rosen's gradient projection method and generalized gradient search, Zoutendijk's method of feasible directions and the generalized reduced gradient method.

Penalty function methods convert a constrained nonlinear problem into a sequence of unconstrained problems which are generally simpler to solve. The penalty represents a trade off between the constraints and the criterion. The algorithms may work from within the feasible region (interior point methods), from outside the feasible region (exterior point methods), or in a combination of these two (mixed methods).

For the problem (A5) the unconstrained problem is

$$\begin{aligned} \min P[x^k, \rho^k] = G(x^k) &+ \sum_{i=1}^{m} \rho_i^k H^1[h_i^1(x^k)] \\ &+ \sum_{i=m+1}^{p} \rho_i^k H^2[h_i^2(x^k)] \end{aligned} \tag{6.14}$$

where P is the 'penalty function'
ρ weighting terms
H^1, H^2 functionals of arguments shown.

Various choices for H^1 and H^2 are available. As k becomes large the effect of the constraints is required to diminish. That is as $k \to \infty$, the extremum of G equals the extremum of P.

Lagrange multipliers, a method of Rosenbrock, a created response surface technique (CRST) modification, a method of Huard, the sequential unconstrained minimization technique (SUMT) and other approaches of Fiacco and McCormick and others employ penalty function ideas.

6.4.2 Example: Elastic Frame Design

Using, for example, a matrix stiffness formulation, the constitutive relationship for a frame may be written

$$R = K\Delta$$

where R is a loading vector, Δ is a nodal displacement vector and K is the structure stiffness matrix containing the control variables of member stiffnesses.

Displacement (including rotational) constraints will be in terms of inequalities on Δ (state variables)

$$\Delta \leq \Delta_{\text{allowable}}.$$

Stress constraints require the consideration of the member internal actions of axial load, bending moment and shear force and their relationship to axial, flexural and shear stresses on the relevant cross section.

Where weight, say, is the design criterion, this may be expressed in terms of the members' areas and lengths.

The nonlinear programming problem is then defined in terms of the variables Δ and the control variables in K.

Consider the specific example of the design of the frame shown in Figure 6.6, subjected to an asymmetrically applied load γ.

The structure stiffness equations read, considering bending effects

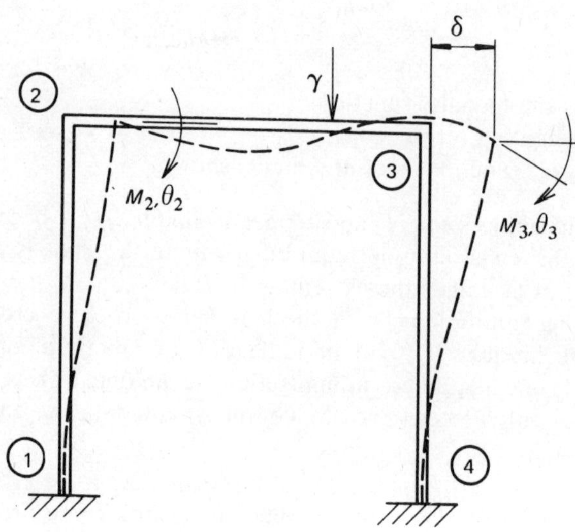

Fig. 6.6

only,

$$\begin{bmatrix} M_2 \\ M_3 \\ 0 \end{bmatrix} = \begin{bmatrix} 8EI/L & 2EI/L & -6EI/L^2 \\ & 8EI/L & -6EI/L^2 \\ & \text{symmetric} & 24EI/L^3 \end{bmatrix} \begin{bmatrix} \theta_2 \\ \theta_3 \\ \delta \end{bmatrix}$$

where θ_2, θ_3, and δ are the structure rotations at nodes 2 and 3, and horizontal displacement respectively, M_2 and M_3 are the 'fixed end' moments for member 2-3, E is the material modulus, I is the member moment of inertia, and L is the member length.

Assume the deflection constraint is

$$\delta \leq \delta_{\text{allowable}}$$

and the flexural stress constraints are, for example, at the base of the column and right-hand end of the beam,

$$[-6EI\delta/L^2 + 2EI\theta_2/L]/Z \leq \sigma_{\text{allowable}}$$
$$[2EI\theta_2/L + 4EI\theta_3/L]/Z \leq \sigma_{\text{allowable}}$$

where Z is the section modulus.

Assume the design criterion is one of weight or volume

$$J = 3AL.$$

The problem is now defined for given overall geometry (L), material (E), allowable deflection and stress ($\delta_{\text{allowable}}$, $\sigma_{\text{allowable}}$) and loading ($\gamma$). The variables in the problem are member size (cross sectional area A) and deformations (δ, θ_2 and θ_3). The problem may be reduced to one in one variable by using the stiffness equations to solve for the remaining three variables, or the problem may be solved in its present form for four variables. For structural steel sections, the following relationships hold approximately

$$Z = 1.45A^{3/2}$$
$$I = 3.20A^2$$

6.5 OPTIMAL CONTROL AND MATHEMATICAL PROGRAMMING

Subsequent sections treat problems (OD), (D), and (P), that is optimal control problems, and outline methods of solution. As noted in section 6.1, however, by various discretization schemes, the problems become amenable to solution by mathematical programming techniques as well. This approach to the solution may be advantageous in certain cases, particularly in the treatment of complicated constraints. It circumvents the solution of a two-point-boundary-value-problem that arises on application of Pontryagin's principle (Chapter 8), while the computer storage requirements are far less than if dynamic programming (Chapter 7) is used.

Considering the general problem (OD1) together with the constraints

$$h^1(x(y), u(y)) \geqslant 0$$
$$h^2(x(y), u(y)) = 0$$

where h^1, h^2 are in general nonlinear vector functions.

To show the connection between this problem and the mathematical programming problem (A), partition the interval (y^L, y^R) into N subintervals of size Δ_k where

$$\Delta_k = y_k - y_{k-1}, \qquad k = 1, \ldots, N. \tag{6.15}$$

As an approximation, integrals may be replaced by summations and derivatives by their finite difference equivalents

$$\frac{\mathrm{d}x}{\mathrm{d}y} = \frac{x(y_k) - x(y_{k-1})}{\Delta_k}. \tag{6.16}$$

Problem (OD1) becomes

$$\min\Big[\sum G[x(k), u(k), k]\Delta_k + g[x(k), k] \Big|_{k=0}^{k=N} \mid (1/\Delta_k)(x(k) - x(k-1))$$
$$= f[x(k-1), u(k-1), k-1], M^2[x(N), N] = 0, M^1[x(0), 0] = 0,$$
$$h^1(x(k), u(k)) \geqslant 0, h^2(x(k), u(k)) = 0, k = 0, \ldots, N\Big] \tag{A7}$$

where y_k, is denoted as k. Other approximations may be used. This is a mathematical programming problem with the finite number of unknowns $x(k)$, $k = 0, 1, \ldots, N$ and $u(k)$, $k = 0, 1, \ldots, N-1$. (The Δ_k may also be considered as unknowns.)

To put this into the form of problem (A) the variables $x_1, x_2, \ldots, x_p$ are assigned to $x(k)$, $k = 0, 1, \ldots, N$ and $u(k)$, $k = 0, 1, \ldots, N-1$. That is $p = N(n+m)+1$. The order of assignment is arbitrary.

Interpreted in another light, the optimal control problem is a mathematical programming problem of infinite dimension. Kuhn–Tucker's theorem is thus applicable and has been used in this manner by many authors but originally by Hurwicz. The approach offers a means of obtaining optimality conditions for the control problem.

Problems (D) are already in a discrete form and their solution as mathematical programming problems follows from the above. Problems (P) require discretization schemes over all their independent variables and the mathematical programming problem follows.

6.5 NOTES, COMMENTS AND BIBLIOGRAPHY

[6.1] See Himmelblau (1972) for an excellent classification and comparison of the various nonlinear programming algorithms. According to Himmelblau the term mathematical programming originated about 1950 by Dorfman and includes linear programming, integer programming, convex programming, nonlinear programming, programming under uncertainty, network flow theory and dynamic programming. The term as used in the present work, however, excludes the last two topics because of the essentially different philosophies involved.

In mathematical programming, some (the residual number of degrees of freedom) of the 'independent' variables x are often termed *decision variables*. Here this usage is not followed as decision variables are used synonymously with control variables and have a definite physical meaning. In mathematical programming usage, which specific variables become decision variables is arbitrary. Likewise in mathematical programming, the term model is sometimes used to describe the problem (A). Here model is used exclusively as a representation of the structural system. See Wilde and Beightler (1967) in regard to the usage of 'state' and 'decision' in mathematical programming.

For other comprehensive treatments of mathematical programming and optimization in general, see Beveridge and Schechter (1970), Luenberger (1969) and Gottfried and Weisman (1973) among others. For stochastic programming see the relevant chapters in Abadie (1967), Hadley (1964) and Dantzig (1963) among others.

For structural applications of mathematical programming see, for example, Fox (1971), Spunt (1971), Spillers (1975a), Gallagher and Zienkiewicz (1973), Kowalik (1966), Majid (1972, 1974), Schmit (1969c), Moses (1974), Sheu and Prager (1968), Przemieniecki (1968) and Cohn (1968) and their bibliographies.

A note on terminology: Problem (A) is sometimes referred to as a *parameter optimization problem* or a *static optimization problem*.

[6.2] For a readable treatment of maxima and minima of functions see Sokolnikoff and Redheffer (1966). The results given here are expressed as theorems in Himmelblau (1972) where sufficient conditions for optimality are also stated.

For comments on convexity and concavity and unimodality see Himmelblau (1972). Convex programming problems have $G(x)$ as a convex function and the constraints forming a convex set. In such cases, the local minimum is the global minimum.

In economic systems, Lagrange multipliers are interpreted as shadow prices (Ray and Szekely 1973). Further interpretation of Lagrange multipliers is given in Bryson and Ho (1975) as well as notes on the topic of parameter optimization. For sufficient conditions for optimality where equality constraints or inequality constraints are present see Bryson and Ho. Sufficient conditions for optimality are also given, for example, in Wilde and Beightler (1967) and Arrow *et al*. (1958), but are rarely used in practice.

The Kuhn–Tucker conditions were given in Kuhn and Tucker (1951). For an alternative statement of the general nonlinear programming optimality conditions see John (1948), and Mangasarian and Fromovitz (1967). Other treatments of the Kuhn–Tucker conditions can be found in Hadley (1964), Himmelblau (1972), Bryson and Ho (1975), Wilde and Beightler (1967), and Luenberger (1969) among others.

Structural examples of the theory in this section can be found, for example, in Stark and Nicholls (1972), Spunt (1971), and Fox (1971) among others.

Inequalities may be reduced to equalities by introducing slack or surplus variables.

An *active* or *binding* inequality constraint is one for which $h_j(x) = 0$ for the value of x under consideration.

Where the feasible region is nonsimply connected several starting vectors are required. Generally, however, most problems have simply connected feasible regions. See Himmelblau (1972) for further comment.

Duality is discussed by Fiacco and McCormick (1968) and Wolfe (1961) among others. For duality in the linear programming problem see Hadley (1962) for example.

A structural example of duality is given in Templeman (1976). In the same reference a comparison is made to the 'optimality criteria' approaches of structural optimization. For structures composed of finite element systems in which the weight of an element is proportional to its stiffness, the mathematical programming and 'optimality criteria' approaches are unified.

[6.3] Much has been written on *linear programming*, its solution efficiency, the availability of computer packages and the simplex method and other standard procedures of linear programming. Refer to Dantzig (1963), Gass (1969), Hadley (1962), Wilde and Beightler (1967), Simmonard (1966), Llewellyn (1964), and Stark and Nicholls (1972) among others. In a structural design and analysis sense see Livesley (1973).

Parametric linear programming examines the effect of changes in the problem parameters and is akin to a sensitivity analysis. See for example Stark and Nicholls (1972) and Cohn and Maier (1977).

Numerous applications of linear programming to structural optimization have been reported. See for example the earlier referenced structural optimization reviews and also Bigelow and Gaylord (1967), Douty (1966), Heyman (1951), Lewis (1966), Moses (1964), Moses and Kinser (1967), Ridha and Wright (1967), Reinschmidt *et al.* (1966), Rubinstein and Karagozian (1966), Chan (1968a,b), Dorn *et al.* (1964), Kumar *et al.* (1967), and Toakley (1968a,b) among others.

Kirsch (1972) reinterprets the optimum design of prestressed concrete beams as a linear programming problem. On the general subject of optimum design of prestressed concrete, though not necessarily in a linear programming sense, see Birkeland (1974), Goble and Lapay (1971), Kirsch (1973), Rozvany and Hampson (1963), Clyde and Sharpe (1965), Rozvany (1964, 1966b), Thakkar and Rao (1974), Touma and Wilson (1973), Naaman (1976), Torres *et al.* (1966), Morris (1978), Francis (1973) and Brotchie (1969). For related work see Schmidt and Brotchie (1973) and Johnson (1972). Sheu and Prager (1968) review work on reinforced and prestressed structures. See also Kirsch and Moses (1977).

The minimum weight design problem for rigid plastic frames is covered extensively in Neal (1963). There the assumptions behind the approach are detailed and physical explanations given. Foulkes' theorems are also given with explanations. See also Foulkes (1953, 1954), Prager (1956). For several loading systems see Heyman (1951), Livesley (1959); for tapered members Heyman (1959, 1960); for computational questions Livesley (1956), Heyman and Prager (1958), Heyman (1953). Horne (1971) devotes a chapter to the problem and treats continuous beams and multistorey frames as well. For multistorey structures see also Rubinstein and Karagozian (1966). Livesley (1973) considers both the design and analysis problems using linear programming and gives an historical perspective to the subject. The emphasis there is on the systematic way of setting up the problems. Note that the shakedown design problem is nonlinear (Heyman 1958). Toakley (1970) considers the effect of axial loads on the design and also discusses the relative merits of a statical approach or a mechanism approach to the design. The problem where axial load effects are included is effectively linear in character. See also Toakley (1968a,b,c), Spillers (1975a), Munro and Smith (1972), Smith and Munro (1976), Heyman (1971) and their bibliographies. For general plasticity problems and mathematical programming see Cohn and Maier (1977). Note in particular the work of Munro, Grierson, DeDonato, Corradi, Zavelani-Rossi, Cohn, Maier, Smith, Best, Polizzotto, Franchi, and Fenves.

The formulation for the lower bound design problem for concrete slabs is based on unpublished notes of D. H. Clyde. For related work see Sharpe and Clyde (1967), Clyde (1965), Clyde and Sharpe (1965), and Carmichael and Clyde (1977). Early work related to Hillerborg's method (Hillerborg 1956) was by Rozvany (1966b) and Wood (1963). The discontinuities introduced by the yield criterion were overcome by Kaliszky (1965) and Mroz (1958) using quadratic terms. Rozvany's approach (Rozvany 1966b), however, requires no such prior manipulation of the problem. The approach rests on the choice of transfer lines. Rozvany's work highlights the discontinuities in the derivative terms. For more recent work in the subject the reader is referred to the comprehensive monographs of Rozvany (1976) and Rozvany and Hill (1976) on flexural systems. For early work on optimization on slabs see Wood (1961) and Wood and Jones (1967). See also Save and Massonet (1972), and Cohn and Maier (1977). Further comments on this problem are given later. See also Borkowski (1975) and Borkowski and Atkociunas (1975).

For *geometric programming* see Zener (1971) and Duffin *et al.* (1967). For a description of the technique see Wilde and Beightler (1967) and Stark and Nicholls (1972) among others. The choice of the term programming is unfortunate as its usage is not in the same sense as the other mathematical programming techniques. Applications include Templeman (1970, 1972, 1975), Stark and Nicholls (1972), Bradley *et al.* (1974), Agrawal (1978) and Palmer (1968a).

For various approaches to *integer programming* see Dantzig (1963), Hu (1969), Hadley (1962, 1964), Kunzi *et al.* (1966), Balinski (1965), Plane and McMillan (1971), Garfinkel and Nemhauser (1972), Zionts (1974), Benders (1962) and others.

Combinatorial, transportation, network and graph theory problems can be formulated as integer programming problems including zero-one programming. Zionts (1974) presents an overview and classification of the available integer programming theory.

Structural applications include those of Cella and Soosaar (1973), Maier (1973), Zavelani *et al.* (1975), and Toakley (1968c). See also Horne (1971) and Masur (1975a).

Quadratic programming problems have quadratic criteria and linear constraints and are of the form

$$\min J = a_0 + c^{\mathrm{T}}x + x^{\mathrm{T}}Qx \quad \text{subject to} \quad Ax + b \leqslant 0 \tag{A8}$$

where Q is a positive definite or semidefinite symmetric square ($n \times n$) matrix.

Assuming J to be convex, then the Kuhn–Tucker conditions are both necessary and sufficient for a global minimum since the linear constraints form a convex feasible region.

In many cases the solution can be found in a finite number of steps.

A quadratic function may arise from a Taylors series approximation to a nonlinear function or from say a statistical analysis of experimental data.

For the development of quadratic programming see Wolfe (1959), Beale (1955), Hadley (1964), Kunzi *et al*. (1966) and Himmelblau (1972). Beale is attributed with the differential method, while Wolfe the Langrangian approach. For comments on showing the criterion J to be a convex function and the constraints a convex set (both equality and inequality) see Himmelblau (1972). See also Abadie (1967), Vajda (1961), Graves and Wolfe (1963), Zoutendijk (1960) and Boot (1964) among others.

For structural applications see Cohn and Maier (1977).

Separable programming problems have criteria and constraints that are separable functions and are of the form.

$$\begin{aligned} &\min J\ (= G(x)) = \sum_{i=1}^{n} f_i(x_i) \\ &\text{subject to} \quad (h_j(x) =) \sum_{i=1}^{n} h_{ji}(x_i) \leq 0 \qquad j = 1, \ldots, m \end{aligned} \tag{A9}$$

See Hadley (1964).

[6.4] Treatments of *nonlinear programming* techniques are given in Himmelblau (1972), Beveridge and Schechter (1970), Luenberger (1969) and Gottfried and Weisman (1973) among others. For the penalty function methods see Fiacco and McCormick (1968).

Majid (1972, 1974) gives a detailed exposition of nonlinear programming applied to the design of rigid framed structures and truss structures in both matrix force and matrix displacement formulations.

For the relationship between cross sectional properties for steel sections see Templeman (1970). (Units of mm for *I, A* and *Z*.)

There are many applications of nonlinear programming applied to structural optimization. For example see Gallagher and Zienkiewicz (1973) where several contributions are given, Kowalik (1966), Przemieniecki (1968), Schmit (1968, 1969a, b, c), Brotchie (1967), Sharpe (1969), Bracken and McCormick (1968), Hughes and Mistree (1975, 1977), Hughes, Mistree and Davies (1977), Moses (1974), AGARD-AG-149-7, and Majid.

For the use of nonlinear programming in the solution of systems of equations see Zangwill (1969).

[6.5] See Tabak and Kuo (1971), Lee and Markus (1967), Canon *et al.* (1970), Sage and White (1977) and Bryson and Ho (1975).

Tabak and Kuo (1971) give a more rigorous transformation from the optimal control problem to the mathematical programming problem than is presented above.

Halkin and Neustadt (1966) and Neustadt (1966, 1967) give general optimality conditions that include Pontryagin's principle and the Kuhn–Tucker conditions as particular cases.

Discussions on discretization schemes for continuous optimal control problems can be found in Cullum (1969), and Tabak and Kuo (1969). Certain schemes may not be suitable for certain problems. Manipulation of the interval size Δ_k may be necessary.

Applications of mathematical programming techniques to optimal control problems of type (D) and (P) are extensively referenced in Tabak and Kuo (1971).

For related structural applications see for example de Silva and Grant (1975), de Silva, Negus and Worster (1976), de Silva, Green and Grant (1976) and de Silva (1975).

Chapter 7

Dynamic Programming

7.1 INTRODUCTION

As originally devised by Bellman, dynamic programming was a technique for solving variational and multistage decision problems but has since been extended to cover a broad range of control problems. At its base is the *principle of optimality* and Markovian properties of the state. The principle states: 'An optimal policy has the property that whatever the initial state and the initial decision, the remaining decisions must constitute an optimal policy with regard to the state resulting from the first decision'. The words decision and control may be interchanged if the optimal control problem is regarded as a multistage decision problem or process. The independent variable need not be time. The principle of optimality may be proved by contradiction and is a general condition for optimality applicable for both the continuous and discrete cases. The resulting recurrence relation expressing optimality is referred to as Bellman's equation and for continuous lumped parameter systems it is equivalent to the Hamilton–Jacobi partial differential equation of variational calculus. The technique is thus logically equivalent to the maximum principle of Pontryagin and the classical calculus of variations.

Dynamic programming is primarily suited to systems with serial 'structure' or staging but can be applied to systems with parallel arrangements. The staging may be physical or conceptual.

Dynamic programming is a different solution philosophy to the similarly named mathematical programming techniques of the previous section. It is in effect an approach to an optimization problem rather than a general solution algorithm. The approach uses an imbedding procedure whereby the original problem is replaced by a sequence of smaller problems. It is noted that there are limitations to its practical application but it is potentially powerful and provides a neat treatment of certain optimization problems.

This chapter outlines the optimality conditions (Bellman's equation) for the optimization problems associated with all system types, namely difference (section 7.2), ordinary differential (section 7.3), algebraic (section 7.4), and partial differential (section 7.5). Invariably a numerical solution is required. An important subclass of problems, namely the linear-quadratic, however, does admit a closed form solution and may serve as an approximation to other problems. Examples are used to illustrate the dynamic programming approach.

7.2 DIFFERENCE EQUATION MODELS

7.2.1 General

Consider the discrete control problem, problem (D1) with g given for $k = N$ only. For the boundary conditions, assume only $x(0)$ is known and work in the reverse y direction; equivalent forward y direction procedures can be used.

Dynamic programming reduces this minimization problem of N vectors $u(0), \ldots, u(N-1)$ to a sequence of N minimizations over a single vector. This is possible as the given optimization problem is imbedded into a wider class of problems. Define

$$\begin{aligned} J_{N-1} &\triangleq G[x(N-1), u(N-1), N-1] + g[x(N)] \\ J_{N-2} &\triangleq G[x(N-2), u(N-2), N-2] + J_{N-1} \quad \text{etc.} \end{aligned} \tag{7.1}$$

and the optimal *return functions*

$$\begin{aligned} S_{N-1} &\triangleq \min_{u(N-1)} J_{N-1} \\ S_{N-2} &\triangleq \min_{u(N-2),u(N-1)} J_{N-2} \\ &\cdots \\ S_{N-j} &\triangleq \min_{u(N-j),\ldots,u(N-1)} J_{N-j} \qquad j = 3, 4, \ldots, N. \end{aligned} \tag{7.2}$$

Here S_{N-j} is the minimum value of the criterion associated with the optimal j-stage discrete process with initial state $x(N-j)$. Applying the principle of optimality, gives the recurrence formula

$$S_{N-j}[x(N-j)] = \min_{u(N-j)} \{G[x(N-j), u(N-j), N-j] + S_{N-j+1}[x(N-j+1)]\} \tag{7.3}$$

where

$$x(N-j+1) = F[x(N-j), u(N-j), N-j]. \tag{7.4}$$

The sequential solution procedure starts with $j = 1$, finding $S_{N-1}[x(N-1)]$ and $\hat{u}(N-1)$, and so on for $j = 2, 3, \ldots, N$ giving a sequence of pairs $S_{N-j}[x(N-j)$ and $\hat{u}(N-j)$ ending with $S_0[x(0)]$ and $\hat{u}(0)$. At each stage S_{N-j} replaces the previous S_{N-j+1} in 'memory'. The sequence $\hat{u}(0), \hat{u}(1), \ldots, \hat{u}(N-1)$ constitutes the optimal control sequence or policy and $S_0[x(0)]$ is the value of criterion. The states $x(1), \ldots, x(N)$ can be found in succession from (7.4) since the controls are now known. This solution procedure can in certain circumstances lead to a closed form solution or it can be used as a computational algorithm. Note that for large n, the amount of computer storage required will be large and some approximating process will be needed. For a numerical solution, the optimum at each stage can be conveniently done by a search procedure in conjunction with interpolation schemes.

All minimizations are assumed to be carried out subject to any constraints on the problem. Some constraints may be handled directly and numerically simplify the computations. Alternatively the constraints can be adjoined to the criterion by means of Lagrange multipliers to given an augmented criterion. The problem then is to find the control and the multipliers which minimize the augmented criterion.

Dynamic programming finds most use in the discrete-continuous and discrete-discrete cases. For the continuous case additional assumptions on the class of functions under consideration are sometimes required.

7.2.2 Example: Torsional Vibration of an Elastic Shaft

Consider a shaft divided into segments of constant diameter (Fig. 7.1). The state equations follow from Chapter 1, and in discrete form are

$$x_1(k+1) = x_1(k) + (\Delta/J(k)G)x_2(k)$$
$$x_2(k+1) = x_2(k) + r^2(k)\gamma\omega^2 x_1(k)$$

where x_1 and x_2 are the rotation ϕ and $JG\mathrm{d}\phi/\mathrm{d}y$.

For a minimum volume design, the optimality criterion may be written

$$V = \sum_{k=0}^{N-1} \Delta\pi R^2(k)$$

where $R(k)$ is the radius of the k'th segment.

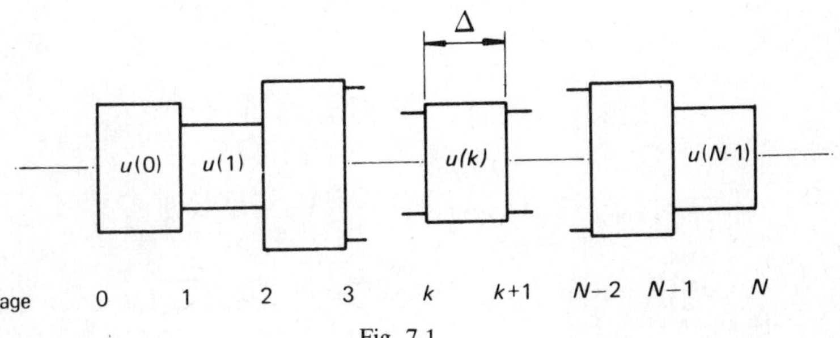

Fig. 7.1

The controls in the problem are $J(k)$, $r(k)$ and $R(k)$ which are related, and the relevant properties may be grouped as $u(k)$. The state equations become

$$x_i(k+1) = F_i[x(k), u(k)] \qquad i = 1, 2$$

and the criterion

$$V = \sum_{k=0}^{N-1} u(k).$$

Constraints may also be placed on the states $x_i(k)$ and controls, but in the numerical solution simplify the computations.

The recurrence relation may be written immediately

$$\begin{aligned} S_{N-j}[x(N-j)] &= \min_{u(N-j)} \{u(N-j) + S_{N-j+1}[x(N-j+1)]\} \\ &= \min_{u(N-j)} \{u(N-j) + S_{N-j+1}(F[x(N-j), u(N-j)])\}. \end{aligned}$$

The initial condition S_N depends on the configuration of the shaft.

7.2.3 The Linear-Quadratic Problem

Closed form results may be obtained for linear system equations and quadratic optimality criteria (problem (D2)).

Consider firstly the criterion

$$J = x^{\mathrm{T}}(k) g_{xx} x(k) \Big|_{k=N} + \sum_{k=0}^{N-1} x^{\mathrm{T}}(k) G_{xx}(k) x(k) + u^{\mathrm{T}}(k) G_{uu}(k) u(k).$$

For $x(0)$ specified, it can be shown by induction that the optimal control and the optimal return function have the form

$$\hat{u}(k) = -\,C(k)x(k) \tag{7.5}$$

$$S[x(k)] = x^{\mathrm{T}}(k)P(k)x(k) \tag{7.6}$$

where $C(k)$ and $P(k)$ are $m \times n$ and $n \times n$ matrices determined from

$$C(k) = Z_{uu}^{-1}(k) Z_{ux}(k) \tag{7.7}$$

$$P(k) = Z_{xx}(k) - Z_{xu}(k) Z_{uu}^{-1}(k) Z_{ux}(k) \tag{7.8}$$

where

$$\left.\begin{aligned} Z_{xx}(k) &= G_{xx}(k) + A^{\mathrm{T}}(k)P(k+1)A(k) \\ Z_{ux}(k) &= B^{\mathrm{T}}(k)P(k+1)A(k) \\ Z_{uu}(k) &= G_{uu}(k) + B^{\mathrm{T}}(k)P(k+1)B(k) \\ P(N) &= g_{xx} \end{aligned}\right. \tag{7.9}$$

Equations (7.5) to (7.9) contain enough information to compute the optimal control and the optimal return function in a backwards sequence.

A more general criterion of the form

$$J = [x^{\mathrm{T}}(k)g_{xx}x(k) + g_x x(k)]_{k=N} + \sum_{k=0}^{N-1} x^{\mathrm{T}}(k)G_{xx}(k)x(k) + x^{\mathrm{T}}(k)G_{xu}(k)u(k)$$
$$+ u^{\mathrm{T}}(k)G_{ux}(k)x(k) + u^{\mathrm{T}}(k)G_{uu}(k)u(k) + G_x(k)x(k) + G_u(k)u(k)$$

may be considered and leads to a similar closed form solution. In particular

$$\hat{u}(k) = -C(k)x(k) - D(k) \tag{7.10}$$

$$S[x(k)] = x^{\mathrm{T}}(k)P(k)x(k) + Q(k)x(k) + R(k). \tag{7.11}$$

7.2.4 Example: Cantilever Design

For a propped cantilever, the relevant state equations in difference equation form are

$$\begin{bmatrix} x_1 \\ x_2 \\ x_3 \\ x_4 \end{bmatrix}_{k+1} = \begin{bmatrix} x_1 + \Delta x_2 \\ x_2 + \Delta u x_3 \\ x_3 + \Delta x_4 \\ x_4 + \Delta q \end{bmatrix}_k$$

with boundary conditions $x_1(0) = 0$, $x_2(0) = 0$, $x_3(N) = 0$, $x_4(N) = Z$, some end reaction. The states are deflection, slope, bending moment and shear force and the control $u = 1/EI$. Δ is the discretization interval.

Assume a square error criterion for which the optimum flexibility (rigidity) of the beam is sought.

Consider

$$J = \sum_{0}^{N-1} \alpha(k)(x_1(k) - x_1^d(k))^2 + \beta(k)(u(k) - u^d(k))^2$$

where $x_1^d(k)$ and $u^d(k)$ denote the desired state (deflection) and flexibility of the beam, corresponding to the state $x_1(k)$ and control $u(k)$ respectively. The measure penalizes large deviations from the desired values more heavily than small deviations. $\alpha(k)$ and $\beta(k)$ are weighting factors which indicate the relative importance of the various terms in the error measure. In any particular design, these weighting factors may be selected to satisfy specified performance requirements, physical constraints or other design briefs. A particular case of interest is when $\alpha = 0$ and u^d large; the criterion is then equivalent to minimizing the stiffness (squared) (which is related to the weight and material) of the beam.

For given Z, the solution is of the form (7.10) and (7.11). The computations are given in Carmichael (1978a).

7.3 ORDINARY DIFFERENTIAL EQUATION MODELS

7.3.1 General

Consider the continuous control problem (OD1) equivalent to the discrete case of section 7.2, namely with $x(y^{\mathrm{L}})$ given and with g only specified at y^{R}. Define an optimal return function,

$$S[x(y), y] \triangleq \min_{u(\tau)} \int_{y}^{y^{\mathrm{R}}} G[x(\tau), u(\tau), \tau]\, \mathrm{d}\tau + g[x(y^{\mathrm{R}}), y^{\mathrm{R}}] \qquad y \leqslant \tau \leqslant y^{\mathrm{R}} \tag{7.12}$$

Applying the principle of optimality and manipulating gives the partial differential equation known as *Bellman's* functional *equation*.

$$-\frac{\partial S[x(y), y]}{\partial y} = \min_{u(y)} \left\{ G[x(y), u(y), y] + \sum_{k=1}^{n} \frac{\partial S[x(y), y]}{\partial x_k} f_k[x(y), u(y), y] \right\} \tag{7.13}$$

From the definition of S, the appropriate boundary condition is

$$S[x(y^{\mathrm{R}}), y^{\mathrm{R}}] = g[x(y^{\mathrm{R}}), y^{\mathrm{R}}]. \tag{7.14}$$

The solution is by integration following the determination of the optimal control by minimization. The minimization is carried out with full regard to any constraints present. Constraints may, as in the discrete case, be adjoined to the criterion by means of Lagrange multipliers to give an augmented criterion.

The continuous result assumes all the derivatives in (7.13) exist and may require justification in certain cases. The result (7.13) is known as the Hamilton–Jacobi–Bellman equation because of its generalization of the Hamilton–Jacobi equation of classical mechanics.

Split boundary conditions may be handled by imbedding the problem within a larger problem.

7.3.2 Example: Optimal Shafts

For the minimum volume design of an elastic shaft in torsional vibration, the state equations are

$$\mathrm{d}x_1/\mathrm{d}y = x_2/JG$$
$$\mathrm{d}x_2/\mathrm{d}y = r^2\gamma\omega^2 x_1$$

where the notation is as given previously in Chapter 1. The states are the rotation ϕ and $JG\mathrm{d}\phi/\mathrm{d}y$. The controls are the torsional rigidity JG

and radius of gyration r. Together with the radius of the shaft, $R(y)$, which occurs in the criterion

$$V = \int_0^L \pi R^2 \,\mathrm{d}y$$

the three controls are interrelated.

Define an optimal return function

$$S[x_1, x_2, y] = \min_{\text{controls}} \int_y^L \pi R^2 \,\mathrm{d}\tau \qquad y \leqslant \tau \leqslant L$$

and by the principle of optimality, Bellman's equation follows

$$-\frac{\partial S}{\partial y} = \min_{\text{controls}} \left(\pi R^2 + \left(\frac{x_2}{JG}\right) \frac{\partial S}{\partial x_1} + \left(r^2 \gamma \omega^2 x_1\right) \frac{\partial S}{\partial x_2} \right).$$

The boundary condition on S depends on the configuration of the shaft. Constraints on the states and controls may be required to produce a physically realizable solution.

7.3.3 The Linear-Quadratic Problem

Typically numerical solutions are required for the general nonlinear problem. However, the linear-quadratic version (problem (OD2)) does admit a closed form solution analogous to the discrete case. Consider firstly the criterion

$$J = \tfrac{1}{2} x^{\mathrm{T}} g_{xx} x \Big|_{y=y^{\mathrm{R}}} + \int_{y^{\mathrm{L}}}^{y^{\mathrm{R}}} \tfrac{1}{2}(x^{\mathrm{T}} G_{xx} x + u^{\mathrm{T}} G_{uu} u) \,\mathrm{d}y.$$

It can be shown that the optimal return function and optimal control assume the form

$$S[x(y), y] = \tfrac{1}{2} x^{\mathrm{T}}(y) K_{xx}(y) x(y) \tag{7.15}$$

where $K_{xx}(y)$ is a symmetric $n \times n$ matrix, and

$$\hat{u}(y) = -G_{uu}^{-1}(y)\{B^{\mathrm{T}}(y) K_{xx}(y) x(y)\}. \tag{7.16}$$

Substituting in Bellman's equation gives an equation in $K_{xx}(y)$

$$-\mathrm{d}K_{xx}/\mathrm{d}y = G_{xx} + A^{\mathrm{T}} K_{xx} + K_{xx} A - K_{xx} B G_{uu}^{-1} B^{\mathrm{T}} K_{xx} \tag{7.17}$$

This is a matrix Riccati equation with boundary conditions $K_{xx}(y^{\mathrm{R}}) = g_{xx}$ from (7.15). Solution is by integration, but note that K_{xx} is symmetric.

This result can be extended to apply to criteria of the form

$$J = [\tfrac{1}{2} x^{\mathrm{T}} g_{xx} x + g_x x]_{y=y^{\mathrm{R}}} + \int_{y^{\mathrm{L}}}^{y^{\mathrm{R}}} \{\tfrac{1}{2}(x^{\mathrm{T}} G_{xx} x + x^{\mathrm{T}} G_{xu} u$$
$$+ u^{\mathrm{T}} G_{ux} x + u^{\mathrm{T}} G_{uu} u) + G_u u + G_x x\} \,\mathrm{d}y$$

where the optimal control and optimal return function become

$$\hat{u}(y) = -(C(y)x(y) + D(y)) \tag{7.18}$$

$$S[x(y), y] = \tfrac{1}{2}x^{\mathrm{T}}(y)K_{xx}(y)x(y) + K_x(y)x(y) + K(y) \tag{7.19}$$

7.4 ALGEBRAIC EQUATION MODELS

7.4.1 General

Systems described by algebraic relationships may also be amenable to the usage of dynamic programming for their associated optimization problem. Structures such as transmission towers and high rise buildings which may be regarded as staged according to storey height or continuous beams which may be regarded as staged according to individual spans lend themselves directly to dynamic programming formulations. Other structures, such as general trusses, although not physically staged, may be regarded as conceptually staged for dynamic programming purposes and this makes the technique of wide applicability. Markov properties are required and this may determine the form of staging adopted.

Consider the standard problem (A1).

$$\min J = G(x, u) \quad \text{subject to} \quad F(x, u) = 0 \quad \text{and constraints} \tag{A1}$$

where x and u are the state and control variables respectively.

For the dynamic programming solution of (A1), the system and problem have to be decomposed into a sequence of single stage systems and problems. Schematically this may be represented as in Fig. 7.2.

Arrows imply dependence relationships and not necessarily a flow of information. The serial multistage system may be regarded as being

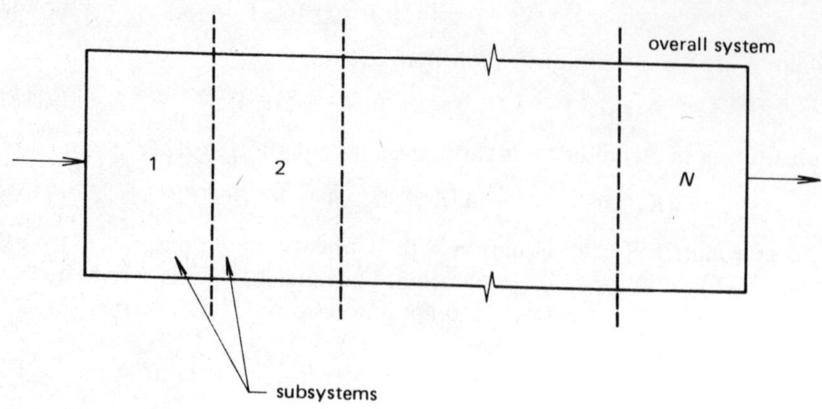

Fig. 7.2

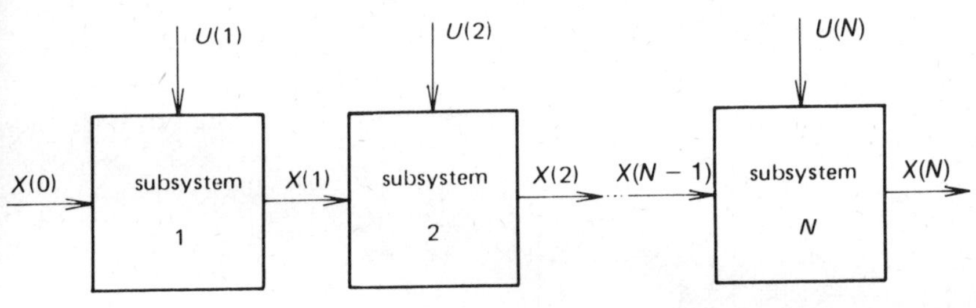

Fig. 7.3

composed of single stage subsystems joined by a transmittal of state variable information from one stage to the following stage. Control variables enter at each stage and influence the values taken by the states.

To allow for the possibility of conceptual staging, let $X(k) = (X_1, X_2, \ldots)^T$ be the state at the k'th stage and $U(k) = (U_1, U_2, \ldots)^T$ be the control at the k'th stage. Schematically this may be shown as in Fig. 7.3. X and U may or may not be functionally related through F depending on the system and the type of staging chosen.

Let the criterion for each stage k be

$$G^k = G^k[X(k-1), X(k), U(k)] \tag{7.20}$$

where for the total problem

$$J = \sum_{k=1}^{N} G^k \tag{7.21}$$

That is, a separable criterion for the system problem is required. The solution by dynamic programming then proceeds as in section 7.2 except that is is more convenient to work in a forward sense, having defined the stages as above. In particular, define

$$S_k[X(k)] = \min_{U(1),\ldots,U(k)} \sum_{j=1}^{k} G^j[X(j-1), X(j), U(j)] \tag{7.22}$$

Applying the principle of optimality gives Bellman's equation

$$S_k[X(k)] = \min_{U(k)}\{G^k[X(k-1), X(k), U(k)] + S_{k-1}[X(k-1)]\} \tag{7.23}$$

with boundary conditions $S_0[X(0)] = 0$.

That is, a series of smaller optimizations replaces the original single optimization. Repeated application of (7.23) solves the problem sequentially.

7.4.2 Example: Truss Design

Consider the elementary braced truss as shown (Fig. 7.4). Nodes have coordinates according to the x, y axes system shown. For the i'th stage the coordinates are

$$(x_{i-1}, y_{i-1}) \qquad (x_i, y_i)$$
$$(x_{i-1}, -y_{i-1}) \qquad (x_i, -y_i).$$

The vertical bars to the left of stage i are considered to belong to stage i. The forces in the four bars for each stage i depend only on x_{i-1}, x_i, y_{i-1}, y_i and the loading but not on other bar locations. Thus for given stage lengths the control variables are the node coordinates y_i and y_{i-1} which directly determine the cost of stage i, denoted $g_i(y_{i-1}, y_i, W)$, where W denotes the applied loading.

Let $c_i(y_i, W)$ = minimum cost of the first i stages

$$= \min_{y_1, y_2, \ldots, y_{i-1}} \sum_{k=1}^{i} g_i(y_{k-1}, y_k, W).$$

Applying the principle of optimality gives the recurrence relation

$$c_i(y_i, W) = \min_{y_{i-1}} \{g_i(y_{i-1}, y_i, W) + c_{i-1}(y_{i-1}, W)\}$$

which may be solved as for the previous Bellman's equations.

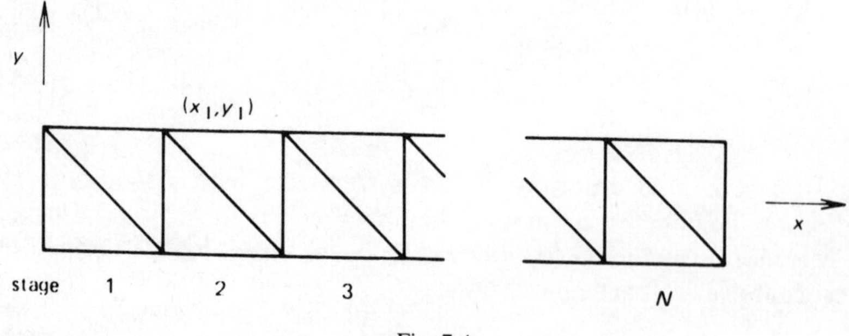

Fig. 7.4

7.5 PARTIAL DIFFERENTIAL EQUATION MODELS

7.5.1 General

The three standard partial differential equation forms, types I, II and III, require distinct manipulations in order that the principle of optimality may be invoked. The resulting equations expressing optimality in all cases are distributed parameter generalizations of Bellman's equation for lumped systems considered above. For the problem relating to system model type I, the derivation is analogous to that for the result in section 7.3 for lumped parameter systems where an increment is taken in the independent variable whose derivatives appear on the left-hand side of the state equations. For the problem relating to system model type II, the parameters defining the imbedded subsystem problems are the state defined on a one-parameter family of surfaces and the parameter of this family of surfaces. The variation is taken in the surfaces' parameter. A similar device can be used for problems relating to system model type III or a region can be incremented.

7.5.2 State Equations Type I

7.5.2.1 BELLMAN'S EQUATION

In order to invoke Bellman's principle of optimality introduce the functional

$$S[x, y_4] = \min_u \int_{y_4}^{y_4^R} \int_{\mathbf{Y}} G[y, x, \ldots, \partial_I x, \ldots, u] \,\mathbf{dy}\, \mathrm{d}y_4 \qquad (7.24)$$

and by making use of the additivity of the functional over an increment in the y_4 coordinate, Bellman's equation results

$$-\frac{\partial S[x, y_4]}{\partial y_4} = \min_u \left[\int_{\mathbf{Y}} \left\{ G[y, x, \ldots, \partial_I x, \ldots, u] + \frac{\partial S[x, y_4]^{\mathrm{T}}}{\partial x} f[y, x, \ldots, \partial_I x, \ldots, u] \right\} \mathbf{dy} \right] \qquad (7.25)$$

with initial condition

$$S[x, y_4^R] = 0. \qquad (7.26)$$

An end state criterion may be incorporated as for the lumped parameter case (section 7.3). $\partial S/\partial x$ denotes a functional partial (variational) derivative. The result assumes the boundary conditions at y_4^R are unknown.

7.5.2.2 EXAMPLE: PLATE ON AN ELASTIC FOUNDATION

For a plate on an elastic foundation the relevant governing equation is

$$D\left(\frac{\partial^4 w}{\partial y_1^4} + 2\,\frac{\partial^4 w}{\partial y_1^2 \partial y_2^2} + \frac{\partial^4 w}{\partial y_2^4}\right) = q - kw$$

where y_1 and y_2 are the plate coordinate variables, w is the lateral deflection, q is the applied lateral load, D is the plate rigidity, and k is the foundation coefficient.

The equation is symmetrical with respect to y_1 and y_2 and so either may be chosen on the left-hand side of the state equations. Let the states be

$$x_1 \triangleq w, \qquad x_2 \triangleq \frac{\partial w}{\partial y_1}, \qquad x_3 \triangleq D\frac{\partial^2 w}{\partial y_1^2}, \qquad x_4 \triangleq D\frac{\partial^3 w}{\partial y_1^3} + 2D\frac{\partial^3 w}{\partial y_1 \partial y_2^2}$$

that is, displacement, and slope, moment and Kirchhoff shearing force in the y_1 direction. The control is the foundation coefficient k for a constant thickness plate.

The state equations become

$$\frac{\partial x_1}{\partial y_1} = x_2 \qquad \frac{\partial x_3}{\partial y_1} = x_4 - 2D\frac{\partial^2 x_2}{\partial y_2^2}$$

$$\frac{\partial x_2}{\partial y_1} = \frac{x_3}{D} \qquad \frac{\partial x_4}{\partial y_1} = q - kx_1 - D\frac{\partial^4 x_1}{\partial y_2^4}$$

For a criterion

$$J = \int_0^a\!\!\int_0^b w^2 \, dy_1 \, dy_2$$

where a and b are the plate dimensions, Bellman's equation is

$$-\frac{\partial S}{\partial y_1} = \min_k \left(\int_0^b \left\{ x_1^2 + \frac{\partial S}{\partial x_1}(x_2) + \frac{\partial S}{\partial x_2}\left(\frac{x_3}{D}\right) + \frac{\partial S}{\partial x_3}\left(x_4 - 2D\frac{\partial^2 x_2}{\partial y_2^2}\right) + \frac{\partial S}{\partial x_4}\left(q - kx_1 - D\frac{\partial^4 x_1}{\partial y_2^4}\right)\right\} dy_2 \right).$$

The initial conditions $S[a, y_2]$ are determined by the configuration of the plate. Bounds on the foundation coefficient will be required as k occurs linearly in Bellman's equation.

7.5.3 State Equations Type II

7.5.3.1 BELLMAN'S EQUATION

Consider the system described over a closed region Y in the $y_1 y_2 y_3$ space with piecewise smooth boundary surfaces ∂Y^a and ∂Y^b (Fig. 7.5), (one octant shown only).

The functional equation approach of dynamic programming imbeds the minimization problem (here (PII)) within a family of problems with 'initial' states and locations of these initial states over Y as parameters.

For this purpose consider the region Y divided into two subregions Y' and Y'' separated by a closed surface Σ (Fig. 7.5) belonging to a one

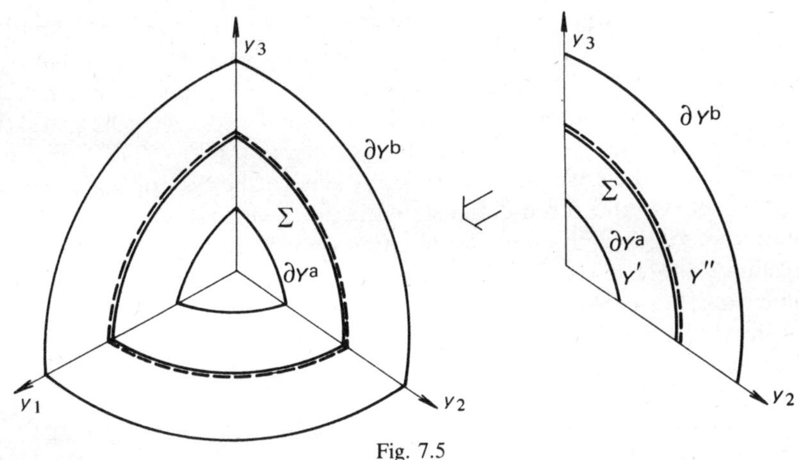

Fig. 7.5

parameter family of surfaces

$$\Phi(y_1, y_2, y_3, c) = 0$$

where c is the parameter of the family. Σ can be reduced to the boundary surfaces ∂Y^a and ∂Y^b by a continuous deformation. The state at Σ, and c may be regarded as parameters defining a family of problems and taking a variation in the surface Σ gives Bellman's equation

$$-\frac{\partial S[x, c]}{\partial c} = \min_u \int_\Sigma \left\{ G[s, c, x, \ldots, \partial_t x, \ldots, u] \, |J(s, c)| + \sum_{j=1}^{n} \frac{\partial S[x, c]}{\partial x_j} \frac{\partial x_j}{\partial c} \right\} \mathrm{d}s \quad (7.27)$$

where s is an areal measurement on Σ, $|J(s, c)|$ denotes the Jacobian and S is the optimal return function. Initial conditions for (7.27) follow from the definition of S and are

$$S[x, c^b] = 0 \quad (7.28)$$

where c takes the value c^b on ∂Y^b.

$\partial S/\partial x_j$ is a functional or variational partial derivative.

End criteria may be handled by introducing extra state and control variables.

If the boundaries of Y are aligned with the y_1, y_2 and y_3 axes (7.27) reduces to

$$-\sum_{i=1}^{3} \frac{\partial S}{\partial y_i} = \min_u \int_\Sigma \left\{ G + \sum_{j=1}^{n} \sum_{i=1}^{3} \frac{\partial S}{\partial x_j} \frac{\partial x_j}{\partial y_i} \right\} \mathrm{d}s \quad (7.29)$$

assuming the Jacobian and the $\partial y_i/\partial c$ terms equal unity.

This simplification is only possible if the increments in Σ are the same in each of the coordinate directions implying that the inner and outer boundaries ∂Y^a and ∂Y^b are concentric cubes. Where the increments differ, ratio terms of the increments according to the particular problem would have to be incorporated. (7.27) remains applicable in all cases. The result (7.29) is nevertheless applicable for all planar regions (and three dimensional regions with two or three interval limits the same) with outer boundaries only by introducing a suitable imaginary inner boundary. For example, the inner boundary in the two dimensional case would correspond to a line parallel to the long side of the rectangle; boundary conditions on this inner boundary would be continuity conditions on the state across the boundary.

7.5.3.2 EXAMPLE: PLATE ON AN ELASTIC FOUNDATION

Consider an elastic plate of constant thickness on a Winkler's foundation with the control being the foundation coefficient $k(y_1, y_2)$, here assumed bounded, $k_{\min} \leq k(y_1, y_2) \leq k_{\max}$.

The state equations for the plate are of the form

$$\frac{\partial x_1}{\partial y_1} = x_2 \qquad \frac{\partial x_1}{\partial y_2} = x_5$$

$$\frac{\partial x_2}{\partial y_1} = x_3 \qquad \frac{\partial x_2}{\partial y_2} = x_8$$

$$\frac{\partial x_3}{\partial y_1} = x_4 \qquad \frac{\partial x_3}{\partial y_2} = x_{10}$$

$$\frac{\partial x_4}{\partial y_1} = \frac{q}{D} - 2\xi_2 - \xi_1 - \frac{k}{D} x_1 \qquad \frac{\partial x_4}{\partial y_2} = 0$$

$$\frac{\partial x_5}{\partial y_1} = x_8 \qquad \frac{\partial x_5}{\partial y_2} = x_6$$

$$\frac{\partial x_6}{\partial y_1} = x_9 \qquad \frac{\partial x_6}{\partial y_2} = x_7$$

$$\frac{\partial x_7}{\partial y_1} = 0 \qquad \frac{\partial x_7}{\partial y_2} = \xi_1$$

$$\frac{\partial x_8}{\partial y_1} = x_{10} \qquad \frac{\partial x_8}{\partial y_2} = x_9$$

$$\frac{\partial x_9}{\partial y_1} = \xi_2 \qquad \frac{\partial x_9}{\partial y_2} = 0$$

$$\frac{\partial x_{10}}{\partial y_1} = 0 \qquad \frac{\partial x_{10}}{\partial y_2} = \xi_2$$

where the states x and parametric variables ξ are

$$x_1 \triangleq w, \quad x_2 \triangleq \frac{\partial w}{\partial y_1}, \quad x_3 \triangleq \frac{\partial^2 w}{\partial y_1^2}, \quad x_4 \triangleq \frac{\partial^3 w}{\partial y_1^3}, \quad x_5 \triangleq \frac{\partial w}{\partial y_2},$$

$$x_6 \triangleq \frac{\partial^2 w}{\partial y_2^2}, \quad x_7 \triangleq \frac{\partial^3 w}{\partial y_2^3}, \quad x_8 \triangleq \frac{\partial^2 w}{\partial y_1 \partial y_2}, \quad x_9 \triangleq \frac{\partial^3 w}{\partial y_1 \partial y_2^2},$$

$$x_{10} \triangleq \frac{\partial^3 w}{\partial y_1^2 \partial y_2}, \quad \xi_1 \triangleq \frac{\partial^4 w}{\partial y_2^4}, \quad \xi_2 \triangleq \frac{\partial^4 w}{\partial y_1^2 \partial y_2^2}$$

w is the lateral displacement of the plate
D is the plate rigidity
q is the lateral loading.

For a squared deflection criterion

$$\min J = \int_Y w^2(y_1, y_2)\, \mathrm{d}y_1\, \mathrm{d}y_2$$

and assuming the plate boundaries coincide with the y_1 and y_2 coordinate axes directions, Bellman's equation becomes

$$\begin{aligned}
-\frac{\partial S}{\partial y_1} - \frac{\partial S}{\partial y_2} = \min_k \int_\Sigma \Bigg\{ & x_1^2 + \frac{\partial S}{\partial x_1}(x_2 + x_5) + \frac{\partial S}{\partial x_2}(x_3 + x_8) \\
& + \frac{\partial S}{\partial x_3}(x_4 + x_{10}) + \frac{\partial S}{\partial x_4}\left(\frac{q}{D} - 2\xi_2 - \xi_1 - \frac{k}{D}x_1\right) \\
& + \frac{\partial S}{\partial x_5}(x_8 + x_6) + \frac{\partial S}{\partial x_6}(x_9 + x_7) + \frac{\partial S}{\partial x_7}(\xi_1) \\
& + \frac{\partial S}{\partial x_8}(x_{10} + x_9) + \frac{\partial S}{\partial x_9}(\xi_2) + \frac{\partial S}{\partial x_{10}}(\xi_2)\Bigg\}\, \mathrm{d}s.
\end{aligned}$$

Depending on the value of the coefficient of k, namely

$$-\frac{\partial S}{\partial x_4}\frac{x_1}{D}$$

so the optimal value of k may be chosen.

7.5.4 State Equations Type III

Bellman's equation for problems associated with systems of this form is not available in the literature but could be straightforwardly derived using the same approaches as for systems type II. For a region Y with inner and outer boundaries ∂Y^a and ∂Y^b respectively, let $Y' \subset Y$ be a variable region with boundary $\partial Y'$ (Fig. 7.6).

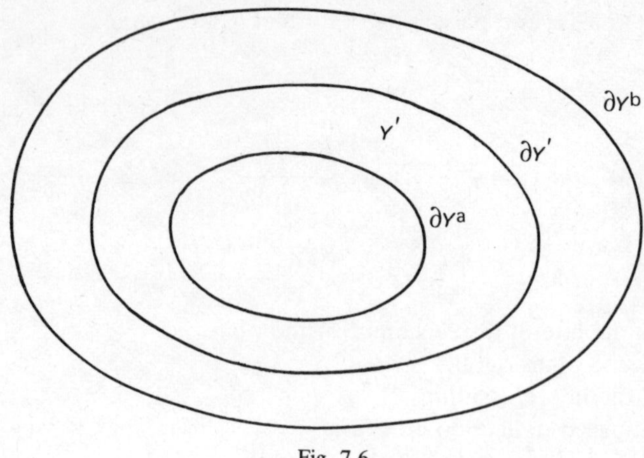

Fig. 7.6

Define an optimal return function

$$S[x, \partial Y'] = \min_u \iint_{Y-Y'} G[x, \ldots, \partial_i x, \ldots, u, y] \, dy_1 \, dy_2$$

and allowing a variation in the region Y', Bellman's equation follows.

7.6 NOTES, COMMENTS AND BIBLIOGRAPHY

[7.1] For the early work of Bellman and a statement of the principle of optimality, see Bellman (1957, 1961), Bellman and Dreyfus (1962), and Bellman and Kalaba (1965).

For a proof of the principle of optimality and a discussion on the nontrivial nature of the principle, see Fel'dbaum (1965) and Porter (1969).

The connection between dynamic programming and the maximum principle of Pontryagin is outlined by Desoer (1961) and Rozonoer (1959), and between dynamic programming and the calculus of variations by Dreyfus (1965). See also Bellman (1961), Lee (1964), Boudarel *et al*. (1971), and Dyer and McReynolds (1970). The solution of the Hamilton–Jacobi–Bellman equation is very difficult in general. Methods for solution are available in works for example on classical mechanics and control theory (Dreyfus 1965, Rozonoer 1959, Denn 1969).

Distefano (1974a) develops the ideas of dynamic programming from a structural mechanics viewpoint. Chapter 6 of this reference deals with the variational methods of analysis as they may be interpreted by dynamic programming. The development is through the use of a string example leading to the biharmonic equation, the Theorem of Castigliano, Betti's Theorem and the Theorem of Complementary Energy. It is an excellent aligning of dynamic programming and structural analysis. Chapters 10 and 11 deal with optimal beam design and the optimal design of rotating discs where the models for the systems are treated as extrema of energy functions. The approach in the present work is through nonvariational models and hence Distefano's treatment is interesting reading for comparison. Chapter 8 gives the dynamic programming version of the optimal truss design problem and the optimal rotating disc problem, using nonvariational models.

For an excellent overview of dynamic programming applied to structural design see Palmer (1973). See also Majid (1974).

Dynamic programming finds use as a structural analysis tool in Palmer (1969), Kalaba (1961), Angel *et al.* (1971) and Distefano (1971). The last reference solves the biharmonic equation by regarding it as the Euler–Lagrange equation of some minimization problem. See also Bellman (1961), Pister (1972) and Sokolnikoff (1956). Connected work of interest is Distefano (1970, 1974b), Distefano and Samartin (1975), Distefano and Chiu (1977), Distefano and Jain (1974), Carver (1967), Distefano and Schujman (1971), Distefano and Todeschini (1975) and Angel and Distefano (1972).

For the use of dynamic programming in time lag systems see the introductory treatment of Noton (1965).

For extensions to branched and cyclic systems (nonserial systems) see Aris *et al.* (1964), Mitten and Nemhauser (1963), Twisdale and Khachaturian (1975a) and Bertele and Brioschi (1972).

[7.2] For a discussion on approximating techniques, the form of computations involved, the numerical methods and the solution of the optimal recurrence relation, see Aris (1964), Larson (1964), Boudarel *et al.* (1971), Dyer and McReynolds (1970), Twisdale and Khachaturian (1975a) and Palmer (1973). Boudarel *et al.* (1971) discusses the sensitivity of the solution.

The problem that arises with n large has been called the 'curse of dimensionality'. See Bellman (1957). Boudarel *et al.* (1971) discusses the problem and the reduction of the dimensionality. Distefano (1975) and Distefano and Bellows (1977) discuss a way of reducing the dimensionality of the problem in a structural mechanics context by the introduction of an energy term.

For dynamic programming done in a forward sense, see for example, Jacobs (1967).

The linear-quadratic problem is well treated by Dyer and McReynolds (1970) and Boudarel *et al.* (1971) but is mentioned in nearly every optimal control text. Dyer and McReynolds also give the closed form solution to the linear-quadratic problem with linear terminal constraints. The result (7.5) implies feedback or closed loop control. The matrix C contains feedback coefficients.

Constraints may be handled by the augmentation of the dimensionality or by the use of Lagrange multipliers (Boudarel *et al.* 1971).

Boudarel *et al.* (1971) among others gives a treatment for systems with both bounded and infinite or unspecified horizons.

For the modelling or rotating shafts in state equation form see Pestel and Leckie (1963).

The optimal design of rotating discs has been considered by Distefano (1972a, b, 1974a), Nagy (1971), Nagy and Distefano (1972) and Distefano and Todeschini (1972). For related work see Chern and Prager (1970), Carmichael (1977b), de Silva (1975), de Silva and Grant (1975), de Silva, Green and Grant (1976), de Silva, Negus and Worster (1976) and Den Hartog (1952).

A stochastic version of the cantilever design problem along with a derivation of the optimal control and optimal return function is given in Carmichael (1978a). See also Carmichael and Elms (1975).

[7.3] For a derivation of the Hamilton–Jacobi–Bellman equation see, for example, Fel'dbaum (1965). It may be obtained directly from infinitesimal arguments for the continuous case or as a limiting result of the equivalent discrete recurrence relation as is done, for example, in Dyer and McReynolds (1970) and Boudarel *et al.* (1971).

The case of split boundary conditions is given by Distefano (1974a, p. 237) and illustrated on a string example. Similar treatments hold for section 7.5.

The treatment of constraints using Lagrange multipliers and questions of abnormality are treated by Dyer and McReynolds, along with the relationship of Bellman's equation to the Hamilton–Jacobi partial differential equation. See also Dreyfus (1965).

Systems with discontinuities in $\dot{x}$ and x are treated in Dyer and McReynolds (1971).

For the linear-quadratic problem, refer to Merriam (1964), Dyer and McReynolds (1970) (including terminal constraints) and Distefano (1974a). The result for the optimal control, as for the discrete case, implies feedback or closed loop control.

[7.4] The optimum design of trusses is treated by Sheppard and Palmer (1972) and Palmer and Sheppard (1970) using dynamic programming. The latter reference also gives comment on Michell structures (Michell 1904) while the former treats the extension to three dimensional transmission towers where geometric constraints on the layout, alternative loadings, buckling constraints and various distinct topologies may be present.

For an overview of dynamic programming in structural optimization see Palmer (1973). Palmer (1968b) considers the continuous beam problem.

The earliest work in dynamic programming and structural optimization is by Goff (1966) on the shape of structures and Kalaba (1962) on statically determinate trusses. See also Razani and Goble (1966) and deSantis (1966) on girders.

Khachaturian and Haider (1966) have followed up the work of Kalaba. See also the extensions and generalizations of Twisdale and Khachaturian (1973, 1975a, 1975b). Twisdale and Khachaturian (1975a) discuss the extension to nonserial systems. See also Distefano and Rath (1975).

Vitiello (1977) treats the standardization problem.

Baker *et al*. (1978) consider the design of shed-type buildings where the arrangement of the components suggests a staged nature and hence the use of dynamic programming as a solution procedure. Additionally dynamic programming allows for the occurrence of discrete member sizes.

The design stages in the problem may be recognized as

a) Roof cladding
b) Purlins
c) Side wall cladding
d) Side wall girts
e) Portal frames
f) Portal footings
g) End wall cladding
h) End wall girts
i) End wall columns
j) Floor slab
k) Roof ventilator
l) Roof drainage system

The design sequence is shown in Fig. 7.7. It is assumed that the building area, eave height, pitch, openings and others are known.

At each stage transition and stage, state and control variables respectively may be recognized. State variables relate to behaviour, while control variables are the quantities directly at the disposal of the structural engineer to vary in order to get a desired behaviour and/or to minimize the design optimality criterion which is usually cost. For example, at the frame stage suitable choices of controls are the moments of inertia and cross sectional areas of the column and rafter members; at

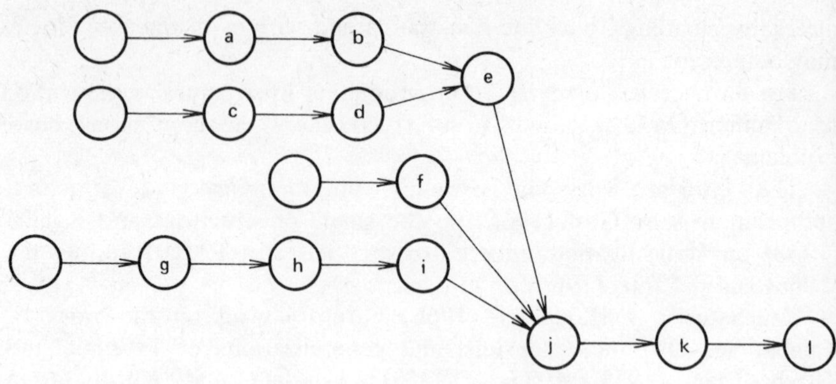

Fig. 7.7

the purlin and girt stages the controls are the purlin and girt sizes and span; at the cladding stage the controls are the cladding size and span and so on. The loadings/reactions transferred from stage to stage may be chosen as the state variables. Other indicators of behaviour are displacements, rotations and stresses among others.

Constraints may be written for each stage representing safety and serviceability limitations. Manufacturers' tables implicitly include constraints and only permissible section sizes are tabulated. The observation that only discrete section sizes are available is also implicit in manufacturers' tables.

Related work on industrial shed-type structures, though not in a dynamic programming sense, can be found in the geometric programming approach of Bradley *et al*. (1974). Grundy and Wathen (1969) and Lipson and Russel (1971) are also relevant. Douty (1972) uses related ideas for slab-beam arrangements.

[7.5] Szefer (1971) uses dynamic programming to derive the optimality conditions for model types I (with an isoperimetric equality constraint) and II and applies these to the optimization of plates on elastic foundations, three dimensional elastic bodies and viscoelastic beams. Historically Szefer's work was the first application of distributed parameter optimal control theory in structural mechanics.

The utilization of dynamic programming concepts in the study of the optimality of distributed parameter systems was initially suggested by Bellman in association with Osborn (1958) and Kalaba (1961, 1962). These fundamental studies were subsequently advanced upon Wang and Tung (1964) and Wang (1964) who derive necessary conditions for a general system described by partial differential equations similar to system model type I. (See also Brogan 1967a, b, 1968a, b.)

Generally, the above authors increment their problem over time only. Angel and Bellman (1972) (see also Angel 1968a, b, 1970, 1973) suggest minimization problems over regions be formulated in a dynamic programming sense through the device of minimizing over subregions. Distefano (1971) on the biharmonic equation uses a related device. The choice of the subregion dictates the form of the final results. If an infinitesimal say is chosen, a differential equation results.

For particular applications of dynamic programming to control problems see Erzberger and Kim (1966a, b), Kim and Erzberger (1967) and Butkovskii (1969) among others. Each of these references is related to linear systems.

Further reviews can be found in Szefer (1971) and Robinson (1971) and there is a text on distributed parameter systems by Lions (1968). See also Pister (1972) for further comment.

The problem of boundary control has been discussed, for example, by Erzberger and Kim (1966a, b), Kim and Erzberger (1967), Brogan (1967a, b, 1968a, b) and Butkovskii (1969).

See Wang (1964) for the definition of a functional partial (variational) derivative.

For Bellman's equation applied to system models type I, Szefer (1971) gives a plate on an elastic foundation example; applied to system models type II see also Carmichael (1975) on an optimal plate example.

This version of the derivation of Bellman's equation for problems associated with state equations type II is given in Carmichael (1978b). There it is shown that such a family of surfaces can be constructed using, for example, a spherical polar coordinate system. A similar derivation can be found in Szefer (1971).

The transformation of Bellman's equation to the lower order conditions of Pontryagin's maximum principle is given in Carmichael also.

Carmichael (1975) shows how end criteria may be treated. Split boundary conditions follow section 7.3.

Szefer (1971) considers plates on elastic foundations. See Carmichael (1978b) for comments on the occurrence of singular optimal controls rather than a bang-bang solution.

Chapter 8

Pontryagin's Principle; Variational Calculus

8.1 INTRODUCTION

The approach to optimum design, based on Pontryagin's (equivalently maximum or minimum) principle, does not in general give an explicit expression for the optimal design but instead optimality is manifested in a set of necessary conditions that have to be satisfied. The technique is a powerful one for the solution of variational problems. In essence the principle extends the results of the calculus of variations to include constraints on the control in the problem statement, although extensions are available within the calculus of variations theory to handle constraints, discontinuities and the like. The control formulation is found, however, to be more suited to posing and solving engineering problems. The technique is applicable to problems (OD), (D) and (P).

For ordinary differential (difference, partial differential) equation systems, the necessary conditions will in general constitute a system of ordinary differential (difference, partial differential) equations of the boundary value type (end conditions are split), the solution of which may present certain complications. To determine the optimal control and the corresponding state, two sets of equations (of total order $2n$)—the state and costate—are solved simultaneously for $2n + r$ unknowns $\{x_i, i = 1, \ldots, n\}$, $\{\lambda_j, j = 1, \ldots, n\}$ and $\{u_k, k = 1, \ldots, r\}$. The u_k may be eliminated with the help of r control conditions leaving $2n$ equations in $2n$ unknowns.

In certain restricted cases (for example linear systems) the results can be shown to be sufficient conditions for optimality.

The development in the following sections firstly gives a special case of Pontryagin's principle where the admissible control set is infinite (section 8.2.1). Section 8.2.4 treats the constrained case leading to a statement of Pontryagin's principle. The derivation of the principle allows piecewise continuous controls, there being no smoothness assumptions as used in the derivation of the Euler–Lagrange necessary conditions of the calculus of variations (section 8.2.7). The approach gives rise to a two point boundary value problem (TPBVP) or a multipoint boundary value problem. For the linear quadratic case (section 8.2.3), which has attracted a large amount of interest in the literature because of its tractability, a linear TPBVP arises with linear boundary conditions. Section 8.2.7 gives the relationship of the control problem and its optimality results to the classical calculus of variations problem and results. The results are illustrated with an optimal elastic column example.

Section 8.2 is concerned with the control problem (OD). Section 8.3 gives the equivalent results for the problem (D) while section 8.4 gives distributed parameter versions for the three system models considered. The basic results are demonstrated on structural applications.

8.2 ORDINARY DIFFERENTIAL EQUATION MODELS

8.2.1 The Unconstrained Case

For the problem (OD1) and considering firstly the interval (y^L, y^R) as fixed and boundary conditions on x at y^L and y^R, define the set of admissible control functions to be the class of piecewise continuous functions. It is assumed that for any admissible u and for given state boundary conditions, the state equations define a unique solution for x over (y^L, y^R). f, G and g are assumed to possess continuous partial derivatives with respect to x and u.

Define (for a minimum principle) a scalar function, the Hamiltonian as

$$H[x(y), u(y), \lambda(y), y] \triangleq G[x(y), u(y), y] + \lambda^T(y) f[x(y), u(y), y] \quad (8.1)$$

where λ is an n vector of costate variables. The necessary conditions for optimality become

(a) costate boundary conditions

$$\delta x^T[\partial g/\partial x - \lambda] = 0 \quad \text{for} \quad y = y^L, y^R$$

(δx is a small variation in x)

(b) state equations (together with state boundary conditions)

$$\mathrm{d}x/\mathrm{d}y = f[x, u, y] = \partial H/\partial \lambda$$

(8.2)

(c) costate equations

$$\mathrm{d}\lambda/\mathrm{d}y = -\partial H/\partial x$$

(d) optimality condition

$$\partial H/\partial u = 0.$$

The conditions (8.2)[b] and (8.2)[c] together with their associated boundary conditions on x and λ represent a two point boundary value problem and a total of $2n$ equations in $2n + r$ variables x, λ and u. The coupling equation is (8.2)[d] which may be used to eliminate the r control variables. (8.2)[d] implies arbitrary variations in u are allowed, that is the control is unbounded.

The conditions (8.2)[a] are sometimes referred to as natural boundary conditions. For x given at y^L or y^R then it follows for (8.2)[a] that $\delta x = 0$.

Consider now the more general boundary conditions

$$M^1[x(y^L), y^L] = 0 \quad \text{and} \quad M^2[x(y^R), y^R] = 0. \tag{8.3}$$

The more general transversality conditions become

$$\begin{aligned} \lambda(y^L) &= \frac{\partial g}{\partial x} + \left[\frac{\partial M^{1T}}{\partial x}\right]\xi \qquad M^1[x(y), y] = 0 \quad y = y^L \\ \lambda(y^R) &= \frac{\partial g}{\partial x} + \left[\frac{\partial M^{2T}}{\partial x}\right]\nu \qquad M^2[x(y), y] = 0 \quad y = y^R \end{aligned} \tag{8.4}$$

which give a total of $2n$ conditions. Here ξ and ν are $p + q$ Lagrange multipliers chosen so as to satisfy the $p + q$ relations (8.3).

The total derivative of the Hamiltonian with respect to y is

$$\frac{dH}{dy} = \frac{\partial G}{\partial y} + \lambda^T \frac{\partial f}{\partial y} + \left[\frac{\partial u}{\partial y}\right]^T \frac{\partial H}{\partial u}. \tag{8.5}$$

For G and f not explicit functions of y, the Hamiltonian is constant on an optimal solution (where (8.2)[d] applies).

Consider now the case where y^R is unspecified (the free terminal time problem). For $x(y^L)$ specified and $M^2[x(y^R), y^R] = 0$, add to the above necessary conditions

$$H[x(y^R), u(y^R), \lambda(y^R), y^R] + \frac{\partial g}{\partial y^R} + \left[\frac{\partial M^{2T}}{\partial y^R}\right]\nu = 0. \tag{8.6}$$

This provides the one additional equation required to determine the unspecified y^R.

8.2.2 Example: Optimum Elastic Column

For a pin-ended column, the differential equation for the deflected shape is

$$EI\frac{d^2w}{dy^2} + Pw = 0 \quad \text{with} \quad w(0) = w(L) = 0$$

where E is the modulus of elasticity, I the second moment of area, w the deflected shape, P the applied axial load and L is the column length.

In state equation form this equation reads

$$\begin{bmatrix} \dfrac{dx_1}{dy} = x_2 \\ \dfrac{dx_2}{dy} = -\dfrac{Px_1}{Eu} \end{bmatrix} \quad \text{with} \quad x_1(0) = x_1(L) = 0$$

where the states are deflection and slope, and the control is the second moment of area.

For a minimum volume solution

$$\min J = \int_0^L A\,dy.$$

For the area A related to I by $A = k\sqrt{I}$ where k is a parameter of the shape of the cross section, the criterion becomes

$$\min J = k\int_0^L u^{1/2}\,dy.$$

The solution follows from the minimum principle. Define a Hamiltonian

$$H = ku^{1/2} + \lambda_1 x_2 - \frac{\lambda_2 P x_1}{Eu}.$$

The necessary conditions for optimality then read

(i) state equations (and state boundary conditions)

$$\begin{bmatrix} \dfrac{dx_1}{dy} = x_2 \\ \dfrac{dx_2}{dy} = -\dfrac{Px_1}{Eu} \end{bmatrix} \quad \text{with} \quad x_1(0) = x_1(L) = 0$$

(ii) costate equations

$$\begin{bmatrix} \dfrac{d\lambda_1}{dy} = \dfrac{\lambda_2 P}{Eu} \\ \dfrac{d\lambda_2}{dy} = -\lambda_1 \end{bmatrix}$$

(iii) costate boundary conditions

$$\lambda_2(0) = \lambda_2(L) = 0$$

(iv) optimality condition

$$0 = \tfrac{1}{2}ku^{-1/2} + \frac{\lambda_2 P x_1}{Eu^2}.$$

(i) to (iv) give the solution to the problem. Note that for this particular problem, these conditions can be simplified if the following relationship (self adjoint property of state and costate equations) is noted;

$$\begin{bmatrix} x_1 \\ x_2 \end{bmatrix} = \gamma \begin{bmatrix} 0 & -1 \\ 1 & 0 \end{bmatrix} \begin{bmatrix} \lambda_1 \\ \lambda_2 \end{bmatrix}$$

where γ is some constant. That is either (i) or (ii) may be removed from the problem. (iv) expresses the relationship between the control and the state and costate, and becomes

$$u^{3/2} = -\frac{2\lambda_2 P x_1}{Ek} = \frac{2Px_1^2}{\gamma Ek}$$

or in the original notation

$$I^{3/2} = \frac{2Pw^2}{\gamma Ek}.$$

8.2.3 The Linear-Quadratic Problem

Consider the linear-quadratic problem (OD2) but with a criterion of the form

$$J = \tfrac{1}{2}x^{\mathrm{T}} g_{xx} x \,|_{y=y^{\mathrm{R}}} + \int_{y^{\mathrm{L}}}^{y^{\mathrm{R}}} \tfrac{1}{2}(x^{\mathrm{T}} G_{xx} x + u^{\mathrm{T}} G_{uu} u)\, \mathrm{d}y \tag{8.7}$$

and boundary conditions on x given at y^{L}.

Define the Hamiltonian

$$H[x(y), u(y), \lambda(y), y] = \tfrac{1}{2}x^{\mathrm{T}} G_{xx} x + \tfrac{1}{2}u^{\mathrm{T}} G_{uu} u + \lambda^{\mathrm{T}}(Ax + Bu). \tag{8.8}$$

The necessary conditions for optimality are

$$\frac{\partial H}{\partial u} = 0 = G_{uu} u + B^{\mathrm{T}}\lambda$$

$$\frac{\mathrm{d}\lambda}{\mathrm{d}y} = -\frac{\partial H}{\partial x} = -G_{xx} x + A^{\mathrm{T}}\lambda \quad \text{with} \quad \lambda(y^{\mathrm{R}}) = g_{xx} x \,|_{y^{\mathrm{R}}} \tag{8.9}$$

$$\frac{\mathrm{d}x}{\mathrm{d}y} = Ax + Bu \qquad \text{with} \quad x(y^{\mathrm{L}}) \text{ given.}$$

If it is assumed that

$$\lambda(y) = P(y)x(y), \tag{8.10}$$

then

$$\frac{\mathrm{d}\lambda}{\mathrm{d}y} = \frac{\mathrm{d}P}{\mathrm{d}y}x + P\frac{\mathrm{d}x}{\mathrm{d}y}. \tag{8.11}$$

Substituting from (8.9), the matrix Riccati equation results

$$\frac{\mathrm{d}P}{\mathrm{d}y} + PA + A^{\mathrm{T}}P - PBG_{uu}^{-1}B^{\mathrm{T}}P + G_{xx} = 0 \tag{8.12}$$

with $P(y^{\mathrm{R}}) = g_{xx}$. P is an $n \times n$ symmetric matrix.
From (8.9) and (8.10)

$$u = -G_{uu}^{-1}B^{\mathrm{T}}Px \tag{8.13}$$

where the coefficient of x on the right-hand side is referred to as a gain matrix.

8.2.4 The Constrained Case

Consider the extension of the previous general unconstrained problem (OD1) to the case where constraints exist on the control and/or the state variables of inequality, equality, global, local or pointwise form.

(a) Integral constraints. Consider the constraint where a certain integral

$$\int_{y^{\mathrm{L}}}^{y^{\mathrm{R}}} I[x(y), u(y), y]\,\mathrm{d}y \tag{8.14}$$

is required to have a specified value, where I is a scalar function. Introduce a new variable x_{n+1} such that

$$x_{n+1}(y^{\mathrm{R}}) = \int_{y^{\mathrm{L}}}^{y^{\mathrm{R}}} I[x, u, y]\,\mathrm{d}y \tag{8.15}$$

$$\frac{\mathrm{d}x_{n+1}}{\mathrm{d}y} = I[x, u, y] \tag{8.16}$$

$$x_{n+1}(y^{\mathrm{L}}) = 0. \tag{8.17}$$

Equation (8.16) may then be treated as another system equation with boundary conditions (8.15) and (8.17). The associated costate variable can be shown to be a constant.

(b) Control variable constraints. For the control constraint of the general form

$$u(y) \in U \qquad y \in [y^{\mathrm{L}}, y^{\mathrm{R}}] \tag{8.18}$$

where U is a given subset of E^r, the result is known as the minimum (or maximum) principle of Pontryagin or McShane. The optimality condition (8.2)[d] becomes

$$H[x(y), \hat{u}(y), \lambda(y), y] \leqslant H[x(y), u(y), \lambda(y), y] \quad \text{for} \quad u \in U. \tag{8.19}$$

That is the control is chosen to minimize the Hamiltonian for all y, taking the constraints into account.

The constraint (8.18) may take on particular forms which are tractable.

Consider, firstly, equality constraints of the form

$$C(u, y) = 0 \tag{8.20}$$

where C is a scalar function. It is assumed that $r \geqslant 2$, as for $r = 1$ the optimization problem disappears.

The constraint may be used directly to eliminate one control variable or alternatively the constraint may be adjoined to the Hamiltonian with a Lagrange multiplier μ.

$$H = G + \lambda^{\mathrm{T}} f + \mu C. \tag{8.21}$$

The form of the necessary conditions for optimality (8.2) remain the same. Additionally (8.20) must be satisfied and this provides the extra equation needed to determine the extra variable $\mu(y)$.

Inequality constraints of the form

$$C(u, y) \leqslant 0 \tag{8.22}$$

may be handled in a similar manner to the equality constraint (8.20) where now

$$\mu \begin{cases} \geqslant 0 & C = 0 \\ = 0 & C < 0. \end{cases} \tag{8.23}$$

The solution involves the piecing together of constrained and unconstrained results.

Alternatively this last form of constraint, (8.22), may be handled by first converting it to an equality constraint of either of the two following types

$$\begin{aligned} \left[\frac{\mathrm{d}\alpha}{\mathrm{d}y}\right]^2 &= C(u(y), y) \qquad \alpha(y^{\mathrm{L}}) = 0 \\ (\beta)^2 &= C(u(y), y) \end{aligned} \tag{8.24}$$

and then adjoining the equality constraint to the criterion by means of Lagrange multipliers.

Constraints of the form

$$u_{\min} \leqslant u \leqslant u_{\max} \tag{8.25}$$

may be broken into two inequality constraints

$$\begin{aligned} C_1(u(y), y) &\equiv u - u_{\max} \leqslant 0 \\ C_2(u(y), y) &\equiv u_{\min} - u \leqslant 0. \end{aligned} \tag{8.26}$$

Bang-bang control. Where the state equations and the criterion are linear in the control, a minimum will only exist if constraints are specified (assuming singular optimal controls are not present). For control constraints, the solution will lie on the constraint boundaries and where a change from one boundary to another occurs, a bang-bang control situation occurs.

Consider state equations and a criterion where the control enters in a linear fashion, but where the other terms are nonlinear.

$$\begin{aligned} \frac{\mathrm{d}x}{\mathrm{d}y} &= f^1[x(y), y] + f^2[x(y), y]u(y) \\ J &= g[x(y^{\mathrm{R}}), y^{\mathrm{R}}] + \int_{y^{\mathrm{L}}}^{y^{\mathrm{R}}} \{G^1[x(y), y] + G^{2\mathrm{T}}[x(y), y]u(y)\}\, \mathrm{d}y. \end{aligned} \tag{8.27}$$

Consider bounds on the control vector $u(y)$ of the form

$$a_i \leqslant u_i \leqslant b_i \qquad i = 1, \ldots, r. \tag{8.28}$$

The Hamiltonian will be linear in the control

$$H[x(y), u(y), \lambda(y), y] = G^1 + G^{2\mathrm{T}}u + \lambda^{\mathrm{T}}(f^1 + f^2u) \tag{8.29}$$

with the coefficient

$$\sigma = G^{2\mathrm{T}} + \lambda^{\mathrm{T}}f^2. \tag{8.30}$$

For the control to minimize the Hamiltonian, this implies

$$u_i = \begin{cases} a_i & \text{if} \quad \sigma_i > 0 \\ b_i & \text{if} \quad \sigma_i < 0. \end{cases} \tag{8.31}$$

This is a bang-bang result. σ is sometimes termed a switching function.

For $\sigma_i = 0$, the Hamiltonian is no longer a function of u_i. Where this occurs over a finite subinterval of $(y^{\mathrm{L}}, y^{\mathrm{R}})$, the problem is one of singular control. For $\sigma_i = 0$ at points only, a bang-bang control situation exists; that is, the control u_i switches from a_i to b_i depending on the sign taken by σ_i.

(c) Constraints on the state and control variables. Equality and inequality constraints of the form

$$C(x, u, y) = 0$$
$$C(x, u, y) \leqslant 0 \tag{8.32}$$

where $\partial C/\partial u \neq 0$ may be handled in the same fashion as the control equality (8.20) and inequality (8.22) constraints respectively.

(d) State variable constraints. For constraints of the form

$$S(x, y) = 0$$
$$S(x, y) \leqslant 0 \tag{8.33}$$

several methods are available for use. Bryson and Ho (1975) suggest differentiating the constraint until control variables appear explicitly, at which stage the last derivative is treated as a combined control and state constraint. All the derivative terms up to that stage may be used to eliminate components of the state or may be added as extra boundary conditions to the problem. Integral penalty functions can also be used for state equality constraints. Sage and White (1977) suggest the inequality constraints be converted to equality constraints using Heaviside step functions or penalty functions.

(e) Interior point constraints; discontinuities in the system equations at interior points; discontinuities in the state variables at interior points. A general formulation of the problem where there are interior point constraints, discontinuities in the system equations at interior points and discontinuities in the state variables at interior points is covered by

$$J = g[x(y_0^-), x(y_0^+), \ldots, x(y_N^-), x(y_N^+); y_0, \ldots, y_N] + \sum_{i=1}^{N} \int_{y_{i-1}^+}^{y_i^-} G^{(i)}[x(y), u(y), y] \, \mathrm{d}y \tag{8.34}$$

$$\frac{\mathrm{d}x}{\mathrm{d}y} = f^{(i)}(x, u, y) \qquad y_{i-1} < y < y_i \qquad i = 1, \ldots, N$$

$$\phi^{(j)}(x(y_0^-), x(y_0^+), \ldots, x(y_N^-), x(y_N^+); y_0, \ldots, y_N) = 0 \qquad j = 0, \ldots, N.$$

Here the + and − notation implies just to the right or left respectively of a particular value of y.

The interior boundary conditions are given by $\phi^{(j)}$. For such a situation, the problem becomes a multipoint boundary value problem.

The criterion in (8.34) admits values associated with interior points. The discontinuities in the system equations are acknowledged by the superscript i.

Necessary conditions for optimality for this problem are given by Bryson and Ho (1975).

(f) Corner conditions. Where the control is discontinuous, the point is referred to as a corner and this may occur at the junction of constrained and/or unconstrained regions or elsewhere. The discontinuity in the control implies a discontinuity in the state derivative. Bryson and Ho (1975) summarize the conditions that must hold at corners.

8.2.5 Example: Optimum Columns with a Constraint on Area

Consider the above column problem but now with a minimum cross sectional area constraint of the form

$$A \geqslant A_0 \quad \text{where} \quad A_0 = P/F_L, \quad F_L \text{ is a given limiting stress.}$$

In terms of the control variable this becomes

$$u \geqslant u_0$$

where

$$u_0 = P^2/k^2F_L^2.$$

Assume the solution comprises a portion off the constraint $(\alpha L/2 < y \leqslant L/2)$ and a portion on the constraint $(0 \leqslant y < \alpha L/2)$ per half column with a junction at $y = \alpha L/2$.

For the portion off the constraint, the necessary conditions for optimality are

$$\begin{bmatrix} \dfrac{\mathrm{d}x_1}{\mathrm{d}y} = x_2 \\ \dfrac{\mathrm{d}x_2}{\mathrm{d}y} = -Px_1/Eu \end{bmatrix} \qquad \begin{array}{l} x_1(\alpha L/2)^+ = x_1(\alpha L/2)^- \\ x_2(\alpha L/2)^+ = x_2(\alpha L/2)^- \\ x_2(L/2) = 0 \end{array} \tag{a}$$

$$\tfrac{1}{2}ku^{-1/2} - \frac{Px_1^2}{\gamma Eu^2} = 0. \tag{b}$$

For the portion on the constraint

$$u = u_0 \tag{c}$$

$$\begin{bmatrix} \dfrac{\mathrm{d}x_1}{\mathrm{d}y} = x_2 \\ \dfrac{\mathrm{d}x_2}{\mathrm{d}y} = -Px_1/Eu \end{bmatrix} \qquad \begin{array}{l} x_1(0) = 0 \\ x_1(\alpha L/2)^- = x_1(\alpha L/2)^+ \\ x_2(\alpha L/2)^- = x_2(\alpha L/2)^+. \end{array} \tag{d}$$

The solution to the whole problem involves solving (a) to (d) together with the stated boundary conditions and the continuity of state conditions.

The alternative means of solution is by the formal arguments given earlier for control constraints.

8.2.6 Hamilton–Jacobi Theory

Pontryagin's result (8.19) may be obtained from the Hamilton–Jacobi equation or from dynamic programming arguments leading to the same equation. The relationship of this functional equation can be shown by relating the gradient vector of the optimal return function to the costate vector characteristic of the canonical equations. In particular defining

$$\lambda(y) = \frac{\partial S[x(y), y]}{\partial x} \tag{8.35}$$

Pontryagin's principle follows.

A derivation of Pontryagin's principle using this approach requires differentiability assumptions on the optimal return function S, and this may not always hold.

8.2.7 The Calculus of Variations

Pontryagin's principle can be shown to lead to the three necessary conditions for optimality of the calculus of variations—Euler–Lagrange, Legendre, and Weierstrass—as a direct consequence of the principle statement when no constraints on the control are present. The Weierstrass–Erdmann corner conditions, transversality conditions and natural boundary conditions follow similarly. A fourth necessary condition for optimality, the Jacobi (conjugate point) condition, is not contained within the principle.

The theory of the calculus of variations, however, exists in its own right and is concerned with finding a continuously differentiable function $x(y)$ which minimizes

$$J(x) = \theta[x(y^{\mathrm{R}}), y^{\mathrm{R}}] + \int_{y^{\mathrm{L}}}^{y^{\mathrm{R}}} \phi[x(y), \dot{x}(y), y]\, \mathrm{d}y \tag{8.36}$$

where the superposed dot denotes differentiation with respect to y. This is known as the problem of *Bolza*. Where $\theta \equiv 0$ it is the problem of *Lagrange* and where $\phi \equiv 0$ it is the problem of *Mayer*. Each form is interchangeable with the others.

Necessary conditions for $x(y)$ to be optimal are obtained by considering a smooth variation in $x(y)$. In particular the Euler–Lagrange equation and the associated natural boundary condition for the Lagrange problem are, respectively, along an optimal solution

$$\frac{\partial \phi}{\partial x} - \frac{\mathrm{d}}{\mathrm{d}y}\left(\frac{\partial \phi}{\partial \dot{x}}\right) = 0 \tag{8.37}$$

$$(\delta x)^{\mathrm{T}} \frac{\partial \phi}{\partial \dot{x}} = 0 \quad \text{for} \quad y = y^{\mathrm{L}}, y^{\mathrm{R}} \tag{8.38}$$

where $\delta x(y)$ is the variation taken in $x(y)$. Equations (8.37) and (8.38) represent a two point boundary value problem. The interval $(y^{\mathrm{L}}, y^{\mathrm{R}})$ is taken as fixed.

For given $x(y^{\mathrm{L}})$ and $x(y^{\mathrm{R}})$, this gives $\delta x(y^{\mathrm{L}}) = \delta x(y^{\mathrm{R}}) = 0$. For x unspecified at the boundary, $\partial \phi / \partial \dot{x} = 0$.

Transversality conditions arise from the specification that the end points must lie on given curves or surfaces, in which case the tranversality conditions give the relation between the direction of the extremal curve and that of the given boundary curve.

An examination of the second variation leads to the Legendre (weak variations) and Weierstrass (strong variations) necessary conditions for optimality. The Legendre condition requires the condition

$$\phi_{\dot{x}\dot{x}} \geqslant 0 \tag{8.39}$$

to be satisfied for a minimum. (The weak variations are as used in the derivation of the Euler–Lagrange equations.) The Weierstrass condition requires the Weierstrass E function to be nonnegative

$$E = \phi(y, x, \dot{X}) - \phi(y, x, \dot{x}) - \sum_{j=1}^{n} \frac{\partial \phi[y, x, \dot{x}]}{\partial \dot{x}_j} (\dot{X}_j - \dot{x}_j) \geqslant 0. \tag{8.40}$$

The results so far are based on the assumption that x is continuously differentiable with respect to y. Where x has a 'corner' or discontinuous first derivative, trouble arises with the $\ddot{x}$ term in the Euler–Lagrange equation. For x having a discontinuous derivative at a point y' the necessary Weierstrass–Erdmann corner conditions are

$$\begin{aligned} \left.\frac{\partial \phi}{\partial \dot{x}}\right|_{y'-} &= \left.\frac{\partial \phi}{\partial \dot{x}}\right|_{y'+} \\ \left.\phi - \dot{x}^{\mathrm{T}} \frac{\partial \phi}{\partial \dot{x}}\right|_{y'-} &= \left.\phi - \dot{x}^{\mathrm{T}} \frac{\partial \phi}{\partial \dot{x}}\right|_{y'+}. \end{aligned} \tag{8.41}$$

In Hamiltonian notation

$$\begin{aligned} H[x(y), \lambda(y), y] &= \phi - \dot{x}^{\mathrm{T}} \frac{\partial \phi}{\partial \dot{x}} \\ &= \phi + \dot{x}^{\mathrm{T}} \lambda, \end{aligned} \tag{8.42}$$

the Weierstrass–Erdmann corner conditions require continuity of H and λ.

The Euler–Lagrange equation may be expanded to give

$$\ddot{x}\phi_{\dot{x}\dot{x}} + \dot{x}\phi_{\dot{x}x} + \phi_{\dot{x}y} - \phi_x = 0 \tag{8.43}$$

which can be solved for $\ddot{x}$ only if $|\phi_{\dot{x}\dot{x}}| \neq 0$, the Hilbert differentiability condition.

Higher derivatives in the integrand may be accommodated. To minimize

$$J = \int_{y^{\mathrm{L}}}^{y^{\mathrm{R}}} \phi[y, x, \dot{x}, \ddot{x}, \ldots, x^{(n)}]\, \mathrm{d}y \tag{8.44}$$

where it is assumed the functions have continuous derivatives up to the $2n$'th order and there exist boundary conditions up to the $(n-1)$'th derivative, the associated Euler–Lagrange equation is $2n$ in order and of the form

$$\phi_x - \frac{\mathrm{d}}{\mathrm{d}y}\phi_{\dot{x}} + \frac{\mathrm{d}^2}{\mathrm{d}y^2}\phi_{\ddot{x}} - \cdots + (-1)^n \frac{\mathrm{d}^n}{\mathrm{d}y^n}\phi_{x^{(n)}} = 0. \tag{8.45}$$

For the Lagrange problem with equality side constraints

$$h[x, \dot{x}, y] = 0 \tag{8.46}$$

Lagrange multipliers can be used to adjoin this constraint to J such that the problem is now one of choosing $x(y)$ and the Lagrange multipliers $\lambda(y)$ to minimize

$$J' = \int_{y^{\mathrm{L}}}^{y^{\mathrm{R}}} \{\phi[x, \dot{x}, y] + \lambda^{\mathrm{T}} h[x, \dot{x}, y]\}\, \mathrm{d}y. \tag{8.47}$$

The above necessary conditions for optimality are applicable to this minimization problem.

Inequality constraints of the form

$$h^{\min} \leqslant h[x, \dot{x}, y] \leqslant h^{\max} \tag{8.48}$$

may be handled, for example, by converting them to equality constraints such as

$$(h_i^{\max} - h_i)(h_i - h_i^{\min}) = \gamma_i^2 \qquad i = 1, 2, \ldots \tag{8.49}$$

where γ is a new introduced variable.

8.2.8. Example: Optimum Elastic Columns

For the problem of section 8.2.2, the equations for the deflected shape may be solved for I to give

$$(x_2 - \dot{x}_1) = 0 \tag{a}$$

$$I = \left(\frac{-P}{E}\frac{x_1}{\dot{x}_2}\right) \tag{b}$$

where the superposed dot denotes differentiation with respect to y. The moment of inertia I and the area A are related by $A = k\sqrt{I}$. The expression for the volume then becomes

$$\begin{aligned} J &= k\int_0^L I^{1/2}\,\mathrm{d}y \\ &= k\int_0^L \left(\frac{-P}{E}\frac{x_1}{\dot{x}_2}\right)^{1/2}\mathrm{d}y. \end{aligned} \tag{c}$$

The calculus of variations problem then is minimize (c) subject to (a), together with the boundary conditions $x_1(0) = x_1(L) = 0$.

Form the augmented criterion

$$J' = \int_0^L \left\{k\left(\frac{-P}{E}\frac{x_1}{\dot{x}_2}\right)^{1/2} + \lambda(x_2 - \dot{x}_1)\right\}\mathrm{d}y.$$

The Euler–Lagrange equations and transversality conditions follow.

The alternative is to use the higher derivative form (8.45) of the Euler–Lagrange equations and apply it to the minimization of

$$J = 2k\int_0^{L/2}\left[\frac{P}{E}\left(\frac{-w}{\ddot{w}}\right)\right]^{1/2}\mathrm{d}y.$$

This gives

$$\frac{\mathrm{d}^2}{\mathrm{d}y^2}\left(\frac{-w}{\ddot{w}^3}\right)^{1/2} = \left(\frac{-1}{w\ddot{w}}\right)^{1/2}.$$

8.3 DIFFERENCE EQUATION MODELS

8.3.1 Necessary Conditions for Optimality

Pontryagin's principle for the preceding continuous case requires a modification for the general discrete case. The general result may be derived from the Kuhn–Tucker conditions of nonlinear programming or through variational or perturbation approaches.

For the problem (D1) with x given at $k = 0$ and N and

$$u(k) \in U \tag{8.50}$$

where U is a given set in E^r, define a Hamiltonian function

$$H[x(k), u(k), \lambda(k+1), k] = G[x(k), u(k), k] + \lambda^T(k+1)F[x(k), u(k), k]. \tag{8.51}$$

Then $\hat{\lambda}$ satisfies

$$\begin{aligned} \hat{\lambda}(k) &= \frac{\partial H[\hat{x}(k), \hat{u}(k), \hat{\lambda}(k+1), k]}{\partial \hat{x}(k)} \\ \left(\hat{\lambda} - \frac{\partial g}{\partial \hat{x}}\right)_{k=0}^{k=N} &= 0 \end{aligned} \tag{8.52}$$

and

$$H[\hat{x}(k), \hat{u}(k), \hat{\lambda}(k+1), k] = \min_{u \in U} H[x(k), u(k), \lambda(k+1), k]$$

$$k = 0, \ldots, N-1. \tag{8.53}$$

Where $u(k)$ is unconstrained

$$\frac{\partial H[x(k), u(k), \lambda(k+1), k]}{\partial u(k)} = 0 \qquad k = 0, \ldots, N-1. \tag{8.54}$$

The necessary conditions constitute a discrete two point boundary value problem, a problem which is more suited to numerical computation than the equivalent continuous problem. The state equations and (8.52)[1] are referred to as canonical equations for the problem.

More general boundary conditions may be considered; for example, at $k = N$

$$M^2[x(N), N] = 0$$

where M^2 is a given vector function of order less than n, the transversality condition becomes

$$\left(\lambda = \frac{\partial g}{\partial x} + \frac{\partial M^{2T}}{\partial x}\nu\right)_{k=N} \tag{8.55}$$

where ν are Lagrange multipliers.

It is seen that the continuous and the discrete versions of Pontryagin's principle lead to different two point boundary value problems but the solutions can be expected to be the same for small discretization intervals. A direct comparison may be made by using a finite difference approximation to the derivatives in the continuous problem.

8.3.2 Example: A Minimum Weight Beam

Consider a simply supported beam with point loads. The boundary conditions and governing equation are

$$w(0) = w(L) = 0$$

$$EI(y)\frac{\mathrm{d}^2w}{\mathrm{d}y^2} = M(y)$$

where the bending moment $M(y)$ may be evaluated from equilibrium considerations. In discrete state equation form these become

$$\begin{pmatrix} x_1 \\ x_2 \end{pmatrix}_{k+1} = \begin{pmatrix} 1 & \Delta \\ \dfrac{\Delta M}{EI} & 1 \end{pmatrix}_k \begin{pmatrix} x_1 \\ x_2 \end{pmatrix}_k \qquad x_1(0) = x_1(N) = 0$$

where the states are the deflection w and slope $\mathrm{d}w/\mathrm{d}y$ respectively. Δ is the discretization interval.

For a beam of rectangular section of constant height h, the moment of inertia $I(k) = \frac{1}{12}u(k)h^3$ where the control variable u is the width. The optimality criterion becomes

$$J = \Delta \sum_{k=0}^{N-1} \rho h u$$

where ρ is the density of the beam material.

Constraints may, for example, be on the deflection, stress or geometry.

The Hamiltonian for the problem is

$$H[x(k), u(k), \lambda(k+1), k] = u(k) + \lambda_1(k+1)(x_1(k) + \Delta x_2(k)) + \lambda_2(k+1)\left(\frac{12\Delta M(k)}{hEu(k)} + x_2(k)\right).$$

The costate equations are

$$\lambda_1(k) = \lambda_1(k+1)$$

$$\lambda_2(k) = \Delta\lambda_1(k+1) + \lambda_2(k+1)$$

with natural boundary conditions

$$\lambda_2(0) = \lambda_2(N) = 0.$$

The control is chosen to minimize the Hamiltonian. For the unconstrained case, the stationarity condition is

$$\frac{\partial H}{\partial u(k)} = 1 - \lambda_2(k+1)\frac{12\Delta M(k)}{hEu^2(k)} = 0.$$

The optimal solution is chosen to satisfy the state and costate equations (together with the four boundary conditions) and the control equation.

8.3.3 The Linear-Quadratic Problem

The general necessary conditions constituting the two point boundary value problem in general require numerical techniques for solution. However, the linear-quadratic problem (D2) does admit a closed form solution.

Consider $x(k)$ given only at $k = 0$ and the criterion

$$J = \tfrac{1}{2}x^{\mathrm{T}}(N)g_{xx}x(N) + \tfrac{1}{2}\sum_{k=0}^{N-1} x^{\mathrm{T}}(k)G_{xx}(k)x(k) + u^{\mathrm{T}}(k)G_{uu}(k)u(k). \quad (8.56)$$

The Hamiltonian becomes

$$H(k) = \tfrac{1}{2}x^{\mathrm{T}}(k)G_{xx}(k)x(k) + \tfrac{1}{2}u^{\mathrm{T}}(k)G_{uu}(k)u(k) + \lambda^{\mathrm{T}}(k+1)(A(k)x(k) + B(k)u(k)) \quad (8.57)$$

and the costate equations

$$\lambda(k) = G_{xx}(k)x(k) + A^{\mathrm{T}}(k)\lambda(k+1) \quad (8.58)$$

with

$$\lambda(N) = g_{xx}x(N). \quad (8.59)$$

For the control unconstrained

$$\partial H/\partial u(k) = 0 = G_{uu}(k)u(k) + B^{\mathrm{T}}(k)\lambda(k+1). \quad (8.60)$$

As before, the solution to this problem is assumed of the form

$$\lambda(k) = P(k)x(k) \quad (8.61)$$

and substitution of this and (8.60) into the state and costate equations gives, upon solving for $x(k+1)$,

$$P(k) = G_{xx}(k) + A^{\mathrm{T}}(k)[P^{-1}(k+1) + B(k)G_{uu}^{-1}(k)B^{\mathrm{T}}(k)]^{-1}A(k) \quad (8.62)$$

with

$$P(N) = g_{xx}. \quad (8.63)$$

This matrix Riccati equation may be solved backward in y.

8.4 PARTIAL DIFFERENTIAL EQUATION MODELS

8.4.1 System Models Type I

For problem (PI) with an integral criterion only, introduce the notation $f_0 \triangleq G$ and

$$J = x_0 = \int_Y f_0[y, x, \ldots, \partial_l x, \ldots, u]\, \mathrm{d}y. \tag{8.64}$$

The necessary conditions for optimality involve $(n + 1)$ auxiliary (costate) variables $\lambda_i (i = 0, 1, \ldots, n)$ defined by the set of equations (costate equations)

$$\frac{\partial \lambda_i}{\partial y_4} = -\frac{\partial H}{\partial x_i} - (-1)^L \partial_l \left(\frac{\partial H}{\partial(\partial_l x_i)} \right) \qquad i = 0, 1, \ldots, n \tag{8.65}$$

with the natural boundary conditions

$$x_i \text{ given} \quad \text{or} \quad (-1)^{L-1} \partial_{(l-1)} \left(\frac{\partial H}{\partial(\partial_l x_i)} \right) = 0 \tag{8.66}$$

$$\text{at} \quad y_k^{\mathrm{L}}, y_k^{\mathrm{R}}, k = 1, 2, 3$$

$$\lambda_i \text{ free (zero) if } x_i \text{ is given (free) at } y_4^{\mathrm{L}}, y_4^{\mathrm{R}} \tag{8.67}$$

$$(\text{as a special case } \lambda_0 |_{y^{\mathrm{R}}} = 1)$$

where the Hamiltonian

$$H = \sum_{i=0}^{n} \lambda_i(y) f_i[y, x, \ldots, \partial_l x, \ldots, u]. \tag{8.68}$$

(Evidently λ_0 = constant = 1.)

Then for an optimum system, it is necessary that the Hamiltonian be minimized over all admissible controls. Formally

$$H[y, x, \ldots, \partial_l x, \ldots, \hat{u}, \lambda] \leqslant H[y, x, \ldots, \partial_l x, \ldots, u, \lambda]. \tag{8.69}$$

This last inequality is variously referred to as the 'optimality condition' or the 'control (in)equation' as it is used to obtain a relation for $\hat{u}$ in terms of the state and costate.

Several extensions of these conditions are possible. For example, consider an end-state criterion of the form

$$\int_{\mathrm{Y}} g[y, x(y)] \Big|_{y_4^{\mathrm{R}}} \mathrm{d}y. \tag{8.70}$$

(An analogous form may also be considered for $y_4 = y_4^{\mathrm{L}}$.) The new problem may be thought of in two ways. A new variable x_γ may be introduced in place of (8.70), or the costate boundary conditions can be shown to become

$$\lambda_i(y) = -\partial g/\partial x_i \quad \text{at} \quad y_4^R \qquad i = 1, \ldots, n. \tag{8.71}$$

Consider the extension to generalized end-states of the form

$$\int_Y S(x, \ldots, \partial_l x, \ldots)\bigg|_{y_4^R} \mathrm{d}\mathbf{y} = 0 \qquad S = (S_1, \ldots, S_q)^T. \tag{8.72}$$

(A similar function may be specified for the states at y_4^L.) Adjoining (8.72) to the criterion with Lagrange multipliers $\Lambda_i(\mathbf{y})$, $i = 1, \ldots, q$ gives the boundary conditions on λ as

$$\lambda_j = -\sum_{i=1}^{q} \frac{\partial S_i}{\partial x_j} \Lambda_i - (-1)^L \partial_l \left(\sum_{i=1}^{q} \frac{\partial S_i}{\partial(\partial_l x_j)} \Lambda_i \right) \bigg|_{y_4^R} \tag{8.73}$$

where the q multipliers Λ_i are chosen to satisfy (8.72).

8.4.2 Example: Optimal Vibrating Plate

Consider the problem of the optimal control of the thickness distribution of a freely vibrating plate such as to minimize the mass of the structure with a bound on the fundamental frequency of vibration of the reference plate.

Assuming a variables separable solution the relevant constitutive equation for a plate of variable thickness under free vibration is

$$\frac{\partial^2}{\partial y_1^2}\left[D\frac{\partial^2 W}{\partial y_1^2} + D\nu\frac{\partial^2 W}{\partial y_2^2}\right] + \frac{\partial^2}{\partial y_2^2}\left[D\frac{\partial^2 W}{\partial y_2^2} + D\nu\frac{\partial^2 W}{\partial y_1^2}\right] + 2\frac{\partial^2}{\partial y_1 \partial y_2}\left[D(1-\nu)\frac{\partial^2 W}{\partial y_1 \partial y_2}\right] - e^2 D^{1/3} W = 0 \quad \text{(a)}$$

where $e^2 = \rho\omega^2[12(1-\nu^2)/E]^{1/3} \geqslant 0$

and D denotes the flexural rigidity, $Eh^3/12(1-\nu^2)$
- h the plate thickness, $h(y_1, y_2)$
- E the modulus of elasticity
- ν the Poissons ratio
- W the lateral displacement, $W(y_1, y_2)$, from the equilibrium position
- ρ the material density (mass per unit area), $\rho(y_1, y_2)$
- y_1, y_2 position coordinates, $0 \leqslant y \leqslant a$, $0 \leqslant y \leqslant b$
- ω the circular frequency (radians per unit time).

The circular frequency is here chosen as

$$\omega = \omega_f = \sqrt{\frac{D_0}{\rho h_0}}\left[\left(\frac{\pi}{a}\right)^2 + \left(\frac{\pi}{b}\right)^2\right],$$

the fundamental frequency of a uniform reference plate.

The boundary conditions are taken as

$$W\Big|_{y_1=0,a} = 0, \qquad D\frac{\partial^2 W}{\partial y_1^2} + D\nu\frac{\partial^2 W}{\partial y_2^2}\Big|_{y_1=0,a} = 0$$
$$W\Big|_{y_2=0,b} = 0, \qquad D\frac{\partial^2 W}{\partial y_2^2} + D\nu\frac{\partial^2 W}{\partial y_1^2}\Big|_{y_2=0,b} = 0. \tag{b}$$

For a minimum mass (ρh) problem

$$J = \int_{y_2}\int_{y_1} D^{1/3}\,\mathrm{d}y_1\,\mathrm{d}y_2. \tag{c}$$

Either y_1 or y_2 may be chosen in the derivative terms on the left-hand side of the state equations. Arbitrarily choosing y_1, the state equations are

$$\frac{\partial x_1}{\partial y_1} = x_2, \quad \frac{\partial x_2}{\partial y_1} = x_3, \quad \frac{\partial x_3}{\partial y_1} = x_4, \quad \frac{\partial x_4}{\partial y_1} = -\frac{\theta}{x_5},$$
$$\frac{\partial x_5}{\partial y_1} = x_6, \quad \frac{\partial x_6}{\partial y_1} = u \tag{d}$$

where
$$\theta = ux_3 + 2x_6x_4 + \nu\left[u\frac{\partial^2 x_1}{\partial y_2^2} + 2x_6\frac{\partial^2 x_2}{\partial y_2^2} + x_5\frac{\partial^2 x_3}{\partial y_2^2}\right]$$
$$+ 2(1-\nu)\frac{\partial}{\partial y_2}\left[x_6\frac{\partial x_2}{\partial y_2} + x_5\frac{\partial x_3}{\partial y_2}\right]$$
$$+ \frac{\partial^2}{\partial y_2^2}\left[x_5\frac{\partial^2 x_1}{\partial y_2^2} + \nu x_5x_3\right] - e^2x_5^{1/3}x_1$$

with boundary conditions

$$x_1\Big|_{y_1=0,a} = 0 \qquad x_5x_3 + \nu x_5\frac{\partial^2 x_1}{\partial y_2^2}\Big|_{y_1=0,a} = 0$$
$$x_1\Big|_{y_2=0,b} = 0 \qquad x_5\frac{\partial^2 x_1}{\partial y_2^2} + \nu x_5x_3\Big|_{y_2=0,b} = 0 \tag{e}$$

and the criterion becomes

$$J = \int_0^b\int_0^a x_5^{1/3}\,\mathrm{d}y_1\,\mathrm{d}y_2 \tag{f}$$

where the states and control are

$$x_1 \triangleq W, \quad x_2 \triangleq \frac{\partial W}{\partial y_1}, \quad x_3 \triangleq \frac{\partial^2 W}{\partial y_1^2}, \quad x_4 \triangleq \frac{\partial^3 W}{\partial y_1^3},$$
$$x_5 \triangleq D, \quad x_6 \triangleq \frac{\partial D}{\partial y_1}, \quad u \triangleq \frac{\partial^2 D}{\partial y_1^2}.$$

With the system differential equations and the criterion now in hand, the Hamiltonian may be written (for a maximum principle),

$$H = -x_5^{1/3} + \lambda_1 x_2 + \lambda_2 x_3 + \lambda_3 x_5 - \frac{\lambda_4 \theta}{x_5} + \lambda_5 x_6 + \lambda_6 u. \tag{g}$$

The maximum principle requires that u must be chosen for all (y_1, y_2) such that $H(u)$ is maximized. However it is noted that the control appears linearly in the Hamiltonian with coefficient

$$\sigma(y_1, y_2) = \frac{-\lambda_4}{x_5}\left\{x_3 + \nu \frac{\partial^2 x_1}{\partial y_2^2}\right\} + \lambda_6 \tag{h}$$

implying the possible occurrence of a singular optimal control. However, the singular control requirement (Chapter 9) that σ be maintained at zero may be avoided (yet satisfied) for this particular problem formulation by noting a relationship between the states and costates.

The costate equations are

$$\begin{bmatrix} \dfrac{\partial \lambda_1}{\partial y_1} \\ \dfrac{\partial \lambda_2}{\partial y_1} \\ \dfrac{\partial \lambda_3}{\partial y_1} \\ \\ \dfrac{\partial \lambda_4}{\partial y_1} \\ \dfrac{\partial \lambda_5}{\partial y_1} \\ \\ \dfrac{\partial \lambda_6}{\partial y_1} \end{bmatrix} = \begin{bmatrix} \nu \dfrac{\partial^2}{\partial y_2^2}(u\phi) + \dfrac{\partial^2}{\partial y_2^2}\left(x_5 \dfrac{\partial^2 \phi}{\partial y_2^2}\right) - e^2 x_5^{1/3}\phi \\ -\lambda_1 + 2\nu \dfrac{\partial^2}{\partial y_2^2}(x_6\phi) + 2(1-\nu)\dfrac{\partial}{\partial y_2}\left(x_6 \dfrac{\partial \phi}{\partial y_2}\right) \\ -\lambda_2 + u\phi + \nu \dfrac{\partial^2}{\partial y_2^2}(x_5\phi) + 2(1-\nu)\dfrac{\partial}{\partial y_2}\left(x_5 \dfrac{\partial \phi}{\partial y_2}\right) \\ + \nu x_5 \dfrac{\partial^2 \phi}{\partial y_2^2} \\ -\lambda_3 + 2x_6\phi \\ \frac{1}{3}x_5^{-2/3} - \dfrac{\phi\theta}{x_5} + \nu\phi \dfrac{\partial^2 x_3}{\partial y_2^2} - 2(1-\nu)\dfrac{\partial \phi}{\partial y_2}\dfrac{\partial x_3}{\partial y_2} \\ + \dfrac{\partial^2 \phi}{\partial y_2^2}\dfrac{\partial^2 x_1}{\partial y_2^2} + \nu x_3 \dfrac{\partial^2 \phi}{\partial y_2^2} - \frac{1}{3}e^2 x_5^{-2/3} x_1 \phi \\ -\lambda_5 + 2x_4\phi + 2\phi \dfrac{\partial^2 x_2}{\partial y_2^2} - 2(1-\nu)\dfrac{\partial \phi}{\partial y_2}\dfrac{\partial x_2}{\partial y_2} \end{bmatrix} \tag{i}$$

where $\phi = \lambda_4/x_5$, and the associated boundary conditions are

$$\lambda_2\Big|_{y_1=0,a} = 0, \qquad \lambda_4\Big|_{y_1=0,a} = 0, \qquad \lambda_6\Big|_{y_1=0,a} = 0,$$

$$\lambda_3 + \Lambda_{0,a} x_5\Big|_{y_1=0,a} = 0, \qquad \lambda_5 + \Lambda_{0,a}\left[x_3 + \nu \frac{\partial^2 x_1}{\partial y_2^2}\right]\Bigg|_{y_1=0,a} = 0,$$

(where $\Lambda_{0,a}$ are Lagrange multipliers)

$$\left[2\nu \frac{\partial}{\partial y_2}(x_6\phi) + 2(1-\nu)x_6\frac{\partial \phi}{\partial y_2}\right]\left[\delta x_2\right]_{y_2=0,b} = 0, \tag{j}$$

$$\left[2\frac{\partial \phi}{\partial y_2}x_5\right]\left[\delta x_3\right]_{y_2=0,b} = 0,$$

$$\left[-2\phi\frac{\partial}{\partial y_2}\left(x_3 + \frac{\partial^2 x_1}{\partial y_2^2}\right) + \frac{\partial}{\partial y_2}\left(\phi\frac{\partial^2 x_1}{\partial y_2^2} + \nu\phi x_3\right)\right]\left[\delta x_5\right]_{y_2=0,b} = 0,$$

$$\left[-2(1-\nu)\phi\frac{\partial x_2}{\partial y_2}\right]\left[\delta x_6\right]_{y_2=0,b} = 0.$$

Equations (d) (including conditions (e)) and (i) (including (j)) constitute the necessary relations that have to be solved for an optimal solution to be gained of the problem. There are twelve equations relating thirteen unknowns $x_i(y_1, y_2)$, $\lambda_i(y_1, y_2)$, $i = 1, \ldots, 6$ and $u(y_1, y_2)$.

The equations are linked by the requirement that the Hamiltonian be maximized with respect to the control. Generally this will give the additional equation (relating the optimal control to the state and costate variables) needed to determine the solution completely. However, as the control appears linearly in H, this singular control condition requires that the coefficient of u in H be maintained at zero.

By inspection of the state and costate equations and their associated boundary conditions, the following relationship can be shown to hold.

$$\begin{bmatrix} \lambda_1 \\ \\ \lambda_2 \\ \\ \lambda_3 \\ \lambda_4 \\ \lambda_5 \\ \lambda_6 \end{bmatrix} = \alpha^2 \begin{bmatrix} \frac{\partial}{\partial y_1}\left[x_5x_3 + \nu x_5\frac{\partial^2 x_1}{\partial y_2^2}\right] + 2(1-\nu)\frac{\partial}{\partial y_2}\left[x_5\frac{\partial x_2}{\partial y_2}\right] + \nu\frac{\partial^2}{\partial y_2^2}\left[x_5x_2 - x_1x_6\right] \\ -\left[x_5x_3 + \nu x_5\frac{\partial^2 x_1}{\partial y_2^2}\right] - 2(1-\nu)\frac{\partial}{\partial y_2}\left[x_5\frac{\partial x_1}{\partial y_2}\right] - \nu\frac{\partial^2}{\partial y_2^2}[x_5x_1] \\ x_5x_2 - x_1x_6 \\ -x_5x_1 \\ [x_2x_3 - x_1x_4] + \nu\left[x_2\frac{\partial^2 x_1}{\partial y_2^2} - x_1\frac{\partial^2 x_2}{\partial y_2^2}\right] + 2(1-\nu)\frac{\partial x_1}{\partial y_2}\frac{\partial x_2}{\partial y_2} \\ -x_1x_3 - \nu x_1\frac{\partial^2 x_1}{\partial y_2^2} \end{bmatrix} \tag{k}$$

Here α^2 is a constant (an amplitude factor on the states as (a) is homogeneous in W).

By relating the state and costate variables in this way, the manipulations normally required in the singular optimal control case have been circumvented. $(\mathrm{i})^1$ can be shown to be equivalent to (a), $(\mathrm{i})^{2,3,4,6}$ are identities and $(\mathrm{i})^5$ becomes, in terms of the original structural variables,

$$\frac{\partial^2 W}{\partial y_1^2}\left(\frac{\partial^2 W}{\partial y_1^2} + \nu\,\frac{\partial^2 W}{\partial y_2^2}\right) + 2(1-\nu)\left(\frac{\partial^2 W}{\partial y_1 \partial y_2}\right)^2 + \frac{\partial^2 W}{\partial y_2^2}\left(\frac{\partial^2 W}{\partial y_2^2} + \nu\,\frac{\partial^2 W}{\partial y_1^2}\right) - \frac{1}{3\alpha^2}[1+\alpha^2 e^2 W^2]D^{-2/3} = 0. \quad (1)$$

The optimum solution then involves the simultaneous solution of (a) or (d) and (1) together with the boundary conditions (b).

8.4.3 System Models Type II

For the integral criterion of problem (PII), in order for the control to be optimal, three n-component vectors $\psi^i(y) = (\psi_1^i, \ldots, \psi_n^i)^{\mathrm{T}}$, $i = 1, 2, 3$ are introduced satisfying the (costate) equations

$$\sum_{i=1}^{3} \frac{\partial \psi_j^i}{\partial y_i} = -\frac{\partial H}{\partial x_j} - (-1)^l \partial_l \left[\frac{\partial H}{\partial[\partial_l x_j]}\right] \qquad j = 1, \ldots, n \qquad (8.74)$$

with natural boundary conditions

$$x_j \text{ given} \quad \text{or}$$

$$-\psi_j^i + (-1)^{l-1}\partial_{l-1}\left[\frac{\partial H}{\partial[\partial_l x_j]}\right] = 0 \qquad (8.75)$$

$$\text{at} \quad y_i^{\mathrm{a}}, y_i^{\mathrm{b}};\ i = 1, 2, 3$$

in order that the Hamiltonian

$$H[y, x, \ldots, \partial_l x, \ldots, \psi^i, u] = G[y, x, \ldots, \partial_l x, \ldots, u] + \sum_{i=1}^{3}\sum_{j=1}^{n} \psi_j^i(y) f_j^i[y, x, \ldots, \partial_l x, \ldots, u] \qquad (8.76)$$

takes on a minimum value with respect to u. State continuity conditions over an imaginary inner boundary may also apply.

Boundary criteria may be treated by defining new state and control variables to give a modified integral criterion and new transversality conditions.

8.4.4 Example: Optimal Vibrating Plate

For the problem of section 8.4.2, the governing equation (section 8.4.2 equation (a) and boundary conditions (b)) may be reinterpreted in a system type II form.

A set of state variables $\{x_j;\ j = 1, \ldots, n\}$ is introduced subscripted for convenience in increasing order of the derivative of W involved. For any derivative of order α there are introduced $\alpha + 1$ state variables. Set

$$
\begin{aligned}
&x_1 \triangleq W, \quad x_2 \triangleq \frac{\partial W}{\partial y_1}, \quad x_3 \triangleq \frac{\partial W}{\partial y_2}, \quad x_4 \triangleq D\frac{\partial^2 W}{\partial y_1^2} + D\nu\frac{\partial^2 W}{\partial y_2^2}, \\
&x_5 \triangleq D(1-\nu)\frac{\partial^2 W}{\partial y_1 \partial y_2}, \quad x_6 \triangleq D\frac{\partial^2 W}{\partial y_2^2} + D\nu\frac{\partial^2 W}{\partial y_1^2}, \\
&x_7 \triangleq \frac{\partial}{\partial y_2}\left[D\frac{\partial^2 W}{\partial y_1^2} + D\nu\frac{\partial^2 W}{\partial y_2^2}\right], \\
&x_8 \triangleq \frac{\partial}{\partial y_1}\left[D\frac{\partial^2 W}{\partial y_1^2} + D\nu\frac{\partial^2 W}{\partial y_2^2}\right] + \frac{\partial}{\partial y_2}\left[D(1-\nu)\frac{\partial^2 W}{\partial y_1 \partial y_2}\right], \\
&x_9 \triangleq \frac{\partial}{\partial y_2}\left[D\frac{\partial^2 W}{\partial y_2^2} + D\nu\frac{\partial^2 W}{\partial y_1^2}\right] + \frac{\partial}{\partial y_1}\left[D(1-\nu)\frac{\partial^2 W}{\partial y_1 \partial y_2}\right], \\
&x_{10} \triangleq \frac{\partial}{\partial y_1}\left[D\frac{\partial^2 W}{\partial y_2^2} + D\nu\frac{\partial^2 W}{\partial y_1^2}\right].
\end{aligned} \tag{a}
$$

The control, $u \triangleq D$.

In addition, certain equation consistency terms or auxiliary dependent (control) variables are required such that when the state variables are differentiated, the resulting sets of equations are consistent with the original fourth order equation. That is their role is essentially one of giving the total order to the set of equations. They may be treated as auxiliary equation controls. Set

$$
\begin{aligned}
&u_1 \triangleq \frac{\partial}{\partial y_1}\left\{\frac{\partial}{\partial y_2}\left[D\frac{\partial^2 W}{\partial y_1^2} + D\nu\frac{\partial^2 W}{\partial y_2^2}\right]\right\}, \quad u_2 \triangleq \frac{\partial}{\partial y_2}\left\{\frac{\partial}{\partial y_2}\left[\frac{\partial^2 W}{\partial y_1^2} + D\nu\frac{\partial^2 W}{\partial y_2^2}\right]\right\}, \\
&u_3 \triangleq \frac{\partial}{\partial y_1}\left\{\frac{\partial}{\partial y_1}\left[D\frac{\partial^2 W}{\partial y_1^2} + D\nu\frac{\partial^2 W}{\partial y_2^2}\right] + \frac{\partial}{\partial y_2}\left[D(1-\nu)\frac{\partial^2 W}{\partial y_1 \partial y_2}\right]\right\}, \\
&u_4 \triangleq \frac{\partial}{\partial y_2}\left\{\frac{\partial}{\partial y_1}\left[D\frac{\partial^2 W}{\partial y_1^2} + D\nu\frac{\partial^2 W}{\partial y_2^2}\right] + \frac{\partial}{\partial y_2}\left[D(1-\nu)\frac{\partial^2 W}{\partial y_1 \partial y_2}\right]\right\}, \\
&u_5 \triangleq \frac{\partial}{\partial y_1}\left\{\frac{\partial}{\partial y_2}\left[D\frac{\partial^2 W}{\partial y_2^2} + D\nu\frac{\partial^2 W}{\partial y_1^2}\right] + \frac{\partial}{\partial y_1}\left[D(1-\nu)\frac{\partial^2 W}{\partial y_1 \partial y_2}\right]\right\}, \\
&u_6 \triangleq \frac{\partial}{\partial y_1}\left\{\frac{\partial}{\partial y_1}\left[D\frac{\partial^2 W}{\partial y_2^2} + D\nu\frac{\partial^2 W}{\partial y_1^2}\right]\right\}, \quad u_7 \triangleq \frac{\partial}{\partial y_2}\left\{\frac{\partial}{\partial y_2}\left[D\frac{\partial^2 W}{\partial y_2^2} + D\nu\frac{\partial^2 W}{\partial y_1^2}\right]\right\}.
\end{aligned} \tag{b}
$$

(During the optimization procedures to be outlined here, the equations involving these auxiliary variables disappear and hence are not carried through the computations.)

Partial differentiation of (a) with respect to y_1 and y_2 yields the $2n$ system equations,

$$\frac{\partial x_1}{\partial y_1} = x_2 \qquad \frac{\partial x_1}{\partial y_2} = x_3$$

$$\frac{\partial x_2}{\partial y_1} = \frac{x_4}{u} - \nu \frac{\partial x_3}{\partial y_2} \qquad \frac{\partial x_2}{\partial y_2} = \frac{x_5}{u(1-\nu)}$$

$$\frac{\partial x_3}{\partial y_1} = \frac{x_5}{u(1-\nu)} \qquad \frac{\partial x_3}{\partial y_2} = \frac{x_6}{u} - \nu \frac{\partial x_2}{\partial y_1}$$

$$\frac{\partial x_4}{\partial y_1} = x_8 - \frac{\partial x_5}{\partial y_2} \qquad \frac{\partial x_4}{\partial y_2} = x_7$$

$$\frac{\partial x_5}{\partial y_1} = x_9 - \frac{\partial x_6}{\partial y_2} \qquad \frac{\partial x_5}{\partial y_2} = x_8 - \frac{\partial x_4}{\partial y_1} \tag{c}$$

$$\frac{\partial x_6}{\partial y_1} = x_{10} \qquad \frac{\partial x_6}{\partial y_2} = x_9 - \frac{\partial x_5}{\partial y_1} \tag{d}$$

$$\frac{\partial x_7}{\partial y_1} = u_1 \qquad \frac{\partial x_7}{\partial y_2} = u_2$$

$$\frac{\partial x_8}{\partial y_1} = u_3 \qquad \frac{\partial x_8}{\partial y_2} = u_4$$

$$\frac{\partial x_9}{\partial y_1} = u_5 \qquad \frac{\partial x_9}{\partial y_2} = e^2 u^{1/3} x_1 - u_3$$

$$\frac{\partial x_{10}}{\partial y_1} = u_6 \qquad \frac{\partial x_{10}}{\partial y_2} = u_7$$

These twenty first-order equations are logically equivalent to the original fourth-order plate equation. They are now in the general form of system type II where now $i = 1, 2$; $y = (y_1, y_2)^T$; $x = (x_1, \ldots, x_{10})^T$; and $u = (u, u_1, \ldots, u_7)^T$.

The reason for the choice of these particular state variables (a) should be clear. Physically they may be interpreted (neglecting sign conventions) as deflection, slopes, internal bending and twisting moments, and internal shears. State variables x_7 and x_{10} have no commonly known appellation but may be given physical interpretation. Notice that as the derivative of W increases, a pyramid effect results with the introduction of additional numbers of state variables per increasing derivative order.

When differentiated with respect to the spatial coordinates y_1 and y_2, the resulting state or system equations ((c) and (d) respectively) also may be given a physical meaning. Equations $(c)^{1,2,3}$ and $(d)^{1,2,3}$ contain all the information regarding constitution and compatibility. For example, $(c)^{1,2}$ and $(d)^1$ combined give constitution and compatibility in the y_1 direction, $(c)^1$ and $(d)^{1,3}$ in the y_2 direction; and $(c)^3$ and $(d)^1$ (or equivalently $(c)^1$ and $(d)^2$) the coupling $y_1 y_2$ effect. Equations $(c)^{4,5}$ (or equivalently $(d)^{5,6}$) represent the required equilibrium relationships in the y_1 and y_2 directions. All remaining equations ensure that the end result of the reduction process is in fact interchangeable with the original fourth-order equation in W. Notice, lastly, that there is a certain repetition of information between (c) and (d) (in the form of common equations) which appears unavoidable with type II systems.

Boundary conditions expressed in terms of the new variables are of a particularly simple form, being

$$\left. x_1 \right|_{y_1=0,a} = 0 \qquad \left. x_4 \right|_{y_1=0,a} = 0$$
$$\left. x_1 \right|_{y_2=0,b} = 0 \qquad \left. x_6 \right|_{y_2=0,b} = 0. \tag{e}$$

(There will also be continuity conditions of state across an imaginary inner line boundary. For the moment, this requirement is put to one side. The final solution will be shown to implicitly satisfy this requirement.)

The criterion may be written

$$J = \int_{y_2}\int_{y_1} u^{1/3}\,\mathrm{d}y_1\,\mathrm{d}y_2.$$

With the state equations and criterion in hand, the Hamiltonian (maximum principle)

$$\begin{aligned} H = {} & -u^{1/3} + \Big\{ \psi_1^1 x_2 + \psi_2^1\left[\frac{x_4}{u} - \nu\frac{\partial x_3}{\partial y_2}\right] + \psi_3^1 \frac{x_5}{u(1-\nu)} + \psi_4^1\left[x_8 - \frac{\partial x_5}{\partial y_2}\right] \\ & + \psi_5^1\left[x_9 - \frac{\partial x_6}{\partial y_2}\right] + \psi_6^1 x_{10} + \psi_7^1 u_1 + \psi_8^1 u_3 + \psi_9^1 u_5 + \psi_{10}^1 u_6 \Big\} \\ & + \Big\{ \psi_1^2 x_3 + \psi_2^2 \frac{x_5}{u(1-\nu)} + \psi_3^2\left[\frac{x_6}{u} - \nu\frac{\partial x_2}{\partial y_1}\right] + \psi_4^2 x_7 \\ & + \psi_5^2\left[x_8 - \frac{\partial x_4}{\partial y_1}\right] + \psi_6^2\left[x_9 - \frac{\partial x_5}{\partial y_1}\right] + \psi_7^2 u_2 + \psi_8^2 u_4 \\ & + \psi_9^2[e^2 u^{1/3} x_1 - u_3] + \psi_{10}^2 u_7 \Big\}. \end{aligned} \tag{f}$$

H is maximized with respect to each control for the optimum solution. This implies a global maximization of H over the controls. Notice that H is nonlinear in u but linear in u_i, $i = 1, \ldots, 7$. This is a singular control problem for the last seven controls. (The requirement in this case, where no constraints on u_i, $i = 1, \ldots, 7$, exist, is that the coefficients of u_i, denoted σ_i, $i = 1, \ldots, 7$, be maintained at zero over the domain of the plate.)

For unconstrained u, the stationary values in H for this variable are given by

$$\frac{\partial H}{\partial u} = 0 = -\tfrac{1}{3}u^{-2/3} - \frac{\psi_2^1 x_4}{u^2} - \frac{\psi_3^1 x_5}{u^2(1-\nu)} - \frac{\psi_2^2 x_5}{u^2(1-\nu)} - \frac{\psi_3^2 x_6}{u^2} + \tfrac{1}{3}\psi_9^2 e^2 x_1 u^{-2/3}. \quad \text{(g)}$$

This is a necessary condition for a local maximum of H with respect to u.

The coefficients of u_i, $i = 1, \ldots, 7$, in (f) are

$$\begin{aligned} &\sigma_1 = \frac{\partial H}{\partial u_1} = \psi_7^1 && \sigma_2 = \frac{\partial H}{\partial u_2} = \psi_7^2 \\ &\sigma_3 = \frac{\partial H}{\partial u_3} = \psi_8^1 - \psi_9^2 && \sigma_4 = \frac{\partial H}{\partial u_4} = \psi_8^2 \\ &\sigma_5 = \frac{\partial H}{\partial u_5} = \psi_9^1 && \sigma_6 = \frac{\partial H}{\partial u_6} = \psi_{10}^1 \\ &\sigma_7 = \frac{\partial H}{\partial u_7} = \psi_{10}^2 . \end{aligned} \quad \text{(h)}$$

It will be shown that by a suitable substitution, the requirement of $\sigma_i = 0$, for all y_1, y_2, will be implicitly satisfied. In so doing much of the formal argument relating to singular control conditions is circumvented.

The differential equations governing the behaviour of the costate variables read

$$\frac{\partial \psi_1^1}{\partial y_1} + \frac{\partial \psi_1^2}{\partial y_2} = -\psi_9^2 e^2 u^{1/3}$$

$$\frac{\partial \psi_2^1}{\partial y_1} + \frac{\partial \psi_2^2}{\partial y_2} = -\psi_1^1 - \nu \frac{\partial \psi_3^2}{\partial y_1}$$

$$\frac{\partial \psi_3^1}{\partial y_1} + \frac{\partial \psi_3^2}{\partial y_2} = -\nu \frac{\partial \psi_2^1}{\partial y_2} - \psi_1^2$$

$$\frac{\partial \psi_4^1}{\partial y_1} + \frac{\partial \psi_4^2}{\partial y_2} = -\frac{\psi_2^1}{u} - \frac{\partial \psi_5^2}{\partial y_1}$$

$$\frac{\partial \psi_5^1}{\partial y_1} + \frac{\partial \psi_5^2}{\partial y_2} = -\frac{\psi_3^1}{u(1-\nu)} - \frac{\partial \psi_4^1}{\partial y_2} - \frac{\psi_2^2}{u(1-\nu)} + \frac{\partial \psi_6^2}{\partial y_1} \tag{i}$$

$$\frac{\partial \psi_6^1}{\partial y_1} + \frac{\partial \psi_6^2}{\partial y_2} = -\frac{\partial \psi_5^1}{\partial y_2} - \frac{\psi_3^2}{u}$$

$$\frac{\partial \psi_7^1}{\partial y_1} + \frac{\partial \psi_7^2}{\partial y_2} = -\psi_4^2$$

$$\frac{\partial \psi_8^1}{\partial y_1} + \frac{\partial \psi_8^2}{\partial y_2} = -\psi_4^1 - \psi_5^2$$

$$\frac{\partial \psi_9^1}{\partial y_1} + \frac{\partial \psi_9^2}{\partial y_2} = -\psi_5^1 - \psi_6^2$$

$$\frac{\partial \psi_{10}^1}{\partial y_1} + \frac{\partial \psi_{10}^2}{\partial y_2} = -\psi_6^1$$

with natural boundary conditions,

along $y_1 = 0, a$

$$\begin{gathered} -\psi_2^1 - \nu\psi_3^2 = 0, \quad -\psi_3^1 = 0, \quad -\psi_5^1 - \psi_6^2 = 0, \quad -\psi_6^1 = 0, \\ -\psi_7^1 = 0, \quad -\psi_8^1 = 0, \quad -\psi_9^1 = 0, \quad -\psi_{10}^1 = 0 \end{gathered} \tag{j}$$

along $y_2 = 0, b$

$$\begin{gathered} -\psi_2^2 = 0, \quad -\psi_3^2 - \nu\psi_2^1 = 0, \quad -\psi_4^2 = 0, \quad -\psi_5^2 - \psi_4^1 = 0, \\ -\psi_7^2 = 0, \quad -\psi_8^2 = 0, \quad -\psi_9^2 = 0, \quad -\psi_{10}^2 = 0. \end{gathered} \tag{k}$$

For an optimal solution to be gained of this problem, equations (c), (d) (with (e)) and equations (i) (with (j), (k)) have to be solved. (c), (d) and (i) are linked by the control equation (g) and the requirement that $\sigma_1, \ldots, \sigma_7$ remain zero over the optimal solution. In total there are ten state variables, twenty costate variables and eight control variables for which solutions have to be found. However, these numbers may be reduced quite significantly as a result of the elementary nature of the equations. Many of the variables are seen to be identically zero, while some variables such as the auxiliary control variables may be eliminated at the very start of the computations.

By inspection it may be seen that

$$
\begin{aligned}
&\psi_1^1 = \beta^2 x_8 && \psi_1^2 = \beta^2 x_9 \\
&\psi_2^1 = -\beta^2 u \frac{\partial x_2}{\partial y_1} && \psi_3^2 = -\beta^2 u \frac{\partial x_3}{\partial y_2} \\
&\psi_3^1 = \psi_2^2 = -\beta^2 x_5 \\
&\psi_4^1 + \psi_5^2 = \beta^2 x_2 \\
&\psi_5^1 + \psi_6^2 = \beta^2 x_3 \\
&\psi_6^1 = \psi_9^2 = -\beta^2 x_1
\end{aligned}
\tag{l}
$$

with the remaining costate variables zero. β^2 is an undetermined constant and may be thought of as a modal amplitude factor on the states (but not the geometry—that is the control—as may be anticipated). From (g), β^2 has to be positive for $u^{-2/3}(0, 0)$ to be positive; hence the choice of a constant squared. The above substitution (l) is consistent with the boundary conditions on ψ^1, ψ^2 and x and maintains σ_i, $i = 1, \ldots, 7$ zero for all (y_1,y_2).

The control equation (g) then simplifies to become (in terms of the original plate symbols)

$$
D^{-2/3} = \frac{3\beta^2}{[1 + \beta^2 e^2 W^2]} \left\{ \frac{\partial^2 W}{\partial y_1^2} \left(\frac{\partial^2 W}{\partial y_1^2} + \nu \frac{\partial^2 W}{\partial y_2^2} \right) + 2(1-\nu) \left(\frac{\partial^2 W}{\partial y_1 \partial y_2} \right)^2 + \frac{\partial^2 W}{\partial y_2^2} \left(\frac{\partial^2 W}{\partial y_2^2} + \nu \frac{\partial^2 W}{\partial y_1^2} \right) \right\} . \tag{m}
$$

Equation (m) corresponds to equation (l) of section 8.4.2 and hence the two system models and associated optimality conditions lead to the same solution as anticipated. β^2 in (m) is equivalent to α^2 in (l) of section 8.4.2.

For comparison purposes (and also to highlight a special form of system model type II as considered in the fundamental work of Lurie 1963), another reduction to a type II format is proposed and the associated solution to the illustration given.

It is noticed that the system equations given in (c) and (d) contain state derivative terms on the right-hand side. These may be eliminated, for example, by modifying x_8 and x_9 and introducing two more state variables. That is, the differential equations are reduced in order but increased in number. In particular, denoting the new states by $\{\xi_j; j = 1,$

$\ldots, 12\}$ then

$$
\begin{aligned}
&\xi_1 \triangleq x_j \qquad j = 1, \ldots, 7 \text{ and } 10, \\
&\xi_8 \triangleq x_8 - \frac{\partial}{\partial y_2}\left[D(1-\nu)\frac{\partial^2 W}{\partial y_1 \partial y_2}\right] = \frac{\partial}{\partial y_1}\left[D\,\frac{\partial^2 W}{\partial y_1^2} + D\nu\,\frac{\partial^2 W}{\partial y_2^2}\right], \\
&\xi_9 \triangleq x_9 - \frac{\partial}{\partial y_1}\left[D(1-\nu)\frac{\partial^2 W}{\partial y_1 \partial y_2}\right] = \frac{\partial}{\partial y_2}\left[D\,\frac{\partial^2 W}{\partial y_2^2} + D\nu\,\frac{\partial^2 W}{\partial y_1^2}\right], \qquad \text{(n)} \\
&\xi_{11} \triangleq \frac{\partial}{\partial y_2}\left[D(1-\nu)\frac{\partial^2 W}{\partial y_1 \partial y_2}\right], \qquad \xi_{12} \triangleq \frac{\partial}{\partial y_1}\left[D(1-\nu)\frac{\partial^2 W}{\partial y_1 \partial y_2}\right].
\end{aligned}
$$

With this change in the definition of state, the auxiliary control variables correspondingly change. Denoting the new controls by μ and $\{\mu_k;\, k = 1, \ldots, 11\}$, then

$$
\begin{aligned}
&\mu \triangleq u, \\
&\mu_k \triangleq u_k, \qquad\qquad k = 1, 2, 6, 7, \\
&\mu_3 \triangleq \frac{\partial \xi_8}{\partial y_1}, \qquad \mu_4 \triangleq \frac{\partial \xi_8}{\partial y_2}, \\
&\mu_5 \triangleq \frac{\partial \xi_9}{\partial y_1}, \qquad\qquad\qquad\qquad \text{(o)} \\
&\mu_8 \triangleq \frac{\partial \xi_{11}}{\partial y_1}, \qquad \mu_9 \triangleq \frac{\partial \xi_{11}}{\partial y_2}, \\
&\mu_{10} \triangleq \frac{\partial \xi_{12}}{\partial y_1}, \qquad \mu_{11} \triangleq \frac{\partial \xi_{12}}{\partial y_2} \quad (= \mu_8).
\end{aligned}
$$

Partial differentiation of the states ξ_j, $j = 1, \ldots, 12$ with respect to y_1 and y_2 gives the state equations

$$
\begin{aligned}
&\frac{\partial \xi_1}{\partial y_1} = \xi_2 && \frac{\partial \xi_1}{\partial y_2} = \xi_3 \\
&\frac{\partial \xi_2}{\partial y_1} = \frac{\xi_4 - \nu\xi_6}{\mu(1-\nu^2)} && \frac{\partial \xi_2}{\partial y_2} = \frac{\xi_5}{\mu(1-\nu)} \\
&\frac{\partial \xi_3}{\partial y_1} = \frac{\xi_5}{\mu(1-\nu)} && \frac{\partial \xi_3}{\partial y_2} = \frac{\xi_6 - \nu\xi_4}{\mu(1-\nu^2)} \\
&\frac{\partial \xi_4}{\partial y_1} = \xi_8 && \frac{\partial \xi_4}{\partial y_2} = \xi_7 \\
&\frac{\partial \xi_5}{\partial y_1} = \xi_{12} && \frac{\partial \xi_5}{\partial y_2} = \xi_{11} \qquad \text{(p)}
\end{aligned}
$$

$$\frac{\partial \xi_6}{\partial y_1} = \xi_{10} \qquad \frac{\partial \xi_6}{\partial y_2} = \xi_9 \tag{q}$$

$$\frac{\partial \xi_7}{\partial y_1} = \mu_1 \qquad \frac{\partial \xi_7}{\partial y_2} = \mu_2$$

$$\frac{\partial \xi_8}{\partial y_1} = \mu_3 \qquad \frac{\partial \xi_8}{\partial y_2} = \mu_4$$

$$\frac{\partial \xi_9}{\partial y_1} = \mu_5 \qquad \frac{\partial \xi_9}{\partial y_2} = e^2\mu^{1/3}\xi_1 - \mu_3 - \mu_8 - \mu_{11}$$

$$\frac{\partial \xi_{10}}{\partial y_1} = \mu_6 \qquad \frac{\partial \xi_{10}}{\partial y_2} = \mu_7$$

$$\frac{\partial \xi_{11}}{\partial y_1} = \mu_8 \qquad \frac{\partial \xi_{11}}{\partial y_2} = \mu_9$$

$$\frac{\partial \xi_{12}}{\partial y_1} = \mu_{10} \qquad \frac{\partial \xi_{12}}{\partial y_2} = \mu_{11}$$

which are equivalent to (c) and (d) and also the original fourth-order equation in W. (p) and (q) are of the general form

$$\partial\xi/\partial y_i = f^i[y, \xi, \mu] \qquad \mu = (\mu, \mu_1, \ldots, \mu_{11})^{\mathrm{T}} \tag{r}$$

and have right-hand sides independent of state derivatives. This general form is the case originally considered by Lurie (1963). The necessary conditions for optimality are again as summarized in section 8.4.3 but with the state derivative terms omitted. That is, it is a special case of the present type II system.

In reducing the state equations to a form free of state derivatives on the right-hand side, the intuitively pleasing characteristic of states having accepted meanings has been partly lost. In particular states ξ_j, $j = 1, \ldots, 6$ only, now have accepted meanings. The subdivision into constitutive, compatibility and equilibrium equations may be identified correspondingly to that outlined above. The resulting state equations are simpler and this in turn produces a simpler Hamiltonian and costate equations (although increased in number).

State boundary conditions and criterion remain the same, substituting ξ_j and μ for x_j and u respectively. See equations (e) and (f).

The Hamiltonian reads (maximum principle)

$$H = -\mu^{1/3} + \{\lambda_1^1\xi_2 + \lambda_2^1\left(\frac{\xi_4 - \nu\xi_6}{\mu(1-\nu^2)}\right) + \lambda_3^1\frac{\xi_5}{\mu(1-\nu)} + \lambda_4^1\xi_8$$

$$+ \lambda_5^1\xi_{12} + \lambda_6^1\xi_{10} + \lambda_7^1\mu_1 + \lambda_8^1\mu_3 + \lambda_9^1\mu_5 + \lambda_{10}^1\mu_6$$

$$+ \lambda_{11}^1\mu_8 + \lambda_{12}^1\mu_{10}\} + \{\lambda_1^2\xi_3 + \lambda_2^2 \frac{\xi_5}{\mu(1-\nu)} + \lambda_3^2\left(\frac{\xi_6 - \nu\xi_4}{\mu(1-\nu^2)}\right)$$
$$+ \lambda_4^2\xi_7 + \lambda_5^2\xi_{11} + \lambda_6^2\xi_9 + \lambda_7^2\mu_2 + \lambda_8^2\mu_4 \tag{s}$$
$$+ \lambda_9^2(e^2\mu^{1/3}\xi_1 - \mu_3 - \mu_8 - \mu_{11}) + \lambda_{10}^2\mu_7 + \lambda_{11}^2\mu_9 + \lambda_{12}^2\mu_{11}\}.$$

For stationary μ

$$\frac{\partial H}{\partial \mu} = 0 = -\tfrac{1}{3}\mu^{-2/3} - \lambda_2^1\left(\frac{\xi_4 - \nu\xi_6}{\mu^2(1-\nu^2)}\right) - \lambda_3^1 \frac{\xi_5}{\mu^2(1-\nu)}$$
$$- \lambda_2^2 \frac{\xi_5}{\mu^2(1-\nu)} - \lambda_3^2\left(\frac{\xi_6 - \nu\xi_4}{\mu^2(1-\nu^2)}\right) + \tfrac{1}{3}\lambda_9^2 e^2\mu^{-2/3}\xi_1. \tag{t}$$

The coefficients of μ_k, $k = 1, \ldots, 11$ are

$$\begin{aligned}
\sigma_1 &= \lambda_7^1 & \sigma_7 &= \lambda_{10}^2 \\
\sigma_2 &= \lambda_7^2 & \sigma_8 &= \lambda_{11}^1 - \lambda_9^2 \\
\sigma_3 &= \lambda_8^1 - \lambda_9^2 & \sigma_9 &= \lambda_{11}^2 \\
\sigma_4 &= \lambda_8^2 & \sigma_{10} &= \lambda_{12}^1 \\
\sigma_5 &= \lambda_9^1 & \sigma_{11} &= \lambda_{12}^2 - \lambda_9^2 \\
\sigma_6 &= \lambda_{10}^1.
\end{aligned} \tag{u}$$

The costate equations become

$$\begin{aligned}
\frac{\partial \lambda_1^1}{\partial y_1} + \frac{\partial \lambda_1^2}{\partial y_2} &= -\lambda_9^2 e^2 \mu^{1/3} \\
\frac{\partial \lambda_2^1}{\partial y_1} + \frac{\partial \lambda_2^2}{\partial y_2} &= -\lambda_1^1 \\
\frac{\partial \lambda_3^1}{\partial y_1} + \frac{\partial \lambda_3^2}{\partial y_2} &= -\lambda_1^2 \\
\frac{\partial \lambda_4^1}{\partial y_1} + \frac{\partial \lambda_4^2}{\partial y_2} &= -\frac{\lambda_2^1}{\mu(1-\nu^2)} + \frac{\nu\lambda_3^2}{\mu(1-\nu^2)} \\
\frac{\partial \lambda_5^1}{\partial y_1} + \frac{\partial \lambda_5^2}{\partial y_2} &= -\frac{\lambda_3^1}{\mu(1-\nu)} - \frac{\lambda_2^2}{\mu(1-\nu)} \\
\frac{\partial \lambda_6^1}{\partial y_1} + \frac{\partial \lambda_6^2}{\partial y_2} &= \frac{\nu\lambda_2^1}{\mu(1-\nu^2)} - \frac{\lambda_3^2}{\mu(1-\nu^2)} \\
\frac{\partial \lambda_7^1}{\partial y_1} + \frac{\partial \lambda_7^2}{\partial y_2} &= -\lambda_4^2 \\
\frac{\partial \lambda_8^1}{\partial y_1} + \frac{\partial \lambda_8^2}{\partial y_2} &= -\lambda_4^1
\end{aligned} \tag{v}$$

$$\frac{\partial \lambda_9^1}{\partial y_1} + \frac{\partial \lambda_9^2}{\partial y_2} = -\lambda_6^2$$

$$\frac{\partial \lambda_{10}^1}{\partial y_1} + \frac{\partial \lambda_{10}^2}{\partial y_2} = -\lambda_6^1$$

$$\frac{\partial \lambda_{11}^1}{\partial y_1} + \frac{\partial \lambda_{11}^2}{\partial y_2} = -\lambda_5^2$$

$$\frac{\partial \lambda_{12}^1}{\partial y_1} + \frac{\partial \lambda_{12}^2}{\partial y_2} = -\lambda_5^1$$

with natural boundary conditions,

along $y_1 = 0,a$

$$\lambda_2^1 = \lambda_3^1 = \lambda_5^1 = \ldots = \lambda_{12}^1 = 0 \tag{w}$$

along $y_2 = 0,b$

$$\lambda_2^2 = \ldots = \lambda_5^2 = \lambda_7^2 = \ldots = \lambda_{12}^2 = 0. \tag{x}$$

The analogous substitutions to (l) are

$$\begin{aligned}
&\lambda_1^1 = \kappa^2(\xi_8 + \xi_{11}) && \lambda_1^2 = -\kappa^2(\xi_9 + \xi_{12}) \\
&\lambda_2^1 = \kappa^2\xi_4 && \lambda_2^2 = -\kappa^2\xi_5 \\
&\lambda_3^1 = -\kappa^2\xi_5 && \lambda_3^2 = -\kappa^2\xi_6 \\
&\lambda_4^1 = \kappa^2\xi_2 && \lambda_5^2 = \kappa^2\xi_2 \\
&\lambda_5^1 = \kappa^2\xi_3 && \lambda_6^2 = \kappa^2\xi_3 \\
&\lambda_8^1 = \lambda_{11}^1 = \lambda_9^2 = \lambda_{12}^2 = -\kappa^2\xi_1
\end{aligned} \tag{y}$$

with the remaining costate variables zero. κ^2 is a constant with a parallel meaning to β^2. The substitutions (y) are consistent with (w) and (x) and the singular control requirements on σ_i, $i = 1, \ldots, 11$, and lead to equations (m) (from (t)) and (l) of section 8.4.2. (from (p) and (q) or (v)) to be solved for optimality. This is the same pair of equations as evolved above and hence leads to the same solution.

8.4.5 System Models Type III

For the problem (PIII), the solution introduces the costate vector η. $\eta(y_1, y_2) = (\eta_1, \ldots, \eta_n)^{\mathrm{T}}$ is defined by

$$\frac{\partial^2 \eta}{\partial y_1 \partial y_2} = \frac{\partial H}{\partial x} + (-1)^l \partial_l \left[\frac{\partial H}{\partial[\partial_l x]}\right] \tag{8.77}$$

over the region Y with boundary conditions –

(a) along boundary ∂Y^{a}, x given or

$$\frac{\partial g_{\mathrm{a}}}{\partial x} - \left((-1)^{l_1 - 1}\partial_{l_1 - 1}\left[\frac{\partial H}{\partial[\partial_{l_1} x]}\right]\frac{\mathrm{d}y_2}{\mathrm{d}\sigma} - (-1)^{l_2 - 1}\partial_{l_2 - 1}\left[\frac{\partial H}{\partial[\partial_{l_2} x]}\right]\frac{\mathrm{d}y_1}{\mathrm{d}\sigma}\right) - \left(\frac{\partial \eta}{\partial y_2}\frac{\mathrm{d}y_2}{\mathrm{d}\sigma} - \frac{\partial \eta}{\partial y_1}\frac{\mathrm{d}y_1}{\mathrm{d}\sigma}\right) = 0 \quad (8.78)$$

(b) along boundary ∂Y^{b}, x given or

$$\frac{\partial g_{\mathrm{b}}}{\partial x} - \left((-1)^{l_1 - 1}\partial_{l_1 - 1}\left[\frac{\partial H}{\partial[\partial_{l_1} x]}\right]\frac{\mathrm{d}y_2}{\mathrm{d}\sigma} - (-1)^{l_2 - 1}\partial_{l_2 - 1}\left[\frac{\partial H}{\partial[\partial_{l_2} x]}\right]\frac{\mathrm{d}y_1}{\mathrm{d}\sigma}\right) - \left(\frac{\partial \eta}{\partial y_2}\frac{\mathrm{d}y_2}{\mathrm{d}\sigma} - \frac{\partial \eta}{\partial y_1}\frac{\mathrm{d}y_1}{\mathrm{d}\sigma}\right) = 0 \quad (8.79)$$

where the Hamiltonian H is defined by

$$\begin{aligned} H[x, \ldots, \partial_l x, \ldots, \eta, u, y_1, y_2] &= \eta(y_1, y_1)^{\mathrm{T}} f[x, \ldots, \partial_l x, \ldots, u, y_1, y_2] \\ &\quad + G[x, \ldots, \partial_l x, \ldots, u, y_1, y_2]. \end{aligned} \quad (8.80)$$

The control is chosen to minimize the Hamiltonian. Continuity conditions exist for curves of discontinuities in the controls.

For the case where the region Y is rectangular the above results assume a particularly simple form. The costate equations become

$$\frac{\partial^2 \eta}{\partial y_1 \partial y_2} = \frac{\partial H}{\partial x} + (-1)^l \partial_l\left[\frac{\partial H}{\partial[\partial_l x]}\right] \quad (8.81)$$

with boundary conditions

(i) at $y_1^{\mathrm{L}}, y_1^{\mathrm{R}}$

$$x_i \text{ given or } \frac{\partial \eta_i}{\partial y_2} + (-1)^{l_1 - 1}\partial_{l_1 - 1}\left[\frac{\partial H}{\partial[\partial_{l_1} x_i]}\right] - \frac{\partial g_2}{\partial x_i} = 0, \quad i = 1, \ldots, n \quad (8.82)$$

(ii) at $y_2^{\mathrm{L}}, y_2^{\mathrm{R}}$

$$x_i \text{ given or } \frac{\partial \eta_i}{\partial y_1} + (-1)^{l_2 - 1}\partial_{l_2 - 1}\left[\frac{\partial H}{\partial[\partial_{l_2} x_i]}\right] - \frac{\partial g_1}{\partial x_i} = 0, \quad i = 1, \ldots, n. \quad (8.83)$$

Also

$$\text{at} \quad (y_1^L, y_2^L), (y_1^R, y_2^R) \quad x_i \text{ given or } \quad \eta_i = 0, \qquad i = 1, \ldots, n. \tag{8.84}$$

The state and costate may be solved simultaneously for the $2n + r$ unknowns $x_1, \ldots, x_n, \eta_1, \ldots, \eta_n, u_1, \ldots, u_r$. The boundary conditions are of the split type; for η they are the differential equations (8.82) and (8.83) which themselves have boundary conditions (8.84)—equations (8.82) and (8.83) with conditions (8.84) uniquely define η along the boundaries for any given control. The coupling relations between the state and costate equations are provided by the condition that the control is chosen to minimize the Hamiltonian.

8.4.6 Example: Optimal Vibrating Plate

Consider the previous plate vibration problem where now a system model type III is used. Essentially two distinct approaches are possible. Firstly, the state may be chosen as the displacement, twisting moment pair and the control as the plate rigidity. Such a choice is intuitively appealing but reduces to a type III form only for the case of constant geometry. Secondly, the derivatives in the high order system equation are expanded first and control and states defined to satisfy the mathematical requirements of the type III format. This leads to a higher number of states and state equations. The second reduction is adopted here.

Differentiations involving mixed-derivative terms in equation (a) of section 8.4.2 are carried out to give an expanded form of this equation with isolated mixed-derivative terms;

$$\frac{\partial^2}{\partial y_1^2}\left(D\frac{\partial^2 W}{\partial y_1^2}\right) + \frac{\partial^2}{\partial y_2^2}\left(D\frac{\partial^2 W}{\partial y_2^2}\right) + \nu\left(\frac{\partial^2 D}{\partial y_1^2}\frac{\partial^2 W}{\partial y_2^2} + \frac{\partial^2 D}{\partial y_2^2}\frac{\partial^2 W}{\partial y_1^2}\right)$$

$$+ 2\left(\frac{\partial D}{\partial y_1}\frac{\partial^3 W}{\partial y_1 \partial y_2^2} + \frac{\partial D}{\partial y_2}\frac{\partial^3 W}{\partial y_1^2 \partial y_2} + D\frac{\partial^4 W}{\partial y_1^2 \partial y_2^2}\right)$$

$$+ 2(1-\nu)\left(\frac{\partial^2 D}{\partial y_1 \partial y_2}\frac{\partial^2 W}{\partial y_1 \partial y_2}\right) - e^2 D^{1/3} W = 0. \tag{a}$$

Introduce state and control notation according to

$$x_1 \triangleq W, \qquad x_2 \triangleq \frac{\partial^2 W}{\partial y_1 \partial y_2}, \qquad x_3 \triangleq D, \qquad u \triangleq \frac{\partial^2 D}{\partial y_1 \partial y_2}. \tag{b}$$

Taking the mixed $y_1 y_2$ derivatives of the states leads to the system equations

$$\begin{bmatrix} \dfrac{\partial^2 x_1}{\partial y_1 \partial y_2} = x_2 \\[2ex] \dfrac{\partial^2 x_2}{\partial y_1 \partial y_2} = \dfrac{-\theta}{2x_3} \\[2ex] \dfrac{\partial^2 x_3}{\partial y_1 \partial y_2} = u \end{bmatrix} \qquad \text{(c)}$$

where
$$\theta = \left\{ \frac{\partial^2}{\partial y_1^2}\left(x_3 \frac{\partial^2 x_1}{\partial y_1^2}\right) + \frac{\partial^2}{\partial y_2^2}\left(x_3 \frac{\partial^2 x_1}{\partial y_2^2}\right) \right.$$
$$+ \nu\left(\frac{\partial^2 x_3}{\partial y_1^2}\frac{\partial^2 x_1}{\partial y_2^2} + \frac{\partial^2 x_3}{\partial y_2^2}\frac{\partial^2 x_1}{\partial y_1^2}\right) + 2\left(\frac{\partial x_3}{\partial y_1}\frac{\partial x_2}{\partial y_2} + \frac{\partial x_3}{\partial y_2}\frac{\partial x_2}{\partial y_1}\right)$$
$$\left. + 2(1-\nu)ux_2 - e^2 x_3^{1/3} x_1 \right\}.$$

Equations (c) are now in the standard form of system type III where $x = (x_1, x_2, x_3)^{\mathrm{T}}$, $\quad u = u$.

State boundary conditions associated with (c) become

$$\begin{aligned} x_1\Big|_{y_1=0,a} &= 0 \qquad x_3\frac{\partial^2 x_1}{\partial y_1^2} + \nu x_3 \frac{\partial^2 x_1}{\partial y_2^2}\Big|_{y_1=0,a} = 0 \\ x_1\Big|_{y_2=0,b} &= 0 \qquad x_3\frac{\partial^2 x_1}{\partial y_2^2} + \nu x_3 \frac{\partial^2 x_1}{\partial y_1^2}\Big|_{y_2=0,b} = 0. \end{aligned} \qquad \text{(d)}$$

The problem is to give optimality to

$$J = \int_{y_1}\int_{y_2} x_3^{1/3}\,\mathrm{d}y_2\,\mathrm{d}y_1 \qquad \text{(e)}$$

(in terms of the introduced variables above) for the system behaving according to (c) and (d).

The Hamiltonian is then of the form (maximum principle)

$$H = -x_3^{1/3} + \eta_1 x_2 - \frac{\eta_2 \theta}{2x_3} + \eta_3 u. \qquad \text{(f)}$$

It is remarked that H is linear in u and without prespecified constraints on the control, the situation corresponds to a singular control problem. The maximum principle requires that H be maximized over u as a necessary condition for optimality. Following arguments similar to the illustration in section 8.4.2 a substitution for the costate variables will be made which implicitly satisfies the requirements for singular controls using the maximum principle. For the present, the coefficient of u in the Hamiltonian is

$$\sigma(y_1, y_2) = -\frac{(1-\nu)x_2\eta_2}{x_3} + \eta_3. \tag{g}$$

The costate variables η_i, $i = 1, 2, 3$ are defined by

$$\left[\begin{aligned}
\frac{\partial^2\eta_1}{\partial y_1\partial y_2} &= \frac{\partial^2}{\partial y_1^2}\left(x_3\frac{\partial^2\phi}{\partial y_1^2}\right) + \frac{\partial^2}{\partial y_2^2}\left(x_3\frac{\partial^2\phi}{\partial y_2^2}\right) \\
&\quad + \nu\frac{\partial^2}{\partial y_2^2}\left(\phi\frac{\partial^2 x_3}{\partial y_1^2}\right) + \nu\frac{\partial^2}{\partial y_1^2}\left(\phi\frac{\partial^2 x_3}{\partial y_2^2}\right) - \phi e^2 x_3^{1/3} \\
\frac{\partial^2\eta_2}{\partial y_1\partial y_2} &= \eta_1 - 2\frac{\partial}{\partial y_2}\left(\phi\frac{\partial x_3}{\partial y_1}\right) - 2\frac{\partial}{\partial y_1}\left(\phi\frac{\partial x_3}{\partial y_2}\right) + 2(1-\nu)\phi u \\
\frac{\partial^2\eta_3}{\partial y_1\partial y_2} &= -\tfrac{1}{3}x_3^{-2/3} - \frac{\phi\theta}{x_3} + \frac{\partial^2\phi}{\partial y_1^2}\frac{\partial^2 x_1}{\partial y_1^2} + \frac{\partial^2\phi}{\partial y_2^2}\frac{\partial^2 x_1}{\partial y_2^2} \\
&\quad + \nu\frac{\partial^2}{\partial y_1^2}\left(\phi\frac{\partial^2 x_1}{\partial y_2^2}\right) + \nu\frac{\partial^2}{\partial y_2^2}\left(\phi\frac{\partial^2 x_1}{\partial y_1^2}\right) \\
&\quad - 2\frac{\partial}{\partial y_1}\left(\phi\frac{\partial x_2}{\partial y_2}\right) - 2\frac{\partial}{\partial y_2}\left(\phi\frac{\partial x_3}{\partial y_1}\right) - \tfrac{1}{3}e^2\phi x_3^{-2/3}x_1
\end{aligned}\right] \tag{h}$$

where $\phi = \dfrac{-\eta_2}{2x_3}$

with natural boundary conditions,

along $y_1 = 0,a$

$$\left[\frac{\partial\eta_2}{\partial y_2} + 2\frac{\partial x_3}{\partial y_2}\phi\right]\delta x_2 = 0$$

$$\left[\frac{\partial\eta_3}{\partial y_2} - \frac{\partial}{\partial y_1}\left(\phi\frac{\partial^2 x_1}{\partial y_1^2}\right) + 2\phi\frac{\partial^3 x_1}{\partial y_1^3} - \nu\frac{\partial}{\partial y_1}\left(\phi\frac{\partial^2 x_1}{\partial y_2^2}\right) + 2\phi\frac{\partial x_2}{\partial y_2}\right]\delta x_3 = 0 \tag{i}$$

along $y_2 = 0,b$

$$\left[\frac{\partial\eta_2}{\partial y_1} + 2\frac{\partial x_3}{\partial y_1}\phi\right]\delta x_2 = 0$$

$$\left[\frac{\partial\eta_3}{\partial y_1} - \frac{\partial}{\partial y_2}\left(\phi\frac{\partial^2 x_1}{\partial y_2^2}\right) + 2\phi\frac{\partial^3 x_1}{\partial y_2^3} - \nu\frac{\partial}{\partial y_2}\left(\phi\frac{\partial^2 x_1}{\partial y_1^2}\right) + 2\phi\frac{\partial x_2}{\partial y_1}\right]\delta x_3 = 0 \tag{j}$$

with $\eta_2(0, 0) = \eta_2(a, b) = \eta_3(0, 0) = \eta_3(a, b) = 0$.

Conditions (i) and (j) are differential equations in η with given initial and final conditions, from which η may be found along the boundaries, for given control.

An optimal solution is thus required to satisfy the boundary value problem expressed by the simultaneous equations (c) and (h) with boundary conditions (d) and (i) and (j). There is a total of six equations in seven unknowns x_1, x_2, x_3, η_1, η_2, η_3 and u. Additionally, the coefficient σ (expression (g)) is required to be maintained at zero over the region; this gives the extra equation needed to completely solve the problem. An alternative approach, analogous to the previous illustrations in section 8.4.2 and section 8.4.4 to the solution, however, will be used here.

By inspection of equations (c) and (h) a valid substitution which satisfies the boundary conditions of (i) and (j) as well as equation (h) is

$$\begin{bmatrix} \eta_1 \\ \eta_2 \\ \eta_3 \end{bmatrix} = -2\gamma^2 \begin{bmatrix} x_3x_2 - \nu x_1 u \\ x_1x_3 \\ (1-\nu)x_1x_2 \end{bmatrix}. \tag{k}$$

The substitution also maintains (over the total plate region) $\sigma = 0$.

Using (k), equation $(h)^1$ reduces to the original system equation when expressed in the original variables, equation $(h)^2$ reduces to an identity, and equation $(h)^3$ reduces to

$$\frac{\partial^2 W}{\partial y_1^2}\left(\frac{\partial^2 W}{\partial y_1^2} + \nu\frac{\partial^2 W}{\partial y_2^2}\right) + 2(1-\nu)\left(\frac{\partial^2 W}{\partial y_1 \partial y_2}\right)^2 + \frac{\partial^2 W}{\partial y_2^2}\left(\frac{\partial^2 W}{\partial y_2^2} + \nu\frac{\partial^2 W}{\partial y_1^2}\right) - \frac{1}{3\gamma^2}[1 + \gamma^2 e^2 W^2]D^{-2/3} = 0. \tag{l}$$

The relevant boundary conditions are (b) of section 8.4.2. That is, for an optimal solution equation (l) has to be solved simultaneously with (a) of section 8.4.2. However, these are in fact the same equations determined in section 8.4.2 and section 8.4.4 for types I and II system formats respectively. All approaches consequently reduce to the same equations to be solved.

The order of equations (c) may be reduced if additional state variables are defined. A reduced order may be helpful in certain computational situations. Consider the set

$$\xi_1 \triangleq W, \qquad \xi_2 \triangleq \frac{\partial W}{\partial y_1}, \qquad \xi_3 \triangleq \frac{\partial W}{\partial y_2}, \qquad \xi_4 \triangleq \frac{\partial^2 W}{\partial y_1 \partial y_2}, \qquad \xi_5 \triangleq D, \tag{m}$$

with control, $\mu \triangleq \dfrac{\partial^2 D}{\partial y_1 \partial y_2}$.

From these, the state equations are

$$\begin{bmatrix} \dfrac{\partial^2 \xi_1}{\partial y_1 \partial y_2} = \xi_4 \\ \dfrac{\partial^2 \xi_2}{\partial y_1 \partial y_2} = \dfrac{\partial \xi_4}{\partial y_1} \\ \dfrac{\partial^2 \xi_3}{\partial y_1 \partial y_2} = \dfrac{\partial \xi_4}{\partial y_2} \\ \dfrac{\partial^2 \xi_4}{\partial y_1 \partial y_2} = \dfrac{-\theta}{2\xi_5} \\ \dfrac{\partial^2 \xi_5}{\partial y_1 \partial y_2} = \mu \end{bmatrix} \tag{n}$$

where $\theta = \dfrac{\partial^2}{\partial y_1^2}\left(\xi_5 \dfrac{\partial \xi_2}{\partial y_1}\right) + \dfrac{\partial^2}{\partial y_2^2}\left(\xi_5 \dfrac{\partial \xi_3}{\partial y_2}\right) + \nu\left(\dfrac{\partial^2 \xi_5}{\partial y_1^2}\dfrac{\partial \xi_3}{\partial y_2} + \dfrac{\partial^2 \xi_5}{\partial y_2^2}\dfrac{\partial \xi_2}{\partial y_1}\right)$

$$+ 2\left(\frac{\partial \xi_5}{\partial y_1}\frac{\partial \xi_4}{\partial y_2} + \frac{\partial \xi_5}{\partial y_2}\frac{\partial \xi_4}{\partial y_1}\right) + 2(1-\nu)\mu\xi_4 - e^2\xi_5^{1/3}\xi_1$$

which are again of the general form (type III)

$$\frac{\partial^2 \xi}{\partial y_1 \partial y_2} = f'[\xi, \ldots, \partial_l \xi, \ldots, \mu, y_1, y_2]$$

where $\xi = (\xi_1, \ldots, \xi_5)^{\mathrm{T}}$, $\mu = \mu$.

Also by using the device employed in connection with the type II systems, namely introducing auxiliary dependent (control) variables, a further reduction can be obtained. In particular define the following states

$$\rho_1 \triangleq W, \quad \rho_2 \triangleq \frac{\partial W}{\partial y_1}, \quad \rho_3 \triangleq \frac{\partial W}{\partial y_2}, \quad \rho_4 \triangleq \frac{\partial^2 W}{\partial y_1 \partial y_2},$$
$$\rho_5 \triangleq \frac{\partial^2 W}{\partial y_1^2}, \quad \rho_6 \triangleq \frac{\partial^2 W}{\partial y_2^2}, \quad \rho_7 \triangleq D, \tag{o}$$

and control $\kappa \triangleq \partial^2 D/\partial y_1 \partial y_2$, with auxiliary dependent (control) variables the remaining second-order derivatives of D and fourth-order derivatives of W except $\partial^4 W/\partial y_1^2 \partial y_2^2$ $(= \partial^2 \rho_4/\partial y_1 \partial y_2)$;

$$\kappa_1 \triangleq \frac{\partial^4 W}{\partial y_1^4}, \quad \kappa_2 \triangleq \frac{\partial^4 W}{\partial y_1^3 \partial y_2}, \quad \kappa_3 \triangleq \frac{\partial^4 W}{\partial y_1 \partial y_2^3}, \quad \kappa_4 \triangleq \frac{\partial^4 W}{\partial y_2^4},$$
$$\kappa_5 \triangleq \frac{\partial^2 D}{\partial y_1^2}, \quad \kappa_6 \triangleq \frac{\partial^2 D}{\partial y_2^2}. \tag{p}$$

Differentiating the state variables ρ leads to

$$\begin{bmatrix} \dfrac{\partial^2 \rho_1}{\partial y_1 \partial y_2} = \rho_4 \\ \dfrac{\partial^2 \rho_2}{\partial y_1 \partial y_2} = \dfrac{\partial \rho_4}{\partial y_1} \\ \dfrac{\partial^2 \rho_3}{\partial y_1 \partial y_2} = \dfrac{\partial \rho_4}{\partial y_2} \\ \dfrac{\partial^2 \rho_4}{\partial y_1 \partial y_2} = \dfrac{-\theta}{2\rho_7} \\ \dfrac{\partial^2 \rho_5}{\partial y_1 \partial y_2} = \kappa_2 \\ \dfrac{\partial^2 \rho_6}{\partial y_1 \partial y_2} = \kappa_3 \\ \dfrac{\partial^2 \rho_7}{\partial y_1 \partial y_2} = \kappa \end{bmatrix} \tag{q}$$

where $\theta = \kappa_5 \rho_5 + 2 \dfrac{\partial \rho_7}{\partial y_1} \dfrac{\partial \rho_5}{\partial y_1} + \rho_7 \kappa_1 + \kappa_6 \rho_6 + 2 \dfrac{\partial \rho_7}{\partial y_2} \dfrac{\partial \rho_6}{\partial y_2} + \rho_7 \kappa_4$

$$+ \nu(\kappa_5 \rho_6 + \kappa_6 \rho_5) + 2\left(\frac{\partial \rho_7}{\partial y_1} \frac{\partial \rho_6}{\partial y_1} + \frac{\partial \rho_7}{\partial y_2} \frac{\partial \rho_5}{\partial y_2}\right)$$

$$+ 2(1 - \nu)\kappa \rho_4 - e^2 \rho_7^{1/3} \rho_1$$

which are now in the form

$$\frac{\partial^2 \rho}{\partial y_1 \partial y_2} = f''\left[\rho, \frac{\partial \rho}{\partial y_1}, \frac{\partial \rho}{\partial y_2}, \kappa, y_1, y_2\right] \tag{r}$$

where $\rho = (\rho_1, \ldots, \rho_7)^{\mathrm{T}}$, $\kappa = (\kappa, \kappa_1, \ldots, \kappa_6)^{\mathrm{T}}$.

It is remarked that the choice of state variables (m) leads to the system equations (n) which contain the lowest order state derivatives on the right-hand side (of system type III form for this structure) without resorting to the device of introducing the auxiliary control variables. In both reductions (m) and (o) the number of state equations ((n) and (q) respectively) is naturally increased. Following the same computations path as above, it can be shown for the two latest proposed reductions, that the same equations (a) of section 8.4.2 and (l) have to be solved for optimality.

8.4.7 The Calculus of Variations

The calculus of variations has extensions which allow finding extrema of multiple integrals of the form

$$J = \iint_Y \phi(y_1, y_2, x, x_{y_1}, x_{y_2})\, \mathrm{d}y_1\, \mathrm{d}y_2 \tag{8.85}$$

over a given region Y with coordinates y_1 and y_2.

Assuming x has continuous derivatives up to the second order the associated Euler (partial differential) equation is

$$\frac{\partial}{\partial y_1}\phi_{x_{y_1}} + \frac{\partial}{\partial y_2}\phi_{x_{y_2}} - \phi_x = 0 \tag{8.86}$$

or in expanded form

$$\begin{aligned}\phi_{x_{y_1}x_{y_1}} x_{y_1y_1} &+ 2\phi_{x_{y_1}x_{y_2}} x_{y_1y_2} + \phi_{x_{y_2}x_{y_2}} x_{y_2y_2} \\ &+ \phi_{x_{y_1}x} x_{y_1} + \phi_{x_{y_2}x} x_{y_2} + \phi_{x_{y_1}y_1} + \phi_{x_{y_2}y_2} - \phi_x = 0.\end{aligned} \tag{8.87}$$

If ϕ contains the derivatives $x_{y_1}, x_{y_2}, \ldots, x_{y_2y_2\cdots y_2}$ up to the n'th order, the Euler equation becomes

$$\begin{aligned}\phi_x - \frac{\partial}{\partial y_1}\phi_{x_{y_1}} - \frac{\partial}{\partial y_2}\phi_{x_{y_2}} + \frac{\partial^2}{\partial y_1^2}\phi_{x_{y_1y_1}} + \frac{\partial^2}{\partial y_1 \partial y_2}\phi_{x_{y_1y_2}} \\ + \frac{\partial^2}{\partial y_2^2}\phi_{x_{y_2y_2}} + \ldots + (-1)^n \frac{\partial^n}{\partial y_2^n}\phi_{x_{y_2y_2\cdots y_2}} = 0.\end{aligned} \tag{8.88}$$

The natural boundary conditions associated with the Euler equation (8.86) or (8.87) are

$$\phi_{x_{y_1}} \frac{\mathrm{d}y_2}{\mathrm{d}\sigma} - \phi_{x_{y_2}} \frac{\mathrm{d}y_1}{\mathrm{d}\sigma} = 0 \quad \text{on } \partial Y \tag{8.89}$$

where σ is a measure of the arc length on the boundary ∂Y.

The more general natural boundary conditions associated with minimizing

$$J = \iint_Y \phi(y_1, y_2, x, x_{y_1}, x_{y_2})\, \mathrm{d}y_1\, \mathrm{d}y_2 + \int_{\partial Y} \theta(\sigma, x, x_\sigma)\, \mathrm{d}\sigma \tag{8.90}$$

are

$$\phi_{x_{y_1}} \frac{\mathrm{d}y_2}{\mathrm{d}\sigma} - \phi_{x_{y_2}} \frac{\mathrm{d}y_1}{\mathrm{d}\sigma} + \theta_x - \frac{\mathrm{d}}{\mathrm{d}\sigma}\theta_{x_\sigma} = 0. \tag{8.91}$$

8.5 NOTES, COMMENTS AND BIBLIOGRAPHY

[8.1] The maximum principle arose out of work by Pontryagin, Boltyanskii and Gamkrelidze in the 1950s on optimal control problems.

Similar results had been given by McShane (1939) while current texts interweave the calculus of variations theory and optimal control theory indicating the common characteristics of these theories. See Fel'dbaum (1965). For proofs of Pontryagin's principle see Pontryagin *et al*. (1962), Rozonoer (1959) and Lee and Markus (1967) among others. For the connection with the calculus of variations see, for example, Berkovitz (1961) and Leitmann (1966), and with dynamic programming see, for example, Fel'dbaum (1965) and Noton (1965).

The minimum principle has been adopted by much of the more recent North American literature. It is equivalent to the original maximum principle of the Russian literature. The difference arises through a change in a sign convention.

For comments on sufficient conditions for optimality see Pontryagin *et al*. (1962) and Lee and Markus (1967).

See Athans (1966) and Paiewonsky (1965) for a discussion on local necessary conditions leading to extremal controls in contrast to globally optimum controls.

[8.2] 1. Sage and White (1977) and Bryson and Ho (1975) give a very readable treatment of the theory. See also Gottfried and Weisman (1973), Luenberger (1969), Beveridge and Schechter (1970) and Tou (1964) among others.

For a maximum principle the Hamiltonian is defined as $H \triangleq -G + \lambda^T f$.

If the substitution

$$\mathrm{d}x_0/\mathrm{d}y = f_0 = G \quad \text{with} \quad x_0(y^L) = 0$$

is made, the Hamiltonian becomes

$$H = \lambda^T f$$

where now λ and f have $n + 1$ components. The costate equations become

$$\mathrm{d}\lambda/\mathrm{d}y = -(\partial f/\partial x)\lambda$$

with x now also an $n + 1$ component vector. These equations can be seen to be homogeneous and linear in λ; that is, if $\alpha(y)$ is a solution of the costate equations, then $-\alpha(y)$ is also a solution. This establishes the equivalence of the maximum and minimum principle forms. Generally, in derivations of the minimum principle λ_0 is taken to be any nonnegative value (usually +1) and the remaining λ_j, $j = 1, \ldots, n$ scaled to suit; in the maximum principle λ_0 is taken to be any nonpositive value (usually −1) and the remaining λ_j, $j = 1, \ldots, n$ scaled to suit. It will be noted from the latest given version of the costate equations above that

$$d\lambda_0/dy = 0$$

and hence λ_0 is constant for all y.

The costate variables are sometimes referred to as adjoint variables, Lagrange multipliers and influence functions. Equation $(8.2)^c$ is sometimes referred to as an adjoint equation.

The costate equations together with the system equations constitute the so-termed 'Hamilton canonical' differential equations when expressed in terms of the Hamiltonian. They are canonical adjoints. See Sage (1968). Coupling is through the control (in)equation. The terminology derives from an analogous construction of equations in analytical mechanics for lumped parameter systems—see Chapter 1 for the form of the canonical equations and their interpretation. (In the analogous mechanics equations, the Hamiltonian is an energy function, x are generalized coordinates, λ are generalized momenta and y is time; the state space is $2n$ dimensional. See Rozonoer 1959.) It is only an analogy and no physical significance should be attached to it. Control variables are explicitly introduced in control theory but are eliminated in analytical mechanics. As noted by Rozonoer (1959), the relationship in control theory between dynamic programming and Pontryagin's principle is analogous to the relationship in mechanics between the Hamilton–Jacobi equations and the Hamilton canonical equations. They are alternative ways of characterizing the optimal control problem or system behaviour respectively. See also Lanczos (1949).

It may also be recalled from Chapter 1 that the state space concepts of control theory are a generalization of phase space concepts of classical dynamics. This generalization and the previously mentioned analogy (of Hamilton's equations) were two separate introductions to control theory.

For an examination of the second derivative given that the first derivative $\partial H/\partial u = 0$ implies stationarity, see Sage and White (1977) and Bryson and Ho (1975).

For all but a few standard problems such as the linear-quadratic, bang-bang and others, some numerical solution procedure is required to solve the resulting two point or multipoint boundary value problem. This represents the main difficulty in applying the technique successfully even though considerable attention has been paid to this problem. Several approaches to this problem have found favour in the literature, including quasilinearization, gradient methods, invariant imbedding, finite differences and others. The alternative is to use mathematical programming, dynamic programming or direct methods ideas. See, for example, Noton (1965), Merriam (1964), Dyer and McReynolds (1970),

Sage and White (1977), Sage (1968), Sage and Melsa (1971), Citron (1969), and Bryson and Ho (1975) among others. Structural applications include the gradient projection method used by Pierson (1975a, 1977) (see also Pierson and Genalo 1977; Pierson and Russell 1973, Pierson 1972b, 1975b and Pierson and Hajela 1979); the steepest ascent method of Haug, Arora and others; the analogue computer approach of Bellamy and West (1969); and the various approaches of de Silva (see, for example, de Silva, Negus and Worster 1976, de Silva and Grant 1975, 1978, de Silva, Green and Grant 1976, de Silva 1975) and others.

2. Trahair and Booker (1970) solve the column problem using the calculus of variations. See a related exercise using a control format by Haug (1969).

Ashley and McIntosh (1969) use the unconstrained results for problems with aeroelastic constraints. A transition matrix algorithm is used to solve the two point boundary value problem. See also Weisshaar (1970, 1976), Vitte *et al.* (1968), Armand and Vitte (1970), Armand (1975, 1976), McIntosh, Weisshaar and Ashley (1969), McIntosh (1974) and Pierson (1972a).

3. The solution for the optimal control implies a linear feedback control law.

The matrix Riccati equation is solved backwards in y from y^{R} to y^{L}. Sage and White (1977) also give the form of the 'inverse' matrix Riccati equation which may be computationally more useful than the matrix Riccati equation. See also Citron (1969) and Bryson and Ho (1975) among others.

A sufficient condition for optimality is that G_{xx} and g_{xx} be positive semidefinite and G_{uu} be positive definite (Sage and White 1977).

See also Casti (1977) and Jacobson (1977).

For bilinear systems, see Mohler (1973).

4. The general problem treated here is sometimes referred to as the constrained Bolza problem.

Integral constraints are sometimes termed isoperimetric constraints.

Equation (8.19) may alternatively be written

$$\hat{u} = \arg\min H[x(y), u(y), \lambda(y), y].$$

For the original ideas behind the principle see Pontryagin *et al.* (1962) and McShane (1939). Numerous approaches to derivations of versions of Pontryagin's principle are available. See, for example, Rozonoer (1959), Lee and Markus (1967), Leitmann (1966) and Fel'dbaum (1965). The calculus of variations type arguments usually require a sufficient degree of smoothness of the function in which a variation is taken. Other derivations are less restrictive on the allowable variations and piecewise continuous controls are admitted. Dynamic programming arguments may be used with the assumption of differentiability of the optimal return function. See, for example, Fel'dbaum (1965), Noton (1965) and Dyer and McReynolds (1970).

In (8.18), U is usually regarded as being independent of values taken by the state. See Rozonoer (1959) for comments. (8.24) follows Valentine (1937) and Berkovitz (1961) and is related to the penalty function ideas of Kelley (1962). See Sage and White (1977). See, for example, Pierson (1977) in the structures literature.

Bang-bang (equivalently on-off or maximum effort) control is similar to the constraint boundary solution of linear programming. It is particularly relevant for the minimum time problems (Pontryagin *et al.* (1962)). Chapter 9 treats the singular optimal control case. In the structures literature, see Szefer (1971) and Carmichael (1978b) for comments.

State variable constraints are treated by Sage and White (1977), Bryson and Ho (1975), Citron (1969), and Leitmann (1966) among others. See also Kelley (1962) and Berkovitz (1962). In the structures literature see, for example, Citron (1969), Haug and Kirmser (1967) and de Silva (1970).

For structural applications where there exist interior point constraints and discontinuities in the state variables, see the support and hinge location problems of Rozvany and Hill (1976), Rozvany (1976), Olhoff and Taylor (1978), and Carmichael and Clyde (1980) among others.

Multipurpose structural design involves the specification of two or more path constraints or system equations in the problem statement. See Karihaloo (1979a, b, c, d), Karihaloo and Parbery (1979a, b) and Karihaloo and Wood (1979).

Interior point constraints are also treated by Dyer and McReynolds (1970).

5. For other applications see Dixon (1967), (see also 1968, 1972 and Boykin and Sierakowski 1972 for discussion), Haug and Kirmser (1967), Haug (1969), Citron (1969), de Silva (1970, 1972), (see also Carmichael 1977a, b for discussion), Distefano and Todeschini (1972), Andreev *et al.* (1972, 1976), Johnson *et al.* (1976), Segenreich, Johnson and Rizzi (1976), Stadler (1977a, b, 1978) Vavrick and Warner (1978a, b) and Huang and Tang (1969) among others.

In general, state constraints complicate the computations inordinately (see, for example, Citron 1969, de Silva 1970, and Haug and Kirmser 1967), and are usually avoided by most authors. In much of the work on free vibration problems, equality constraints are handled by direct substitution of the appropriate constraint in the system equations. The systems are then effectively without loading and unconstrained. In such circumstances the state and costate variables can often be shown to exhibit a simplifying property in that they are constant multiples of each other and the solution computations, though still nontrivial, are relatively uncomplicated. However, for most design problems, this simplifying property is not apparent from inspection of the equations.

For lower bound plasticity design, the system equation is not the constitutive relationship at the appropriate level, but rather an equilibrium equation. It is noted that the equilibrium equation is a relationship between state variables and hence contains no variables that are control variables in the conventional design sense. In this form the system is theoretically uncontrollable. To counter this, the dependent variables in the equilibrium equation may be arbitrarily classified as control and state variables and the solution follows conventional state-control treatments. The mathematics can still handle the problem; it is only the conceptual basis which is lacking. See Lepik (1972, 1973) and Carmichael and Clyde (1980) for other ideas.

6. See Lanczos (1949) and Synge (1960), for example, for the mechanics version. For comments on the control problem see Sage and White (1977), Denn (1969), Hinderer (1970) and Porteus (1975) as well as the previously referenced works.

See also Benton (1977) and MacFarlane (1970).

7. For the relationship between Pontryagin's principle and the calculus of variations see Blum (1967), Berkovitz (1961), Kalman (1963 b), A. I. Egorov (1966) and Leitmann (1966) among others. From an historical viewpoint see McShane (1978). The control problem may be converted to one in the calculus of variations by defining

$$\mathrm{d}x_{n+i}/\mathrm{d}y \triangleq u_i \quad \text{and} \quad x_{n+i}(y^{\mathrm{L}}) = 0 \qquad i = 1, \ldots, r$$

See Sage and White (1977) for the transformation between the Lagrange, Mayer and Bolza forms. For example, the Lagrange form may be converted to the Mayer form by suitably augmenting the x vector by defining

$$\mathrm{d}x_0/\mathrm{d}y = \phi \quad \text{with} \quad x_0(y^{\mathrm{L}}) = 0.$$

The Lagrange problem is sometimes referred to as the 'simplest' problem in the calculus of variations.

Courant and Hilbert (1953) give the theory of the calculus of variations, which gives the conditions for the extrema of functionals, a functional being a quantity or function, which depends on the entire course of one or more functions. (See also the definition of Luenberger 1969.) Courant and Hilbert also treat the transformation of variational problems to canonical form where the second-order Euler–Lagrange equation becomes two first-order equations. See also the approach where any second-order ordinary differential may be regarded as the Euler–Lagrange equation of some equivalent minimization problem. The distinction adopted above between natural boundary conditions and transversality conditions is used in Courant and Hilbert.

In practice the second variations are rarely checked, the solution resulting from the Euler–Lagrange equation usually being accepted or rejected on physical arguments alone. The problem of determining the minimum of the second variation of J is known as the accessory minimum problem with the Euler–Lagrange equation for the problem being referred to as the Jacobi or accessory differential equation (Citron 1969).

Constraints may be treated with the use of Lagrange multipliers as in the parameter optimization problem. The technique of Lagrange multipliers adjoins the constraint to the functional being minimized and removes the necessity of prior elimination of free variables (whether this is feasible or infeasible in particular problems). The use of Lagrange multipliers allows the problem to be treated as if it were unconstrained.

The Euler–Lagrange equation and the Legendre condition are sometimes referred to as the Euler equation and the Legendre–Clebsch condition respectively. The term extremal is often used to refer to a function satisfying the Euler–Lagrange equation.

For the direct solution of variational problems, using for example Rayleigh–Ritz or finite difference methods, see Sage (1968), Sokolnikoff and Redheffer (1966) and Courant and Hilbert (1953) among others.

The Euler–Lagrange equation and associated boundary conditions given above apply to the fixed interval $[y^L, y^R]$ case. For the case where y^R is allowed to vary see Sage and White (1977). The derivation of the necessary conditions for optimality involves taking a variation in y^R as well as x.

For general references on the calculus of variations including discussions on sufficient conditions for optimality as well as on relative (weak) versus absolute (global) extrema see the above works and also Denn (1969), Gottfried and Weisman (1973), Bliss (1946), Elsgolc (1961), Gelfand and Fomin (1963), Kalman (1963b), Leitmann (1962), Pierre (1969) and Tou (1964) among others.

Frequently in control texts, conventional calculus of variations arguments are used to derive necessary conditions for optimality. This involves setting the first variation of the (augmented) criterion to zero and allowing free variations of the state and control, to obtain the control that yields the stationary value of the criterion. (This is manifested in the result $\partial H/\partial u = 0$.) For this control to be also minimizing the first variation of the criterion has to be positive which leads on to a version of the minimum principle; that is some scalar quantity H, the Hamiltonian, has to be minimized over the admissible controls for optimality. This, however, is only possible when the admissible state and control sets are unbounded. Where the admissible control set is bounded the variations in the control cannot be completely arbitrary and the usual approach of the calculus of variations no longer holds. The same situation for controls arises in the presence of constraints on the state space where the control must be chosen without violating these constraints.

This is an inherent restriction of the calculus of variations but may be overcome with extensions due to Weierstrass; in particular the Weierstrass–Erdmann corner conditions which give the requirements at discontinuities in extremals, and extend the admissible class of controls to include piecewise continuous functions (and hence allow constraints on the controls).

For the control discontinuous, the point is referred to as a corner. These points may arise at the junction of constrained and unconstrained portions of the solution. Corner points may also arise in an unconstrained problem where a discontinuous control is a valid solution to the Euler–Lagrange equations. Corner points impose special requirements on the optimal solution. These requirements are contained in the Weierstrass–Erdmann corner conditions.

8. Trahair and Booker (1970) use the higher derivative form of the Euler–Lagrange equation. For other applications see, for example, Karihaloo (1979a, b, c, d).

For an application of the Weierstrass–Erdmann corner conditions see Banichuk and Karihaloo (1977). The singularities referred to in this reference are not the same as for the singular optimal control problem.

[8.3] 1. For the discrete version of Pontryagin's principle see Tou (1964), Fan and Wang (1964), Rozonoer (1959), Gottfried and Weisman (1973) and Denn (1969).

See Sage and White (1977) for a comparison between the discrete and continuous maximum principles. See also Budak (1969) and Cullum (1969, 1970).

For the solution of the discrete two point boundary value problem see, for example, Sage and White (1977) and Sage and Melsa (1971).

2. The minimum weight beam design problem is treated in Citron (1969) for the continuous case.

Singaraj and Rao (1975) give a non-standard discrete formulation for trusses. See also Singaraj and Rao (1972).

3. The solution to the linear-quadratic problem is a closed loop

control as for the continuous case. The comments for the continuous linear-quadratic problem carry over to the discrete case. See Bryson and Ho (1975).

[8.4] 1. Using a calculus of variations approach, Sage (1968) gives the Euler–Lagrange equations for the problem (PI) but does not admit constraints or discontinuities in the controls.

Numerous uses of the type I form for particular problems in optimal control have been reported. In addition to those referenced in the previous chapter, Sage and Chaudhuri (1967) discuss discretization problems; Katz (1964) discusses both lumped and distributed parameter systems of type I form under a general operational equation using functional analysis arguments; Denn (1966, 1969) and Chaudhuri (1965) use a Green's function approach to derive necessary conditions for linear equations.

Several authors have found Rozonoer's approach (Rozonoer 1959) amenable to an extension to distributed parameter systems. In particular, A. I. Egorov has given necessary conditions for quasilinear partial differential equations (1963), hyperbolic, parabolic and elliptic equations (1966), general second order partial differential equations (1964), hyperbolic and parabolic equations (1967a, b). In many of these derivations, local sufficiency is also shown for the linear case. The independent variables need not be fixed in range. The systems are essentially interpreted in a type III format. For systems of a type I form, A. I. Egorov (1965a, b) treats the linear heat conduction equation. Sirazetdinov (1964) considers quasilinear system equations in a simplified type I form with derivatives of state up to the first order on the right-hand side. Butkovskii (1969) discusses the work of the last two authors and includes a special control case.

Historically systems modelled according to a type III format were the first distributed parameter systems described by a set of partial differential equations for which a maximum principle was obtained. Their introduction was the beginning of the transfer from integral equation systems as pioneered by Butkovskii and Lerner to the more general differential equation systems.

The use of the classical calculus of variations philosophy in optimal control, because of their essentially equivalent problem constructions, was early. Lurie (1963) solves the Mayer–Bolza problem for multiple integrals with as side constraints special forms of type II partial differential equations in that derivative's of state are omitted from the right-hand sides of the system equations. These derivatives have been avoided by the introduction of additional dependent variables to replace the derivative terms. The case treated is the multiple (double) integral case of the calculus of variations and leads to a two dimensional generalization of the Euler–Lagrange equation and the Legendre and Weierstrass conditions. The relationship to the maximum principle is shown. The Euler–Lagrange equation for the m-dimensional case is sometimes referred to as the Ostrogradski equation. See Elsgolc (1961) and Gelfand and Fomin (1963). For works related to Lurie's see Armand (1971, 1972). Jackson (1966) treats the same variational problem and derives special results for the case where the system equations are hyperbolic and particular boundary conditions apply. Kim and Gajwani (1968), for a system type I over two independent variables and an integral criterion over the time domain only, use the methods of the calculus of variations to derive the canonical equations as necessary conditions.

In addition to variational and dynamic programming arguments two other routes to obtaining necessary conditions have been noted in the literature (in particular see Robinson 1971) and may be broadly classified as 'function space' and 'moment' methods. Moment methods are generally only applicable to linear integral equations with known eigenfunctions. (See Butkovskii 1969.) The more abstract function space methods illustrate a recent trend in the ways of obtaining necessary conditions. (See, for example, Butkovskii 1969, Neustadt 1969, Lions 1968.) However, as commented by A. I. Egorov (1966), the introduction of abstract spaces imposes auxiliary constraints on the class of admissible controls not called for by the nature of the problem. Restrictions on the form of design criteria are also present.

2. This problem was posed by Armand (1972). Armand formulates the problem in the format of a particular type II system. See Carmichael (1975), Carmichael and Goh (1977). Notation and conventions generally follow Timoshenko and Woinowsky–Krieger (1959). Ashley and McIntosh (1969) discuss the concept of fixing the fundamental frequency at a given value. Pierson (1972a) reviews the dynamic optimization problem. Haug, Pan and Streeter (1972) solve a related problem. See also the comments of Lurie and Cherkaev (1976).

It is noted that the reduction to a system type I format for this structure (assuming variable thickness) can only be accomplished in one way—namely where the mathematical meaning alone is satisfied. Choosing all variables, in the reduction, with physical meanings creates state equations with derivatives of the control appearing on the right-hand side. Several reductions, it is noted, are possible to type II and III forms. All formulations lead ultimately to the same equations to be solved for optimality and further are singular control problems to varying degrees. The requirements for singular optimal control problems can be implicitly satisfied in this particular problem by making suitable substitutions in the courses of the solutions.

The given treatment follows Carmichael and Goh (1977). The solution can be shown to satisfy both necessary and sufficient conditions for optimality for the lumped parameter case while the solution can be shown to satisfy sufficient conditions for optimality for the distributed parameter case.

The state/costate substitution is developed in Carmichael and Goh (1977) from the lumped parameter case to the distributed parameter case.

For further applications of the maximum principle to distributed parameter systems see Szefer (1975).

3. See Carmichael (1975) for a treatment of end criteria.

4. See also Butkovskii *et al.* (1968) for systems expressed in the form (r). Equation (m) is also equivalent to the equation obtained by Armand (Armand (1972), equation 2.10, p. 120) using a different approach.

See Armand (1971) for other applications, and Carmichael and Goh (1977) for a note on this problem.

5. See Carmichael (1975).

The simplification of the results to a rectangular domain implies certain assumptions on the differentials dy_1 and dy_2 in the transversality conditions. The results could alternatively be derived directly for the rectangular case without this assumption.

6. A. I. Egorov (1964) and Butkovskii (1969) treat the general form of type III models where state derivatives up to the first order are allowed on the right-hand side.

See Carmichael and Goh (1977) for a note on this problem.

7. See Courant and Hilbert (1953).

For the application of the calculus of variations to structural optimization problems see Rozvany and Hill (1976), Rozvany (1976) and Hemp (1973) among others. See also Rozvany and Adidam (1972).

Chapter 9

Singular Control

9.1 INTRODUCTION

For certain special control problems, neither Pontryagin's principle nor classical variational theory provide an adequate test for solution optimality and supplementary conditions for optimality need to be introduced. Typically singular control formulations occur when the Hamiltonian is linear in one or more of the control variables (irrespective of the nonlinearity or linearity in the states), although other cases exist. Such formulations can be shown to be characteristic of some problems in optimum structural design.

Singular optimal control formulations may be largely avoided if attention is paid to the modelling detail. In particular controls should be chosen as geometry/material type variables and states as behaviour type variables. Both the model and variables will then take on physical significance. Against this, the state vector is not a unique quantity and may be chosen in many ways to produce the standard equation forms. This nonuniqueness of choice of variables produces two situations. The first, where the choice is based on physical grounds, leads in most cases to the direct application of Pontryagin's principle or the calculus of variations. The second, where the choice is without a physical basis, requires the use of additional optimality conditions. The latter may be preferable in some cases on, say, computational grounds and so obviously a trade off between the two situations arises.

This chapter first reviews the singular optimal control problem and outlines supplementary necessary conditions for optimality. These supplementary conditions are then applied on illustration structural design problems which have singular control formulations. Typically the computations are given for the lumped parameter case on which essentially all of the control literature has been concentrated. The last illustration (section 9.3.5) discusses the distributed parameter singular control problem which has not had the same extensive attention devoted to it as the lumped parameter singular control problem. Section 9.4

gives the associated notes, comments and bibliography. A maximum principle formulation is used in this chapter.

9.2 THE SINGULAR OPTIMAL CONTROL PROBLEM

Consider problem (OD1) with control constraints of the form

$$u(y) \in U \qquad y \in [y^L, y^R] \tag{9.1}$$

where the set U is defined by

$$U = \{u(y);\, a_i \leq u_i(y) \leq b_i,\, i = 1, 2, \ldots, r\} \tag{9.2}$$

a_i and b_i being either constants or known functions of y.

From Pontryagin's principle, the control is chosen to maximize the Hamiltonian. For the control appearing linearly in the Hamiltonian this gives

$$u_i = \begin{cases} a_i & \text{for} \quad \sigma < 0 \\ b_i & \text{for} \quad \sigma > 0 \end{cases} \tag{9.3}$$

where σ is the coefficient of the control in the Hamiltonian and is often termed a 'switching function' since the control switches from one constraint boundary to another whenever σ changes sign. This in principle creates a well defined piecewise continuous ('bang-bang') control, it being assumed that σ only changes sign at isolated values of y. However, σ may take on zero value over a subinterval of $[y^L, y^R]$. The corresponding control is termed singular and it may comprise part of the optimal solution. (The presence of singular control need not imply that the optimal solution contains singular controls.)

The optimal control problem is said to be singular if for any subinterval in $[y^L, y^R]$

$$H_u[x, u, \lambda, y] \equiv 0, \qquad \det|H_{uu}[x, u, \lambda, y]| \equiv 0 \tag{9.4}$$

where the subscripts on the Hamiltonian denote differentiation. The subinterval on which these identities hold is termed the singularity interval and the corresponding control is termed a singular control.

An examination of $\sigma(= H_u)$ is necessary to show the existence or nonexistence of a singular control in the optimum solution. The singular solution may be found from the requirement that σ remains zero on the singularity interval or equivalently from the vanishing of the derivatives of σ,

$$\frac{d\sigma}{dy} = \frac{d^2\sigma}{dy^2} = \ldots = 0. \tag{9.5}$$

Each derivative is applied successively until an expression containing u is obtained. The first derivative, in this series, that contains the control explicitly determines the order of the singularity. In particular the problem is singular of order κ if the 2κ'th derivative is the first to contain the control explicitly with a non zero coefficient.

Optimality of the singular control may be examined through supplementary optimality conditions. For example the generalized Legendre–Clebsch condition for the case of vector control is

$$\frac{\partial}{\partial u}\left[\frac{\mathrm{d}^q}{\mathrm{d}y^q}(H_u)\right] = 0, \qquad q \text{ odd} \quad \text{and} \quad (-1)^\kappa \frac{\partial}{\partial u}\left[\frac{\mathrm{d}^{2\kappa}}{\mathrm{d}y^{2\kappa}}(H_u)\right] \leq 0. \quad (9.6)$$

(It will be noted that the conventional Legendre–Clebsch condition $(\partial/\partial u)(H_u) \leq 0$ is trivially satisfied for this singular case.)

Other necessary conditions for optimality and sufficient conditions for optimality have been developed.

Subintervals of singular controls may comprise part of the total optimal control solution. The nonsingular parts where the control lies on the constraint boundary as given by (9.2) are pieced together with the singular parts with continuity conditions applying at the junctions.

9.3 ILLUSTRATIONS

9.3.1 General

Several existing optimal control formulations of structural design problems can be shown to be singular control candidates. The means of handling this situation are twofold. Firstly the singular control formulation can be retained and supplementary conditions for optimality can be invoked, or secondly the problem can often be reformulated to give a nonsingular control problem. It is generally seen that where state variables are chosen as descriptors of behaviour and control variables as descriptors of geometry or materials, the problem is of a nonsingular control form. Where, however, the variables are chosen to satisfy the mathematics alone without regard to the physical significance of the variables, the problem is often of a singular control form.

9.3.2 Minimum Mass Design for Specified Fundamental Frequency

Consider the minimum mass design of a one dimensional member exhibiting elasticity only in shear. The member is constrained to a prescribed fundamental frequency and in geometry.

For states chosen as $x_1 \triangleq w(y)$ (deflection), $x_2 \triangleq \mathrm{d}w(y)/\mathrm{d}y$ (slope) and $x_3 \triangleq h^*(y)$ (structural thickness) and control $u \triangleq \mathrm{d}h^*(y)/\mathrm{d}y$, the

Hamiltonian becomes,

$$H = -x_3 + \lambda_1 x_2 - \frac{\lambda_2}{x_3}\left[ux_2 + \frac{\rho}{G}\,\omega_f^2(\delta_1 x_3 + \delta_2)x_1\right] + \lambda_3 u + \zeta(x_3 - h_0^*)$$

where ζ is a Lagrange multiplier; $\zeta(y) \leq 0$ for $x_3 = h_0^*$ and $\zeta(y) = 0$ for $x_3 \geq h_0^*$. h_0^* is a minimum thickness value. G is the modulus of elasticity in shear, ρ is the density of the material, ω_f the fundamental frequency of a reference structural element, and δ_1 and δ_2 relate to structural and nonstructural parts of the thickness.

The possibility of singular control may be investigated through differentiating the coefficient of the control in the Hamiltonian. Differentiating twice (implying the order $\kappa = 1$) and setting the result to zero gives for $\zeta = 0$ and $l^2 = \rho\omega_f^2\delta_2/G$

$$u = \left[\frac{\lambda_2}{\lambda_1} - \frac{x_1}{x_2}\right]\left[k^2 x_3 + \frac{l^2}{2}\right]$$

which is the control law applicable on singular arcs. The generalized Legendre–Clebsch condition may be invoked to test for optimality

$$(-1)^1 \frac{\partial}{\partial u}\left(\frac{\mathrm{d}^2}{\mathrm{d}y^2} H_u\right) = \frac{2\lambda_1 x_2}{x_3^2}$$

which can be shown to be negative always (Carmichael 1977a). The solution for $[0, L/2]$ is thus in two parts; a nonsingular part on the state constraint ($\zeta \leq 0$) for $[0, y')$ and a singular part off the state constraint ($\zeta = 0$) for $(y', L/2]$ where $0 \leq y' \leq L/2$.

The equivalence of this problem formulation with the calculus of variations may be shown if a device of Berkovitz (1961) is used. In particular introduce a new variable x_4 according to

$$\frac{\mathrm{d}x_4}{\mathrm{d}y} \triangleq u \quad \text{and} \quad x_4(0) = 0.$$

The standard calculus of variations form for the problem follows where the system model is now interpreted as a set of side conditions. As noted in Carmichael (1977a) computations show that the Euler–Lagrange equations are of a reduced order (coefficients of the $\ddot{x}$ terms vanish), being in essence ‘degenerate’ forms of complete Euler–Lagrange equations and not having all the boundary conditions satisfied. The Weierstrass and Legendre conditions are also seen to be satisfied in a trivial sense and cannot be used to establish minimization.

9.3.3 Optimal Discs

For a turbine disc idealization of variable thickness, consider a criterion consisting of a linear combination of the natural frequencies of vibration. Constraints are on the total weight and thickness. The Hamiltonian, in the notation of de Silva (1972), is

$$\begin{aligned} H[x, u, \lambda, r] = &- \sum_{i=1}^{l} c_i p_i + \sum_{i=1}^{3} \lambda_i x_{i+1} \\ &+ \lambda_4\Bigg[\left(\frac{12(1-\nu^2)}{Ex_5^2}\rho p^2 + \frac{3n^2\nu u}{x_5 r^2} - \frac{9n^2 x_6}{x_5 r^3} + \frac{6n^2\nu x_6^2}{x_5^2 r^2} - \frac{n^2(n^2-4)}{r^4}\right)x_1 \\ &- \left(\frac{3\nu u}{x_5 r} - \frac{6n^2+3}{x_5 r^2}x_6 + \frac{6\nu x_6^2}{x_5^2 r} + \frac{2n^2+1}{r^3}\right)x_2 \\ &- \left(\frac{3u}{x_5} + \frac{6+3\nu}{x_5 r}x_6 + \frac{6x_6^2}{x_5^2} - \frac{2n^2+1}{r^2}\right)x_3 - 2\left(\frac{3}{x_5}x_6 + \frac{1}{r}\right)x_4\Bigg] \\ &+ \lambda_5 x_6 + \lambda_6 u \end{aligned}$$

where the independent variable r is a radial coordinate.

For the unconstrained region (x_5 unconstrained), the possibility of singular controls is investigated. Differentiating the coefficient of the (linearly appearing) control in the Hamiltonian, the order (κ) may be shown to be two.

A non-singular formulation for the problem may be achieved if the state is reduced to four variables and the control defined as the thickness. This implies not expanding the derivatives in the original governing equation (de Silva 1972, equation (8)).

The 'dual' problem to the above involves a criterion of weight with constraints on the natural frequencies of vibration and on the stresses. The problem is described in de Silva (1970) and Carmichael (1977a, b). The possibility of singular controls arises not from the choice of the radial and tangential stresses (σ_r and σ_θ) as states but from the thickness of the disc (h) as a state leaving dh/dr as the control. The Hamiltonian for one version of this problem, after Carmichael (1977b) is

$$\begin{aligned} H = -2\pi\rho r h - \frac{\lambda_1}{h}\left[\sigma_r u + \frac{h}{r}(\sigma_r - \sigma_\theta) + \rho\omega^2 r h\right] \\ + \lambda_2\left[\frac{(\sigma_r - \sigma_\theta)}{r} - \frac{\nu}{h}\sigma_r u - \nu\rho\omega^2 r\right] + \lambda_3 u. \end{aligned}$$

The problem is singular of order one.

The choice of behaviour quantities as states and geometry properties as a control yields a nonsingular formulation.

9.3.4 Optimization of a Plate on an Elastic Foundation

Consider the optimization of a plate on an elastic foundation. Using a lumped parameter formulation equivalent to Szefer (1971) and section 7.5, the Hamiltonian is

$$H = -x_1^2 + \lambda_1 x_2 + \lambda_2 x_3 + \lambda_3 x_4 + \lambda_4\left(\frac{q}{D} - \frac{k}{D}x_1\right)$$

where the states are the beam deflection and its three successive derivatives with respect to the independent variable. q is the applied loading, k is the foundation coefficient (control variable) and D is the beam rigidity.

The control takes the values

$$\hat{k} = \begin{cases} k_{\min} & \text{for} \quad \sigma < 0 \\ k_{\max} & \text{for} \quad \sigma > 0 \end{cases}$$

where $k_{\max}$ and $k_{\min}$ are upper and lower admissible values on the foundation coefficient.

Where $\sigma = -\lambda_4 x_1/D$ takes on zero values, the possibility of singular controls should be investigated. For $\kappa = 2$,

$$k = \frac{D}{2x_1\lambda_4}\left(-2x_1^2 - 4\lambda_1 x_2 + 6\lambda_2 x_3 - 4\lambda_3 x_4 + \frac{\lambda_4 q}{D}\right)$$

and the generalized Legendre–Clebsch condition becomes

$$(-1)^2\left(-\frac{1}{D}\left(-\frac{2x_1\lambda_4}{D}\right)\right) = \frac{2x_1\lambda_4}{D^2} \leq 0.$$

This implies that the singular control forms part of the optimal solution, coupled with k lying on its constraint boundaries.

9.3.5 Optimal Vibrating Plates

The optimal design problem for vibrating plates with frequency constraints has singular control formulations exhibited in all three canonical distributed parameter types (section 8.4). Such problems, however, because they are linear homogeneous in the displacement, may be solved directly and conventional singular control arguments may be avoided. The direct solution follows from noting a characteristic relationship between the states and costates. The solution coincides with the sufficient conditions for optimality of Prager (Prager 1968, 1969, Prager and Taylor 1968) derived on an energy basis. Consider the lumped parameter equivalent of section 8.4.

For the nonsingular control formulation, the Hamiltonian is

$$H = -u^{1/3} + \lambda_1 x_2 + \lambda_2 \frac{x_3}{u} + \lambda_3 x_4 + \lambda_4 e^2 u^{1/3} x_1$$

where the states are deflection (W), slope, bending moment and shear force and the control is the flexural rigidity.

The relationship between the states and costates is of the form

$$\begin{bmatrix}\lambda_1\\ \lambda_2\\ \lambda_3\\ \lambda_4\end{bmatrix} = A\begin{bmatrix}0 & 0 & 0 & 1\\ 0 & 0 & -1 & 0\\ 0 & 1 & 0 & 0\\ -1 & 0 & 0 & 0\end{bmatrix}\begin{bmatrix}x_1\\ x_2\\ x_3\\ x_4\end{bmatrix}$$

where A is some constant, giving the optimal rigidity as

$$D^{-2/3} = \frac{3A\left(\dfrac{d^2W}{dy^2}\right)^2}{[1 + Ae^2W^2]}$$

This is a necessary condition for optimality. Using the energy arguments of Prager (1968, 1969), this result can also be shown to be a sufficient condition for optimality.

For a singular control formulation of the same problem

$$H = -x_5^{1/3} + \lambda_1 x_2 + \lambda_2 x_3 + \lambda_3 x_4 - \frac{\lambda_4}{x_5}[ux_3 + 2x_6x_4 - e^2x_5^{1/3}x_1] + \lambda_5 x_6 + \lambda_6 u$$

where the states are deflection and its three successive derivatives with respect to the independent variable y, and rigidity and its first derivative with respect to y while the control is the second derivative of the rigidity.

The relationship between the states and costates in this case is

$$\begin{bmatrix}\lambda_1\\ \lambda_2\\ \lambda_3\\ \lambda_4\\ \lambda_5\\ \lambda_6\end{bmatrix} = B\begin{bmatrix}\dfrac{d}{dy}(x_5x_3)\\ -x_5x_3\\ x_5x_2 - x_1x_6\\ -x_5x_1\\ x_2x_3 - x_1x_4\\ -x_1x_3\end{bmatrix}$$

and this maintains the coefficient of the control in the Hamiltonian, $\sigma = (\partial H/\partial u) = (-\lambda_4 x_3/x_5) + \lambda_6$, zero along the singular solution. B is some constant.

The same result for the rigidity evolves in this case.

The generalized Legendre–Clebsch condition becomes ($\kappa = 2$)

$$\frac{-2B}{D}\left\{\left(\frac{d^2W}{dy^2}\right)^2 - \frac{1}{9B}(1 + Be^2W^2)D^{-2/3}\right\} < 0 \quad \text{for all} \quad y.$$

9.4 NOTES, COMMENTS AND BIBLIOGRAPHY

[9.1] The occurrence of singular control formulations in optimal structural design is noted in Carmichael (1977a, 1977b, 1978b), Carmichael and Goh (1977) and Carmichael and Clyde (1980).

In the control literature, Bell and Jacobson (1975) collects together the contributions to singular control theory. An early exploratory article was by Johnson (1965). Gabasov and Kirillova (1972), Bell (1975) and Jacobson (1971) give reviews. See also Bryson and Ho (1969).

[9.2] See Bell and Jacobson (1975), Johnson (1965), Gabasov and Kirillova (1972, 1976), Bell (1975) and Jacobson (1971) for reviews as well as the generalized Legendre–Clebsch condition for the case of scalar control (Kelley *et al*. 1966) and vector control (Goh 1966b, 1973).

For singular control formulations where the Hamiltonian is not linear in the control, see Kelley *et al*. (1966).

Bell and Jacobson (1975) outline Jacobson's necessary condition and sufficiency conditions for optimality.

A totally singular control function u satisfies $H_u = 0$ for all $y \in [y^L, y^R]$. A partially singular control function satisfies $H_u = 0$ only over subintervals of $[y^L, y^R]$ called singularity intervals.

The formulation given in Section 9.2 is for problems of the form (OD). Bell and Jacobson (1975) reference works related to problems (D) while Jacobson (1971) considers the linear-quadratic problem. For distributed parameter singular control see Seinfeld and Lapidus (1968). There are inherent difficulties in translating the lumped parameter conditions to the distributed parameter case. For the present it seems that the problem of singular solutions in the design of distributed parameter systems can only be handled by alluding to the equivalent finite dimensional problem.

Transformations are available for converting singular optimal control problems to nonsingular ones. See, for example, Kelley *et al*. (1966) and Goh (1966b) for the early development in singular optimal control theory. The state dimension may or may not change under the transformation.

Other publications on singular optimal control of interest are Goh (1966a, 1967, 1969), Snow (1965), and Speyer and Jacobson (1971).

[9.3] The problem of the minimum mass design for specified fundamental frequency is outlined in Armand (1971) and Armand (1972, pp. 26–79), with the suggested state equations given on pp. 13–14 and Appendix 1 of Armand (1972). The lumped parameter equivalent problem is given here.

The results for the distributed parameter case are shown by Armand (1972) to satisfy the sufficient conditions for optimality obtained from the energy arguments of Prager (1968, 1969). Armand uses a self-adjoint property of the optimization equations and avoids solving the necessary conditions for optimality in the conventional manner.

The problem of the optimal vibrational modes of a disc is given in de Silva (1972).

The problem of the minimum weight of a rotating disc is given in de Silva (1970) and Carmichael (1977b).

The problem of the optimization of a plate on an elastic foundation is given in Szefer (1971).

The original formulation of the problem of optimal vibrating plates is given in Armand (1972). A related exercise using a steepest descent algorithm is given in Haug *et al.* (1972). Carmichael and Goh (1977) develop the problem in both singular and nonsingular control senses. See section 8.4.

For the fixed and simply supported boundary condition cases the optimal result reflects a constancy of energy characteristic ('conservation of Lagrangian density', Ashley and McIntosh 1969).

The simplifying relationship between the state and costate appears peculiar to homogeneous problems of the above form and a complete generalization does not appear possible. The approach holds for simply supported and fixed boundary conditions but not free edges, agreeing in scope with the results of Prager.

Chapter **10**

Multicriteria Optimization

10.1 INTRODUCTION

The problem where several requirements are asked of an optimal design, such as extrema of cost, reliability, stiffness, deflection, weight, aesthetics, . . ., is termed a multicriteria (multiobjective, multigoal) optimization problem or vector optimization problem. The criteria may be expressed in the same units (commensurable) or in different units (noncommensurable). This is a fundamental problem in structural design although historically the single criterion or scalar optimization problem is the one which has been given the most attention; sensitivity studies have sometimes been used to augment the single criterion approach and to treat judgement based and hard to quantify criteria.

Multicriteria problems may be formulated for optimization problems dealing with all system types (algebraic, differential and difference) but for explanation purposes and computational purposes, that relating to algebraic models is the most suitable. In particular the multicriteria version of problems (A) is

$$\begin{aligned} &\min J = G(x) \\ &\text{subject to} \qquad h_j(x) \le 0 \qquad j = 1, 2, \ldots, m \end{aligned} \tag{A2$'$}$$

where $x = (x_1, \ldots, x_n)^{\mathrm{T}}$, and $(J =)\ G = (G_1, \ldots, G_N)^{\mathrm{T}}$ is a vector of optimality criteria. Typically $n \gg N$ for most problems. Denote the feasible set of values for x, as determined by the constraints, as $X = \{x;\ h_j(x) \le 0, j = 1, \ldots, m\}$.

The computations may be viewed in the space of the variables $x(E^n)$ or in the space defined by the criteria (E^N).

The solution which gives the minimum value to each of the criteria simultaneously is termed the *optimum solution* or *superior solution* and in general it will not exist. To circumvent this the concept of *Pareto optimum solutions, noninferior solutions, nondominated solutions* or *efficient solutions* is introduced. Such solutions have the property whereby no decrease can be obtained in any of the criteria without causing a simultaneous increase in at least one of the other criteria. They are in general nonunique.

The *best* or *preferred* solution is the Pareto optimum solution chosen as the final solution. Some criterion for choice is required. In this regard *utility function* (or *social preference*, or *social welfare function*) ideas are useful, where broadly a utility function may be regarded as a monotonic decreasing function of the problem criteria. The concept of *indifference* or *isopreference surfaces*, which are surfaces of equal utility, may also be used. The choice of the preferred solution involves subjective interaction between the designer and the Pareto optimum solutions.

Multicriteria optimization problems may be converted to single criterion problems

(i) by formulating a compound criterion using penalty function or Lagrange multiplier ideas,
(ii) by solving for each criterion individually and trading off all the solutions, or
(iii) by interpreting all but one of the criteria as constraints.

These ideas are employed in differing ways in the various multicriteria methodologies in an attempt to handle the vector problem and generate Pareto optimum solutions from which the preferred solution may be extracted. The developed theory of multicriteria optimization has added significance for the treatment of hard-to-quantify criteria and noncommensurable criteria.

The following section outlines the principles behind many of the various existing approaches to the multicriteria problem. One approach, a constraint approach, is developed for illustration purposes particularly to show the generation of Pareto optimum solutions; a frame design is used as a numerical example. Notes are given on the extension of the approach to problems involving differential equation systems. The constraint approach selects one criterion and constrains the remaining criteria to certain levels. The Lagrange multipliers associated with the criteria treated as constraints, are either zero or nonzero. The latter implies the constraint is active and hence the constraint influences the optimum solution. It can be shown that the nonzero Lagrange multipliers are associated with the Pareto optimum set of solutions.

10.2 SOLUTION BASES

10.2.1 General

A discussion of the available solution methodologies can be done according to the following classification; namely whether a composite single criterion, a single criterion with constraints, or many single criteria are the *basis* for the approach. Overlapping of, combinations of and connections between many of the approaches is present. Certain approaches require subjective *a priori* statements on the part of the designer. Additionally there are methodologies of an interactive nature and methodologies based on game theory ideas and decision theory under uncertainty. Both numerical algorithms and necessary and sufficient conditions for optimality use these bases as a starting point for their development.

10.2.2 Basis: A Combined Single Criterion

Various forms of a composite single criterion exist

(a)

$$\begin{aligned} &\min J = \| G(x) - \tilde{G} \| \\ &\text{subject to} \quad x \in X \end{aligned} \tag{10.1}$$

where $\tilde{G}$ denotes an *a priori* set goal (*goal programming*) and $\| \,.\, \|$ any suitable norm such as the absolute value of the deviations. Using a least square norm and $\tilde{G}_i$ as the minimum value of G_i considered alone leads to the *mean square approach* which gives a Pareto optimum solution.

(b) A weighted version of (a),

$$\begin{aligned} &\min J = \| G(x) - \tilde{G} \|_w \\ &\text{subject to} \quad x \in X \end{aligned} \tag{10.2}$$

where emphasis can be placed on some criteria relative to others. The weights are often normalized.

(c) The individual criteria may be weighted directly according to their relative importance (*parametric approach*) to give

$$\begin{aligned} &\min J = \sum_{i=1}^{N} w_i G_i(x) \\ &\text{subject to} \quad x \in X. \end{aligned} \tag{10.3}$$

The weighting coefficients w_i may be varied to get different solutions (Pareto optimum). The choice of weights is often subjective. This implies linear and additive utilities.

(d) If a *utility function* (a monotonic decreasing function of the various criteria) can be found which commensurates the various criteria, this gives the preferred solution directly (by maximization of the utility function). The idea of a utility associates some value to each G_i. It is often assumed that the utility for each criterion is additive to and independent of the values for the other criteria. The alternative is to use an *indifference function* which uses an ordinal comparison between criteria or preference of one criterion over another.

10.2.3 Basis: A Single Criterion Together with Constraints

A variation on approach (b) in section 10.2.2 is the *goal attainment method* which solves the problem

$$\begin{aligned} &\min J = z \\ &\text{subject to} \quad G(x) - wz \leq \tilde{G} \\ &\qquad\qquad\qquad w > 0 \\ &\qquad\qquad\qquad x \in X \end{aligned} \tag{10.4}$$

where w is a vector of weights, z is a scalar. The term wz indicates how closely $\tilde{G}$ is attained. z is obtained during the process of solution. As in the mean square approach, varying w gives Pareto optimum solutions.

Alternatively maximum values $\varepsilon_2, \varepsilon_3, \ldots, \varepsilon_N$ for the $N-1$ criteria $G_2, G_3, \ldots, G_N$ can be specified *a priori* and the following problem solved (*a constraint approach*) to give the preferred solution

$$\begin{aligned} &\min J = G_1(x) \\ &\text{subject to} \quad G_j(x) \leq \varepsilon_j \qquad j = 2, 3, \ldots, N \\ &\qquad\qquad\quad x \in X. \end{aligned} \tag{10.5}$$

G_1 may be chosen as any of the N criteria. The ε_j may be varied to get different solutions (Pareto optimum). This approach implies a constant utility for $G_j \leqslant \varepsilon_j$, but a utility of $-\infty$ for $G_j > \varepsilon_j$.

10.2.4 Basis: Solving for Each Criterion Separately

Where the criteria are ranked, this leads to the *lexicographic approach*. The problems are solved down the line in order of criterion ranking stopping whenever a unique optimum solution is obtained.

Various *adaptive search approaches* are available for finding Pareto optimum solutions.

10.3 A CONSTRAINT APPROACH

10.3.1 General

The constraint approach, as noted above, treats each criterion in turn while setting the remaining criteria as constraints and varying the constraint bounds to generate the set of Pareto optimal values. The approach allows for the treatment of noncommensurable criteria. In effect the constraints, while reducing the set of available x to a feasible region, admit only a half space in E^N.

The constraint method is developed and illustrated below for problems type (A) (multicriteria case) and the extension is shown to problems type (OD) (multicriteria case).

10.3.2 Problems (A): Optimal Frame Example

Consider each criterion in turn with the remaining $N-1$ criteria treated as constraints. This problem may be written as

$$\begin{aligned} &\min G_i(x) \\ &\text{subject to} \quad G_j(x) \le \varepsilon_j \qquad j = 1, 2, \ldots, N \\ &\qquad\qquad\quad x \in X \qquad\qquad i \ne j \end{aligned} \tag{10.6}$$

where $\varepsilon_j = G_j(\bar{x}_j) + \Delta_j$ and $\bar{x}_j$ is the minimum value for the criterion j, and Δ_j are positive increments that are varied to obtain the complete Pareto optimal set.

Form a Lagrangian

$$L = G_i(x) + \sum_{j=1}^{N} \lambda_{ij}[G_j(x) - \varepsilon_j] + \sum_{k=1}^{m} \mu_k h_k(x) \tag{10.7}$$

where λ and μ are Lagrange multipliers. For active G_j constraints, λ_{ij} are positive and also it can be shown that

$$\lambda_{ij} = -\frac{\partial G_i(x)}{\partial G_j(x)} \,. \tag{10.8}$$

This implies that G_i improves at the expense of G_j degrading. That is active constraints give rise to Pareto optimal solutions and inactive constraints (λ_{ij} zero) to other than Pareto optimal solutions.

The constraint value may be bounded according to

$$G_{j\text{MIN}} \le \varepsilon_j \le G_{j\text{MAX}}. \tag{10.9}$$

$G_{j\text{MIN}}$ equals $G_j(\bar{x}_j)$ while $G_{j\text{MAX}}$ equals $G_j(\bar{x}_i)$ and the latter may be reasoned as follows. For any feasible solution $\bar{\bar{x}}_i \in X$

$$G_i(\bar{\bar{x}}_i) \ge G_i(\bar{x}_i). \tag{10.10}$$

If also

$$G_j(\bar{\bar{x}}_i) > G_j(\bar{x}_i) \tag{10.11}$$

the implication is that $\bar{\bar{x}}_i$ is not Pareto optimal as both G_i and G_j may be decreased, and thus $G_j(\bar{x}_i)$ represents an upper bound on ε_j.

Consider the development of the constraint method through an example of an optimal frame design with non-commensurate criteria. The problem is an extended version of the frame problem considered in section 6.4.2 without stress constraints. A complete statement is

$$\min G_1 = A$$

$$\min G_2 = \delta$$

$$\text{subject to} \quad \begin{bmatrix} M_2 \\ M_3 \\ 0 \end{bmatrix} = \begin{bmatrix} 8EI/L & 2EI/L & -6EI/L^2 \\ & 8EI/L & -6EI/L^2 \\ \text{symmetric} & & 24EI/L^3 \end{bmatrix} \begin{bmatrix} \theta_2 \\ \theta_3 \\ \delta \end{bmatrix}$$

$$\delta \le 10 \text{ mm}$$

$$A \le 3 \times 10^3 \text{ mm}^2$$

$$A \ge 0.$$

Particular values chosen for the structure and loading are: $E = 210 \times 10^3$ MPa, $L = 5000$ mm, and $\gamma = 100$ kN at the quarter point.

The criteria are of weight (or volume) and response, and are conflicting and non-commensurable.

Ignoring G_1, the solution to the single criterion minimization problem is

$$G_{2\text{MIN}} = 6.91, \qquad A = 3 \times 10^3 \text{ mm}^2, \qquad \delta = 6.91 \text{ mm}.$$

Ignoring G_2, the solution to the single criterion minimization problem is

$$G_{1\text{MIN}} = 2.49 \times 10^3, \qquad A = 2.49 \times 10^3, \qquad \delta = 10 \text{ mm}.$$

These numbers provide bounds for the ε_2 values on G_2 treated as a constraint. In particular using the latest value of δ

$$G_{2\text{MAX}} = \delta = 10.$$

This delineates the interval range of ε_2

$$G_{2\text{MIN}} \le \varepsilon_2 \le G_{2\text{MAX}}.$$

Table 10.1 summarizes the results.

ε_2	$G_1 \times 10^3$	A $\times 10^3$ mm^2	δ mm	λ_ε
10.0	2.49	2.49	10.0	0.0500
9.5	2.56	2.56	9.5	0.0526
9.0	2.63	2.63	9.0	0.0556
8.5	2.71	2.71	8.5	0.0588
8.0	2.79	2.79	8.0	0.0625
7.5	2.88	2.88	7.5	0.0667
7.0	2.98	2.98	7.0	0.0714

Table 10.1

Note that all the constraints are active, implying that all the solutions correspond to Pareto optimal solutions from which the preferred solution comes.

10.3.3 Outline—Problems (OD)

The approach applicable to problems with algebraic systems carries over to problems (OD). All concepts remain the same as for the algebraic case.

For integral criteria, it may be convenient to convert the constraint by introducing extra state variables x_{n+i}, $i = 1, \ldots, N$ where

$$\frac{\mathrm{d}x_{n+i}}{\mathrm{d}y} = G[x(y), u(y), y] \quad \text{with} \quad x_{n+i}(y^{\mathrm{L}}) = 0. \tag{10.12}$$

This increases the number of state equations but the constraint becomes more manageable in the form

$$x_{n+i}(y^{\mathrm{R}}) \leqslant \varepsilon_i. \tag{10.13}$$

Active constraints again correspond to Pareto optimum solutions.

10.4 NOTES, COMMENTS AND BIBLIOGRAPHY

[10.1] For a comment on the rationale of several criteria existing simultaneously, see Fel'dbaum (1965), the early work of Kuhn and Tucker (1951) and Zadeh (1963).

The usage of the term 'multicriterion design' by Rozvany (1976) (see also Cohn and Maier 1977, Cohn 1965 and Rozvany and Cohn 1970) is in the sense of ensuring satisfactory serviceability and safety, and is not in the same sense as used here.

Many works now exist covering the multicriteria problem. See the collection of papers in Thiriez and Zionts (1976), Leitmann (1976), Leitmann and Marzollo (1975), and Cochrane and Zeleny (1973), and the books Zeleny (1974), Haimes *et al.* (1975), Johnsen (1968) and Keeney and Raiffa (1976). See also Sage (1977), Von Neumann and Morgenstern (1953), Raiffa (1970), Raiffa and Luce (1958) and Gottfried and Weisman (1973).

For an application to optimal loading in structures see Leitmann (1977) and to some tractable structural elements and commensurable criteria see Stadler (1977a, 1978) (see also Stadler 1977b). Graphical solutions and trade off curves have been used by Bartel and Marks (1974) on the two criteria problem. Carmichael (1980) acknowledges the fundamentally multicriteria nature of structural design problems.

On Pareto optimal solutions see Kuhn and Tucker (1951). A modified definition is given there. See also Geoffrion (1968), Klinger

(1964), Reid and Citron (1971), Chu (1970) and DaCunha and Polak (1967) among others. On superior solutions see Athans and Geering (1973). The term utility is used in the sense of Haimes (1977). See also Rosenblueth (1973), Legerer (1970) and Gottfried and Weisman (1973) for a discussion of utility. The last reference also discusses 'multifactor objectives', equivalently multiple criteria grouped into a single criterion.

[10.2] For a discussion on the various multicriteria techniques see Haimes *et al*. (1975) with applications to water resources problems.

[10.3] See Haimes *et al*. (1975) and Haimes (1977).

Chapter 11

Multilevel Optimization

11.1 INTRODUCTION

Multilevel systems theory treats the decomposition of systems into subsystems. The concept of subsystems is fundamental. Multilevel optimization theory, in a similar vein, looks at the *decomposition* of a single level design problem into subproblems with interaction. *Coordination* ideas are invoked in order that the solutions to the subproblems result in the solution to the original problem.

Multilevel optimization theory has been advanced historically as a theory capable of handling complexity and large scale systems. However, it is seen to be far more general and is a fundamental approach and effective solution method to any optimization problem, although the effectiveness is more evident for large scale systems. Generally, with the current state of the art of optimization, it may be said that several small problems of low order are easier to solve than a single large problem of high order irrespective of the strength of the interaction between the subproblems. Decomposition may be chosen with a physical significance in mind or computational reasons may warrant alternative decompositions.

The coupling between subproblems prevents the direct solution of the overall problem. Instead computational schemes typically handle the coupling in an iterative fashion. The lower level (infimal level, first level) is coordinated at an upper level (supremal level, second level) in order that the solution to the original problem is obtained (Fig. 11.1). Figure 11.1 is given for a two level formulation, the extension to many levels being straightforward. At any level and for any particular subproblem, the designer has the choice of which optimization technique to use.

As outlined in Chapter 3 there are four types of possible system model decomposition.

(a) According to the organization of the model equations. This involves a partitioning of the component equations.
(b) According to an hierarchy. Such a decomposition allows for a

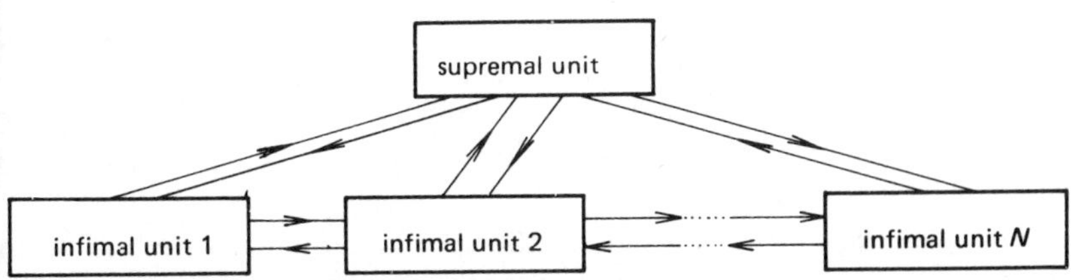

Fig. 11.1 Problem Decomposition and Interaction

convenient treatment of nonlinearities and lower level constraints at the lower levels.

(c) According to the nature and type of control. This implies a different methodology for each subsystem.

(d) Related to the y interval. Here the independent variable (whether time or space) interval is broken into subintervals. The subintervals in this case become the subsystems. This permits the treatment of problems such as continuous beam design where the discontinuities in the states occur at interval supports.

A certain overlapping may occur between the various decomposition types. A choice of the form of decomposition and the method of multilevel optimization adopted is at the discretion of the designer. In all cases a multilevel framework is obtained. Subproblems may have conflicting objectives. Decomposition types (b) and (c) do not allow general formulations, but instead vary from problem to problem, unlike (a) and (d). In general, (c) can be made to fit the other forms and so will not be considered here.

The two basic processes of multilevel optimization, namely *decomposition* (the generation of subproblems) and *coordination* (ensuring overall problem solution) are developed in section 11.2 and illustrated with examples. The decomposition ideas are given according to the previously mentioned types and may follow a logical problem composition or may be arbitrary for computational reasons. The type of coordination depends on the coordination variables that are chosen and the manner in which they are adjusted. The division of the following presentation is according to the mathematical characteristics of the system model, that is whether ordinary differential, algebraic, partial differential or difference equations are used to describe the model. Section 11.3 gives the notes, comments and bibliography on the approach.

11.2 DECOMPOSITION AND COORDINATION

11.2.1 Basic Ideas

Decomposition involves the dissection of the design problem components; namely the system into subsystems and the criterion and constraints at the system level into criteria and constraints associated with the subproblems. Interaction variables are introduced into the formulation in order to decouple the problem components and produce independent subproblems.

Coordination of the solutions of the subproblems is carried out such that the resulting solution of the multilevel problem is equivalent to the solution of the original single level problem. Coordination involves a repeated two way transfer, in an iterative fashion, between the upper and lower levels. At each transfer the interaction (interpreted in terms of coordination variables) between subproblems is gradually enforced.

In decomposing the problem components, modification is required to all components. Modification of the criterion ensures that the upper level is able to coordinate the lower level results. No modification of the system model implies the subsystems are already uncoupled yielding independent subproblems automatically. The various available coordination methodologies differ only in their usage and adjustment of the coordination variables and are popularly (though not universally) classified as interaction balance methods or interaction prediction methods. The form of decomposition adopted obviously influences the subsequent coordination strategy that may be used. Note also that, while interaction variables are introduced to decompose the problem, coordination variables are employed in the coordination process. Interaction variables may be chosen as coordination variables depending on the coordination methodology adopted.

The common steps to all coordination methodologies are as follows:

(i) From the available entities, namely system variables, interaction variables, Lagrange multipliers or penalty weights, the coordination variables may be chosen and do not necessarily have to reflect the subsystem interaction.

(ii) The independent lower level problems are solved for fixed values of the coordination variables.

(iii) The solution values for the lower level problems are used at the upper level to update the values of the coordination variables. The updating is done in some optimum fashion.

(iv) The problem returns to the lower level with new values of the coordination variables and the procedure is repeated. The lower level is coordinated by the upper level.

11.2.2 Problems (A)

11.2.2.1 DECOMPOSITION ACCORDING TO THE CONSTRUCTION OF THE MODEL

Consider the problems (A1) or (A2) where a distinction is made between the state and control variables. The problem may be written as

$$\begin{aligned} &\min J = G(x, u) \\ &\text{subject to} \quad F(x, u) = 0 \\ &\qquad\qquad\quad\; H(x, u) \leq 0 \end{aligned} \tag{11.1}$$

distinguishing between the system model and the constraints.

Interaction variables π may be introduced, where π is some general function $\gamma(x, u)$ of state and control variables (including individual states and controls as special cases) such that the criterion is separable and the subsystem models and constraints contain no common variables. That is

$$\begin{aligned} G(x, u, \pi) &= \sum_{i=1}^{N} G^i(x^i, u^i, \pi^i) \\ F^i(x^i, u^i, \pi^i) &= 0 \\ H^i(x^i, u^i, \pi^i) &\leq 0 \qquad i = 1, \ldots, N. \end{aligned} \tag{11.2}$$

The superscript denotes the relevant subsystem, N total. The interconnection relations are of the form

$$\pi^i = \gamma^i(x^j, u^j) \quad \text{all} \quad j \neq i. \tag{11.3}$$

Note that the choice of π is essentially arbitrary.

To ensure that the upper level is able to coordinate the lower levels, the interconnection relation (11.3) is adjoined to the criterion according to

$$\min J' = \sum_{i=1}^{N} \{G^i(x^i, u^i, \pi^i) + \beta^{i\mathrm{T}}[\gamma^i(x^j, u^j) - \pi^i]\} \tag{11.4}$$

where $\beta = (\beta^1, \ldots, \beta^N)^{\mathrm{T}}$ are Lagrange multipliers. Further manipulation of (11.4) is required to ensure a separable criterion. The particular coordination scheme chosen determines the form of this manipulation, as it does determine the choice of coordination variables.

Interaction balance methods select the β^i value at the upper level and this is then considered as a constant for the lower level. The interaction prediction methods select the π and β values at the upper level. Both place the $\beta^{i\mathrm{T}}\pi^i$ term in the i'th subproblem criterion with the j'th variables in the j'th subproblem criterion. [Another method referred to as a 'feasible' method—see section 11.3—chooses π^i values at the upper level and puts the terms in $\beta^{i\mathrm{T}}[\gamma^i(x^j, u^j) - \pi^i]$ associated with the j'th variables in the j'th subproblem criterion.] See Fig. 11.2.

The values of the coordination variables are adjusted between iterations, generally according to a gradient or related scheme. The use of such schemes requires a specification of the starting values and step size. Using a gradient scheme, β is updated between iterations k and

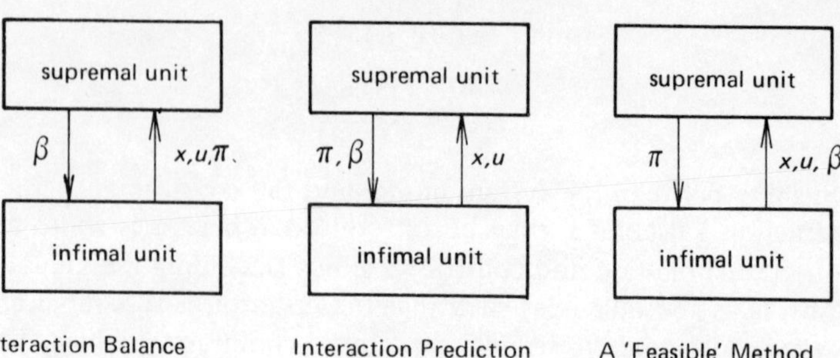

Fig. 11.2

$k + 1$ according to

$$\begin{aligned}\beta(k+1) &= \beta(k) + \Delta\beta(k) \\ &= \beta(k) + \kappa_\beta \frac{\partial L}{\partial \beta} \qquad \kappa_\beta > 0 \\ &= \beta(k) + \kappa_\beta[\gamma - \pi]\end{aligned} \tag{11.5}$$

and π according to

$$\begin{aligned}\pi(k+1) &= \pi(k) + \Delta\pi(k) \\ &= \pi(k) - \kappa_\pi \frac{\partial L}{\partial \pi} \qquad \kappa_\pi > 0\end{aligned} \tag{11.6}$$

where κ_β and κ_π are quantities to be determined and L is the Lagrangian defined by

$$L = \sum_{i=1}^{N} G^i + \sum_{i=1}^{N} \lambda^{i\mathrm{T}} F^i + \sum_{i=1}^{N} \mu^{i\mathrm{T}}(H^i - \sigma^i) + \sum_{i=1}^{N} \beta^{i\mathrm{T}}[\gamma - \pi]. \tag{11.7}$$

Here σ^i are slack variables and λ and μ are Lagrange multipliers.

Example. Consider the frame design problem of section 6.4.2 with the deflection constraint only. A convenient breakdown into subsystems is one in which the subsystems correspond to the rotations and the deflection. This essentially implies partitioning of the equations.

In subsystem one, let $\pi^1 \triangleq \delta$, and in subsystem two, let $\pi_1^2 \triangleq EI$, $\pi_2^2 \triangleq \theta_2$, and $\pi_3^2 \triangleq \theta_3$. The modified criterion becomes

$$J' = 3AL + \beta^1[\delta - \pi^1] + \beta_1^2[EI - \pi_1^2] + \beta_2^2[\theta_2 - \pi_2^2] + \beta_3^2[\theta_3 - \pi_3^2].$$

Consider the interaction balance method as an example. The subproblems are

Subproblem one: $\min J^1 = 3AL - \beta^1\pi^1 + \beta_1^2 EI + \beta_2^2\theta_2 + \beta_3^2\theta_3$

subject to $M_2 = 8EI\theta_2/L + 2EI\theta_3/L - 6EI\pi^1/L^2$

$M_3 = 2EI\theta_2/L + 8EI\theta_3/L - 6EI\pi^1/L^2$

Subproblem two: $\min J^2 = \beta^1\delta - \beta_1^2\pi_1^2 - \beta_2^2\pi_2^2 - \beta_3^2\pi_3^2$

$$\text{subject to} \quad 0 = -6\pi_1^2\pi_2^2/L^2 - 6\pi_1^2\pi_3^2/L^2 + 24\pi_1^2\delta/L$$
$$\delta \leq \delta_{\text{allowable}}.$$

The interaction balance method fixes the values of β at the second level. The solutions of the subproblems then return values for A (or I), δ, θ_2, θ_3 and π to the second level. At the second level β is updated in such a fashion that δ approaches π^1, EI approaches π_1^2, θ_2 approaches π_2^2 and θ_3 approaches π_3^2 in value. The process is then repeated.

An alternative formulation of the problem and decomposition is given in the literature for the case where the interaction variables appear in the problem formulation at the outset such that for problem (A2), the x vector may be partitioned directly according to $x = (\pi^{\mathrm{T}}, X^{\mathrm{T}})^{\mathrm{T}}$ where $X = (X^{1\mathrm{T}}, \ldots, X^{N\mathrm{T}})^{\mathrm{T}}$. Superscripts again denote the relevant subsystem. The problem becomes

$$\begin{aligned} &\min J = G(\pi, X) = \sum_{i=1}^{N} G^i(\pi^i, X^i) \\ &\text{subject to} \quad h^i(\pi, X^i) \leq 0 \qquad\qquad i = 1, \ldots, N. \end{aligned} \tag{11.8}$$

That is the problem is immediately decomposable into subproblems through the recognition of certain variables as interaction variables. (Note there is a requirement for π to occur in G for the feasible method described below. Note also that the problem is essentially at the lower level at the outset.)

For a feasible (model coordination) method, the iterations start by the second (upper) level fixing values for the coordination variables π, say $\pi = \pi_0$. The first (lower) level then solves the problem

$$\begin{aligned} &\min J^i = G^i(\pi_0^i, X^i) \\ &\text{subject to} \quad h^i(\pi_0, X^i) \leq 0 \qquad i = 1, \ldots, N. \end{aligned} \tag{11.9}$$

The calculations return values for X^i to the second level; defining

$$H^i(\pi_0^i) = \min J^i \tag{11.10}$$

and

$$H(\pi_0) = \sum_{i=1}^{N} H^i(\pi_0^i) = \sum_{i=1}^{N} \min J^i \tag{11.11}$$

the second level problem becomes one in finding π_0 that minimizes $H(\pi_0)$ while observing any constraints present on π_0. Gradient or similar methods as before may be used for this minimization problem. The problem transfers again to the first level with the new value for π_0, and so on for other iterations.

The terminology 'model coordination' derives from the coordination variables being chosen primarily to decompose the system model and in the computations given as a fixed constraint on the model. All values of π and X throughout the iterations are feasible. Solutions intermediate in the iterations are feasible yet suboptimal.

For a nonfeasible (goal coordination) method, the values of the interaction variables π are no longer supplied by the second level, but rather the values for π are allowed to differ between subsystems; that is the subsystems are decoupled. At the optimum it is required that the values for π be the same between subsystems and hence no feasible solution is obtained for iterations short of the optimum. For the i'th subsystem the relevant variables are $x^i = [\pi^{i\mathrm{T}}, X^{i\mathrm{T}}]^{\mathrm{T}}$ where X^{a} and X^{b} denote different variables, but π^{a} and π^{b} denote the same variables though with different values. At the optimum it is required that

$$\pi^{\mathrm{a}} - \pi^{\mathrm{b}} = 0. \tag{11.12}$$

This may be regarded as a constraint and adjoined to the criterion by means of Lagrange multipliers β to give

$$J' = \sum_{i=1}^{N} G^i(\pi^i, X^i) + \beta^{\mathrm{T}}(\pi^{\mathrm{a}} - \pi^{\mathrm{b}}). \tag{11.13}$$

This may be written as

$$J' = \sum_{i=1}^{N} \{G^i(\pi^i, X^i) + \beta^{i\mathrm{T}}\pi^i\} \tag{11.14}$$

where β^i is a vector of components of β.

The computations involve values for β being determined at the upper level and π being treated as an extra unknown at the first level. The term goal coordination derives from the fact that the manipulation of the first level criteria provides the coordination at the first level.

11.2.2.2 DECOMPOSITION ACCORDING TO HIERARCHY

Decompositions based on an hierarchical organization of the system follow no general mathematical format, the decomposition being peculiar to every problem. The only generality that can be used is that on decomposing a constitutive relationship, which is the model at the upper level, the lower level model will also be a constitutive relationship and the interaction between subsystems will be equilibrium and compatibility. Obviously general mathematical relationships could be used to describe this decomposition for certain structure types such as rigid framed structures, trusses and so on. This form of decomposition highlights and enables the straightforward treatment of nonlinearities and constraints that arise at subsystem levels, such as for example, stress constraints in a member or structure level problem.

Example. Consider the frame design problem of section 6.4.2. The problem, considering both deflection and stress constraints is

$$\min J = 3AL$$

$$\text{subject to} \quad \begin{bmatrix} M_2 \\ M_3 \\ 0 \end{bmatrix} = \begin{bmatrix} 8EI/L & 2EI/L & -6EI/L^2 \\ & 8EI/L & -6EI/L^2 \\ \text{symmetric} & & 24EI/L^3 \end{bmatrix} \begin{bmatrix} \theta_2 \\ \theta_3 \\ \delta \end{bmatrix}$$

$$\delta \leq \delta_{\text{allowable}}$$

$$[-6EI\delta/L^2 + 2EI\theta_2/L]/Z \leq \sigma_{\text{allowable}}$$

$$[2EI\theta_2/L + 4EI\theta_3/L]/Z \leq \sigma_{\text{allowable}}$$

where the equality constraint is the constitutive relationship for the structure.

Choosing the three members as the subsystems, then their relevant constitutive relationships and interaction (compatibility and equilibrium) are respectively

$$\begin{bmatrix} M_{12} \\ M_{21} \\ M_{23} \\ M_{32} \\ M_{34} \\ M_{43} \end{bmatrix} = \begin{bmatrix} 4EI/L & 2EI/L & & & & \\ & 4EI/L & & & & \\ & & 4EI/L & 2EI/L & & \\ & & & 4EI/L & & \\ & & & & 4EI/L & 2EI/L \\ \text{symmetric} & & & & & 4EI/L \end{bmatrix} \begin{bmatrix} \phi_{12} \\ \phi_{21} \\ \phi_{23} \\ \phi_{32} \\ \phi_{34} \\ \phi_{43} \end{bmatrix}$$

or $F = k\delta$

$$\begin{bmatrix} \phi_{12} \\ \phi_{21} \\ \phi_{23} \\ \phi_{32} \\ \phi_{34} \\ \phi_{43} \end{bmatrix} = \begin{bmatrix} 0 & 0 & -1/L \\ 1 & 0 & -1/L \\ 1 & 0 & 0 \\ 0 & 1 & 0 \\ 0 & 1 & -1/L \\ 0 & 0 & -1/L \end{bmatrix} \begin{bmatrix} \theta_2 \\ \theta_3 \\ \delta \end{bmatrix}$$

or $\delta = A_* \Delta$

$$\begin{bmatrix} M_2 \\ M_3 \\ 0 \end{bmatrix} = \begin{bmatrix} 0 & 1 & 1 & 0 & 0 & 0 \\ 0 & 0 & 0 & 1 & 1 & 0 \\ -1/L & -1/L & 0 & 0 & -1/L & -1/L \end{bmatrix} \begin{bmatrix} M_{12} \\ M_{21} \\ M_{23} \\ M_{32} \\ M_{34} \\ M_{43} \end{bmatrix}$$

or $R = A_*^{\mathrm{T}} F$

where the M's and ϕ's are the member end moments and rotations respectively.

The modification of the criterion involves adjoining the interaction relations to give

$$J' = J + \beta_c^{\mathrm{T}}[A_*\overline{\Delta} - \delta] + \beta_e^{\mathrm{T}}[A_*^{\mathrm{T}}F - R]$$

where β_c and β_e are vector Lagrange multipliers.

Considering the interaction balance method or the interaction prediction method, the subproblem associated with the beam for example, becomes

$$\min J^2 = AL + \beta_{c2}[\theta_2] + \beta_{c3}[\theta_2 - \phi_{23}] + \beta_{c4}[-\phi_{32}]$$
$$+ \beta_{e1}[M_{23} - M_2] + \beta_{e2}[M_{32}]$$

$$\text{subject to} \quad \begin{bmatrix} M_{23} \\ M_{32} \end{bmatrix} = \begin{bmatrix} 4EI/L & 2EI/L \\ 2EI/L & 4EI/L \end{bmatrix} \begin{bmatrix} \phi_{23} \\ \phi_{32} \end{bmatrix}$$

$$[2EI\phi_{23}/L + 4EI\phi_{32}/L]/Z \le \sigma_{\text{allowable}}.$$

Other formulations can be given.

11.2.3 Problems (OD)

11.2.3.1 DECOMPOSITION ACCORDING TO THE CONSTRUCTION OF THE MODEL

Consider the problem (OD1). Modification of the model involves the introduction of the terms $\pi(y)$ which may be substituted for state, control or combinations of state and control variables. They are a representation of subsystem interaction. The system equation decomposes to

$$\frac{\mathrm{d}x^i(y)}{\mathrm{d}y} = f^i[x^i(y), u^i(y), \pi^i(y), y] \qquad i = 1, 2, \ldots, N \qquad (11.15)$$

with interaction

$$\pi^i(y) = \gamma^i(x^j, u^j, y) \quad \text{all} \quad j \ne i \qquad (11.16)$$

where γ^i is some general function of the arguments shown. The superscript notation refers to the relevant subsystem, $i = 1, \ldots, N$, for N subsystems. $\pi(y) = (\pi^{1\mathrm{T}}, \ldots, \pi^{N\mathrm{T}})^{\mathrm{T}}$. The notation x^i, u^i, π^i, and γ^i in general refers to vectors; that is groups of state variables x_l may be implied in the notation x^i, and similarly for u^i, π^i and γ^i.

Modification of the criterion is undertaken in two parts. Initially the interconnection relationship (11.16) is adjoined to the original criterion

$$J' = g[x(y), y]\Big|_{y=y^{\mathrm{L}}}^{y=y^{\mathrm{R}}} + \int_{y^{\mathrm{L}}}^{y^{\mathrm{R}}} \Big\{ G[x(y), u(y), y] + \sum_{i=1}^{N} \beta^{i\mathrm{T}}(y)[\pi^i(y) - \gamma^i(x^j, u^j, y)] \Big\} \mathrm{d}y \qquad (11.17)$$

where $\beta(y) = (\beta^1, \ldots, \beta^N)^{\mathrm{T}}$ are Lagrange multipliers.

Consider the decomposition further in the manner in which it is associated with the interaction balance and interaction prediction methods. The following assumption is made and can usually be satisfied in most cases because of the usually simple nature of π.

$$\gamma^i(x^j, u^j, y) = \sum_{j \neq i}^{N} \gamma^{ij}(x^j, u^j, y). \qquad (11.18)$$

Then

$$\sum_{i=1}^{N} \beta^{i\mathrm{T}}[\pi^i - \gamma^i(x^j, u^j, y)] = \sum_{i=1}^{N} \beta^{i\mathrm{T}}\Big[\pi^i - \sum_{j\neq i}^{N} \gamma^{ij}(x^j, u^j, y)\Big]$$
$$= \sum_{i=1}^{N} \Big\{ \beta^{i\mathrm{T}}\pi^i - \sum_{j\neq i}^{N} \beta^{j\mathrm{T}}\gamma^{ji}(x^i, u^i, y) \Big\}. \qquad (11.19)$$

Thus separate optimality criteria may be written for each subproblem if it can be assumed that the criterion components g and G are separable of the form

$$g = \sum_{i=1}^{N} g^i[x^i, y] \quad \text{and} \quad G = \sum_{i=1}^{N} G^i(x^i, u^i, y) \qquad (11.20)$$

to give

$$J^i = g^i[x^i, y]\Big|_{y=y^{\mathrm{L}}}^{y=y^{\mathrm{R}}} + \int_{y^{\mathrm{L}}}^{y^{\mathrm{R}}} \Big\{ G^i(x^i, u^i, y) + \beta^{i\mathrm{T}}\pi^i - \sum_{j\neq i}^{N} \beta^{j\mathrm{T}}\gamma^{ji}(x^i, u^i, y) \Big\} \mathrm{d}y. \qquad (11.21)$$

The subproblems are given by (11.15) and (11.21). Where constraints are also present in the original problem, a separable form has to also apply such that constraints of the form

$$h[x(y), u(y), y] \lesseqgtr 0 \qquad (11.22)$$

become

$$h^i[x^i, u^i, y] \lesseqgtr 0 \qquad i = 1, \ldots, N. \tag{11.23}$$

The interaction variables π may be freely chosen to give the desired separability property for the criterion and constraints.

The Hamiltonian for each subproblem is

$$H^i = G^i + \lambda^{i\mathrm{T}} f^i + \beta^{i\mathrm{T}} \pi^i - \sum_{j \neq i}^{N} \beta^{j\mathrm{T}} \gamma^{ji} \tag{11.24}$$

where

$$H = \sum_{i=1}^{N} H^i. \tag{11.25}$$

The subproblems may be solved using any of the techniques in Chapters 6, 7 or 8 once certain of the variables λ, β, π or u are known. Coordination schemes are distinguished by the variables chosen as coordination variables. For example interaction balance methods (nonfeasible methods) choose β at the upper level, while interaction prediction methods (combined methods) β and π. (Other methods such as costate coordination choose λ, control coordination u and feasible methods choose π.) The iterations on the coordination variables at the second level may be done by gradient or related or other methods. Where π appears as a control type variable in the subproblems (interaction balance methods), it occurs linearly and the possibility of singular optimal control has to be checked. Alternatively the interaction relation may be expressed in a quadratic form or else a feasible-type penalty function approach may be used.

Consider various updating schemes. A gradient scheme updates β and π according to

$$\beta_j(y)\bigg|_{k+1} = \beta_j(y)\bigg|_k + \kappa_{\beta_j}\bigg|_k \frac{\partial H}{\partial \beta_j} \qquad \kappa_{\beta_j}\bigg|_k > 0 \tag{11.26}$$

$$\pi_j(y)\bigg|_{k+1} = \pi_j(y)\bigg|_k - \kappa_{\pi_j}\bigg|_k \frac{\partial H}{\partial \pi_j} \qquad \kappa_{\pi_j}\bigg|_k > 0. \tag{11.27}$$

These results are similar to the algebraic case. The designer is still required to choose κ.

An equality updating scheme gives

$$\begin{gathered}\pi^i(y) = \gamma^i(x^j, u^j) \qquad j \neq i \\ \sum_{j \neq i}^{N} \frac{\partial}{\partial x^i} [f^{jT}(x^j, u^j, \gamma^j(x^i, u^i), y)] \lambda^j = -\sum_{j \neq i}^{N} \frac{\partial}{\partial x^i} [\gamma^{ji\mathrm{T}}(x^i, u^i)] \beta^j \\ i = 1, 2, \ldots, N\end{gathered} \tag{11.28}$$

which is based on a comparison of the solution to the original problem and the solutions to the subproblems with coordination.

Example: the design of a lumped mass system. Consider a two degree of freedom frame with rigid girders (Fig. 11.3) subjected to ground motion. The equations of motion are

$$m_1\ddot{w}_1 + k_1w_1 - k_2(w_2 - w_1) - c_{11}\dot{w}_1 = -m_1\ddot{w}_g$$
$$m_2\ddot{w}_2 + k_2(w_2 - w_1) - c_{22}\dot{w}_2 = -m_2\ddot{w}_g$$

together with appropriate boundary conditions.

Consider constraints of the general form

$$h_1(w_1) \leq 0 \qquad h_2(w_2) \leq 0$$
$$h_3(k_1) \leq 0 \qquad h_4(k_2) \leq 0$$

and a criterion

$$(\min) J = k_1 + k_2$$

k_1 and k_2 represent stiffnesses, and c_{11} and c_{22} damping constants.

The single level problem is now decomposed into subproblems associated with subsystems. The subproblems when solved give the solution to the original problem. The obvious subsystems to choose are those associated with each mass where the interconnection relationships are very simple (the coupling is provided by the terms containing k_2) although other subsystems could be chosen. In state equation form, where the states are position and velocity and the controls are stiffnesses, the subsystem models are;

Subsystem 1

$$\dot{x}_1 = x_2$$
$$\dot{x}_2 = \frac{1}{m_1}[-u_1x_1 + \pi_1(\pi_2 - x_1) + c_{11}x_2 - m_1\ddot{w}_g].$$

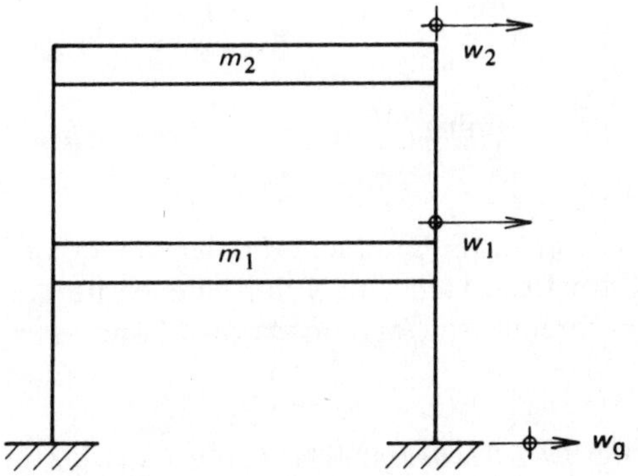

Fig. 11.3

Subsystem 2

$$\dot{x}_3 = x_4$$
$$\dot{x}_4 = \frac{1}{m_2}[-u_2(x_3 - \pi_3) + c_{22}x_4 - m_2\ddot{w}_g]$$

with interconnection relationships

$$\pi^1 = (\pi_1, \pi_2)^{\mathrm{T}} = (u_2, x_3)^{\mathrm{T}}$$
$$\pi^2 = (\pi_3) = (x_1).$$

Since the constraints and the criterion are in a form which allows a part of the constraints and a part of the criterion respectively to be associated with each subsystem, the subproblems become,

Subproblem 1

subsystem model $\dot{x}_1 = x_2$

$$\dot{x}_2 = \frac{1}{m_1}[-u_1x_1 + \pi_1(\pi_2 - x_1) + c_{11}x_2 - m_1\ddot{w}_g]$$

constraints $h_1(x_1) \leq 0 \quad h_3(u_1) \leq 0$

criterion $(\min)\, J^1 = u_1 + \int_{t_0}^{t_f} \left\{ [\beta_1 \beta_2] \begin{bmatrix} \pi_1 \\ \pi_2 \end{bmatrix} - \beta_3 x_1 \right\} \mathrm{d}t.$

Subproblem 2

subsystem model $\dot{x}_3 = x_4$

$$\dot{x}_4 = \frac{1}{m_2}[-u_2(x_3 - \pi_3) + c_{22}x_4 - m_2\ddot{w}_g]$$

constraints $h_2(x_3) \leq 0 \quad h_4(u_2) \leq 0$

criterion $(\min)\, J^2 = u_2 + \int_{t_0}^{t_f} \left\{ \beta_3 \pi_3 - [\beta_1 \beta_2] \begin{bmatrix} u_2 \\ x_3 \end{bmatrix} \right\} \mathrm{d}t.$

Using, for example, the interaction balance method, the subproblems may be solved for fixed values of β during each iteration cycle while for the interaction prediction method both β and π are fixed for the subproblems.

Example: the design of a beam. The beam equation in first order form may be written as

$$\frac{dw}{dy} = \theta$$

$$\frac{d\theta}{dy} = \frac{M}{EI}$$

$$\frac{dM}{dy} = S$$

$$\frac{dS}{dy} = q$$

where w, θ, M, S and q are the deflection, slope, bending moment, shear force and distributed load respectively. Suitable boundary conditions have to also be specified.

Consider the criterion of minimizing the flexural rigidity

$$(\min) J = \int_0^L EI \, dy$$

and constraints related to deflections.

Choose 'contrived' subsystems of equilibrium type relationships and compatibility type relationships. The subproblems then involve solving an equilibrium type problem and a compatibility type problem.

Modifying the system model, the subsystems become;

Subsystem 1 (compatibility)

$$\frac{dw}{dy} = \theta$$

$$\frac{d\theta}{dy} = \frac{\pi^1}{EI}$$

Subsystem 2 (equilibrium)

$$\frac{dM}{dy} = S$$

$$\frac{dS}{dy} = q$$

with interaction $\pi^1 = M$.

Modifying the criterion gives an augmented criterion,

$$J' = \int_0^L \{EI + \beta^1(\pi^1 - M)\} \, dy.$$

The subproblems become,

Subproblem 1

subsystem model

$$\frac{\mathrm{d}w}{\mathrm{d}y} = \theta$$

$$\frac{\mathrm{d}\theta}{\mathrm{d}y} = \frac{\pi^1}{EI}$$

criterion

$$(\min) J^1 = \int_0^L \{EI + \beta^1\pi^1\} \,\mathrm{d}y$$

constraints – related to w.

Subproblem 2

subsystem model

$$\frac{\mathrm{d}M}{\mathrm{d}y} = S$$

$$\frac{\mathrm{d}S}{\mathrm{d}y} = q$$

criterion

$$(\min) J^2 = \int_0^L \{-\beta^1 M\} \,\mathrm{d}y.$$

11.2.3.2 DECOMPOSITION ACCORDING TO HIERARCHY

For such decompositions, there is a change of magnitude and units between levels. The formulations are particular to each problem.

Consider as an illustration, the beam design problem again. The moment–curvature relationship

$$\frac{M}{EI} = \frac{1}{r}$$

is the subsystem (element level) model. Equilibrium and compatibility relationships, which are both second order differential equations, represent subsystem interaction. The subproblems, if this differential form is retained, are infinite in number. If an equivalent difference form is used then the solution methodology follows section 11.2.2.2.

11.2.3.3 DECOMPOSITION OF THE y INTERVAL

The ideas of decomposition according to the construction of the model, and the associated coordination extend straightforwardly to the case where decomposition is applied to the independent variable interval. The decompositions in this case yield subintervals as the 'subsystems' and the junctions of subintervals are logically chosen at discontinuities, for example, in the model, state variables or the criterion. Following the format of the earlier multilevel optimization, the subproblems are solved independently and coordinated at a higher level.

Consider problem (OD1) with an integral criterion only and without control constraints. Assume that a discontinuity occurs in the model, state or criterion at $y = y'$, given by

$$\psi(x(y'), y') = 0 \tag{11.29}$$

where $\psi = (\psi_1, \ldots, \psi_p)^T$, $p \leq n + 1$. The subinterval from y^L to y' will be termed subsystem 1 and denoted by a superscript 1, and from y' to y^R by a superscript 2. In general x^1, u^1, f^1 and G^1 will be different to x^2, u^2, f^2 and G^2, but at y', $x^1(y')$ is related to $x^2(y'^+)$ by

$$h(x^1(y')) - x^2(y'^+) = 0 \tag{11.30}$$

and

$$y' - y'^+ = 0. \tag{11.31}$$

The subproblem solutions are given by Bauman to be the solution of the following necessary conditions for optimality. For subproblem one:

$$\begin{aligned}
&\frac{d\lambda^1}{dy} = -\left(\frac{\partial G^1}{\partial x^1} + \left[\frac{\partial f^1}{\partial x^1}\right]^T \lambda^1\right) \\
&\frac{dx^1}{dy} = f^1 \\
&\frac{\partial G^1}{\partial u^1} + (\lambda^1)^T \frac{\partial f^1}{\partial u^1} = 0 \\
&\left[l + G^1 + (\lambda^1)^T f^1 + \gamma^T \frac{\partial \psi}{\partial y'} + \rho^T \frac{\partial h}{\partial y'}\right]_{y'} = 0 \\
&\left[-\lambda^1 + \rho^T \frac{\partial h}{\partial x^1} + \gamma^T \frac{\partial \psi}{\partial x^1}\right]_{y'} = 0 \\
&h\,|_{y'} = x^2\,|_{y'+} \qquad y' = y'^+ \\
&\psi\,|_{y'} = 0
\end{aligned} \tag{11.32}$$

where l, γ and ρ are Lagrange multipliers resulting from adjoining (11.31), (11.29) and (11.30) respectively to the criterion in the derivation of the necessary conditions for optimality. For subproblem two:

$$\frac{\mathrm{d}\lambda^2}{\mathrm{d}y} = -\left(\frac{\partial G^2}{\partial x^2} + \left[\frac{\partial f^2}{\partial x^2}\right]^{\mathrm{T}} \lambda^2\right)$$

$$\frac{\mathrm{d}x^2}{\mathrm{d}y} = f^2$$

$$\frac{\partial G^2}{\partial u^2} + (\lambda^2)^{\mathrm{T}} \frac{\partial f^2}{\partial u^2} = 0 \tag{11.33}$$

$$\left[G^2 + (\lambda^2)^{\mathrm{T}} f^2 + \nu^{\mathrm{T}} \frac{\partial M^2}{\partial y^{\mathrm{R}}}\right]_{y^{\mathrm{R}}} = 0$$

$$\left[-\lambda^2 + \nu^{\mathrm{T}} \frac{\partial M^2}{\partial x^2}\right]_{y^{\mathrm{R}}} = 0$$

where ν is the Lagrange multiplier associated with the state boundary conditions at y^{R}, namely

$$M^2[x^2(y^{\mathrm{R}}), y^{\mathrm{R}}] = 0 \tag{11.34}$$

The feasible method proposed by Bauman selects x^2 and y'^{+} at the second level with $n + 1 - p$ of the coupling equations $(11.32)^f$ retained. x^2 and y'^{+} may be updated according to

$$\begin{aligned} x^2\,|_{k+1} &= x^2\,|_k + \delta x^2 \qquad \text{at} \quad y'^{+} \\ y'^{+}\,|_{k+1} &= y'^{+}\,|_k + \mathrm{d}y'^{+} \end{aligned} \tag{11.35}$$

where

$$\begin{aligned} \delta x^2 &= -\kappa(\lambda^2 - \rho) \quad \text{at} \quad y'^{+} \qquad & \kappa > 0 \\ \mathrm{d}y'^{+} &= -\kappa(-G^2 - (\lambda^2)^{\mathrm{T}} f^2 - l) \qquad & \kappa > 0. \end{aligned} \tag{11.36}$$

The choice of κ is left to the designer. Implementation is by first selecting a solution for subproblems 1 and 2 that satisfies the state constraints at y^{L}, y' and y^{R}; solving subproblem 1 for the existing state conditions at y' and y^{L}; solving subproblem 2 for the existing state conditions at y'^{+} and y^{R}; update $x^2(y'^{+})$ and y'^{+}.

Example. Consider the design of a continuous beam, Fig. 11.4

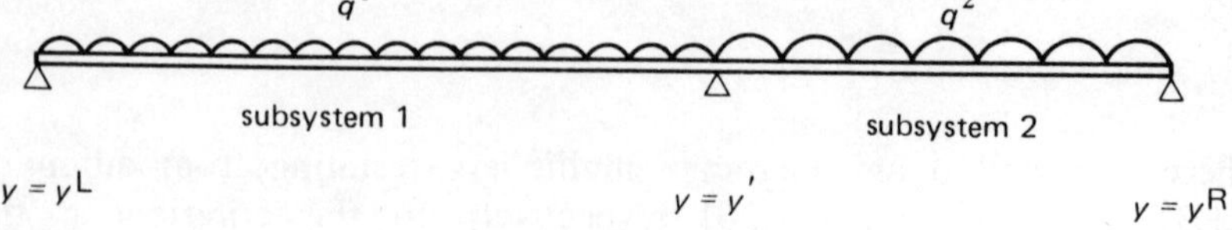

Fig. 11.4

The relation between the states (11.30) at the junction of the two subsystems is

$$\begin{aligned} x_1^1(y') - x_1^2(y'^+) &= 0 \qquad \text{deflection} \\ -x_2^1(y') - x_2^2(y'^+) &= 0 \qquad \text{slope} \\ x_3^1(y') - x_3^2(y'^+) &= 0 \qquad \text{bending moment} \\ -x_4^1(y') - x_4^2(y'^+) &= 0 \qquad \text{shearing force.} \end{aligned}$$

The known state conditions at $y = y'$ are

$$\psi(x(y'), y') = \begin{bmatrix} x_1(y') = 0 \\ 0 \\ 0 \\ 0 \end{bmatrix}.$$

Assuming the design criterion is

$$J = \int_{y^L}^{y^R} EI \, \mathrm{d}y$$

with constraints on the deflection; then for subsystem 1, the relevant necessary conditions for optimality are for $u \triangleq EI$;

$$\frac{\mathrm{d}\lambda_1^1}{\mathrm{d}y} = 0 \qquad \frac{\mathrm{d}x_1^1}{\mathrm{d}y} = x_2^1$$

$$\frac{\mathrm{d}\lambda_2^1}{\mathrm{d}y} = \lambda_1^1 \qquad \frac{\mathrm{d}x_2^1}{\mathrm{d}y} = \frac{x_3^1}{u^1}$$

$$\frac{\mathrm{d}\lambda_3^1}{\mathrm{d}y} = \frac{\lambda_2^1}{u^1} \qquad \frac{\mathrm{d}x_3^1}{\mathrm{d}y} = x_4^1$$

$$\frac{\mathrm{d}\lambda_4^1}{\mathrm{d}y} = \lambda_3^1 \qquad \frac{\mathrm{d}x_4^1}{\mathrm{d}y} = q^1$$

$$1 - \frac{\lambda_2^1 x_3^1}{(u^1)^2} = 0$$

$$l + u^1 + \lambda_1^1 x_2^1 + \lambda_2^1(x_3^1/u^1) + \lambda_3^1 x_4^1 + \lambda_4^1 q^1 \,|_{y'} = 0$$

$$-\begin{bmatrix} \lambda_1^1 \\ \lambda_2^1 \\ \lambda_3^1 \\ \lambda_4^1 \end{bmatrix} + \begin{bmatrix} \rho_1 \\ \rho_2 \\ \rho_3 \\ \rho_4 \end{bmatrix} + \begin{bmatrix} \gamma_1 \\ 0 \\ 0 \\ 0 \end{bmatrix} = 0 \quad \text{at} \quad y'$$

together with the previously given state relations at y' and between subsystems 1 and 2 at y' and y'^{+}. For subsystem 2;

$$\frac{d\lambda_1^2}{dy} = 0 \qquad \frac{dx_1^2}{dy} = x_2^2$$

$$\frac{d\lambda_2^2}{dy} = \lambda_1^2 \qquad \frac{dx_2^2}{dy} = \frac{x_3^2}{u^2}$$

$$\frac{d\lambda_3^2}{dy} = \frac{\lambda_2^2}{u^2} \qquad \frac{dx_3^2}{dy} = x_4^2$$

$$\frac{d\lambda_4^2}{dy} = \lambda_3^2 \qquad \frac{dx_4^2}{dy} = q^2$$

$$1 + \frac{\lambda_2^2 x_3^2}{(u^2)^2} = 0$$

$$u^2 + \lambda_1^2 x_2^2 + \lambda_2^2(x_3^2/u^2) + \lambda_3^2 x_4^2 + \lambda_4^2 q^2 \,|_{y^{\mathrm{R}}} = 0$$

$$- \begin{bmatrix} \lambda_1^2 \\ \lambda_2^2 \\ \lambda_3^2 \\ \lambda_4^2 \end{bmatrix} = 0.$$

11.2.4 Problems (D) and (P)

Difference equations and the associated design problem are decomposed in an entirely similar fashion to the continuous version of section 11.2.3. The means by which problems, in which the systems are modelled by partial differential equations, are treated in a multilevel sense in the literature is by discretizing the problem to give problems of type (D) or (OD). The earlier approaches thus are applicable. The dimensionality of the problem is proportional to the discretization grid size used. Decomposition of the system may be effected between states or over the space and time domains.

11.3 NOTES, COMMENTS AND BIBLIOGRAPHY

[11.1] The theory of multilevel hierarchical systems has its real beginnings in the early 1960s with the work of Mesarovic, Macko, Takahara and Pearson among others. Most of this early work is contained in Mesarovic *et al.* (1970). Books published since this time include Wismer (1971a), Himmelblau (1973), Lasdon (1970), Singh (1977), Haimes (1977), Siljak (1978), and Wismer and Chattergy (1978). See also Savage and Roe (1978), Sage (1977) and Klir (1972).

Essentially the early work was aimed at the optimization problem. Extensions to the identification problem can be found, for example, in Guinzy and Sage (1973), Smith and Sage (1973b) and Fry and Sage (1973), the state estimation problem in Chen and Perlis (1967), Noton (1971) and Pearson (1971), and the combined optimization–identification problem in Haimes (1973, 1977). See Mahmoud (1977a) for a comprehensive listing, and also Singh *et al.* (1975). The ideas of Aoki (1968, 1971), on aggregation are also relevant. The theory is still developing.

In the structural optimization literature, Kirsch (1975) and Kirsch and Moses (1979) use model and goal coordination techniques on algebraic format problems. Baker *et al.* (1978) used a two level formulation to design shed-type structures; the upper level corresponded to management decisions such as floor area, openings and building size while the lower level corresponded to structural designer's decisions such as member and cladding sizes and member spacings—the lower level problem was solved using dynamic programming. Related work is reported in Vanderplaats and Moses (1972), Kirsch *et al.* (1972) and Arora and Govril (1977). For other ideas, see Fenves (1973), Spillers (1973), Baty and Williams (1973) and Schmit and Farshi (1974).

For a discussion on coordination and coordination principles as developed originally in Mesarovic *et al.* (1970), see Mahmoud (1977a).

Occasionally the term stratum is used to describe the levels in a decomposition type (b), and the term layer in (c) (Schoeffler 1971b).

Ray and Szekely (1973) suggest four reasons for the employment of decomposition ideas in optimization: (a) to cope with the size of a large problem, (b) to obtain a modular structure, (c) to isolate the effect of a dominant unit, and (d) to handle the case where quantitative models are lacking.

This chapter is based on Carmichael and Clyde (1979).

[11.2] 1. Mesarovic *et al.* (1970) discusses general coordination. Two coordination principles, the interaction balance principle and the interaction prediction principle, were introduced to judge the effectiveness of coordination. Smith and Sage (1973a) and Mahmoud (1977a) discuss the physical interpretation of these principles.

An alternative, but not equivalent, classification to that of interaction balance methods and interaction prediction methods is a feasible/nonfeasible classification. The interaction balance method would be classed as a nonfeasible method while the interaction prediction method is a combination approach. The term feasible derives from the fact that all solutions through the iterations are feasible because the interconnection or coupling constraint (11.3) is always satisfied. For the nonfeasible methods the opposite applies.

Interaction balance methods belong to the goal (criterion) coordination group. Feasible methods belong to the model coordination group.

2.1 The so called 'static' multilevel optimization technique development is due principally to Lasdon, Brosilow, Schoeffler and Pearson among others.

The first formulation of the problem and decomposition follows Bauman (1968a) and Ray and Szekely (1973). The gradient coordination scheme follows Lasdon and Schoeffler (see Schoeffler 1971a). Bauman (1968a) has proposed a Newton–Raphson scheme and discusses convergence for this, the gradient scheme, and the interaction prediction method (direct iteration method). The interaction prediction method follows Takahara on dynamic systems (see Bauman 1968a). See also Wismer (1971b) and Haimes (1977). The feasible and nonfeasible methods are a dual pair (Mahmoud 1977a). See also Wismer and Chattergy (1978).

The second formulation of the problem and decomposition follows Schoeffler (1971a), Kirsch (1975) and Kirsch and Moses (1979). Schoeffler gives a primal-dual approach to the multilevel problem; the goal coordination approach is termed a dual-feasible method. Kirsch (1975) solves a two-bar truss example, a slab-beam-column system example and another statically determinate truss example using both the model coordination method and the goal coordination method. Kirsch and Moses (1979) extend the use of the model coordination method to a statically indeterminate continuous beam and truss.

Large scale linear and nonlinear programming is discussed in Geoffrion (1971), Lasdon (1970), Dantzig and Van Slyke (1971) and Ray and Szekely (1973) among others, where decomposition and solution procedures for specialized problem structures are given.

3.1 This development follows Guinzy and Sage (1973) and Smith and Sage (1973a). For a review of early work applied to dynamic systems see Bauman (1968a). Where π is a control type variable at the lower level (interaction balance methods) the possibility of singular control exists with its attendant special requirements for consideration of optimality. Using an interaction relation in a quadratic form, to overcome this singular control problem, may introduce extraneous solutions (Bauman 1968a), while a penalty function approach does not guarantee satisfaction of the interaction relation (Guinzy and Sage 1973, Smith and Sage 1973a). Bauman (1968a) discusses convergence for the feasible and nonfeasible methods using gradient and Newton–Raphson updating schemes. In the same paper it is demonstrated how a single level problem with a state constraint may be converted to a multilevel problem with a control constraint at the lower level.

General coordination methods are discussed by Mahmoud (1977a) including costate, control, feasible, nonfeasible and combined. See also Mahmoud (1977b), Mahmoud *et al.* (1977a, b), Guinzy and Sage (1973) and Fry and Sage (1973).

Pearson (1971) gives a primal-dual approach and a pseudo-model coordination method. The pseudo-model coordination method is introduced to handle the case where the number of coupling variables is not less than the number of control variables, leading to a breakdown of the model coordination method. Bauman (1968a) comments similarly for static systems where for the feasible method to work, a control u^i has to be available to satisfy each interaction constraint. See also Singh *et al.* (1975).

3.3. The trajectory decomposition approach follows Bauman (1968a, b, 1971). See also Sugar (1974a, b). Bauman suggests means of choosing κ to aid convergence. The feasible type method is preferred as at each iteration the solution is valid. See Mahmoud (1977a) for comments.

Schoeffler (1971a) details an approach whereby a problem of type (D) over N stages reduces to $N + 1$ problems of the type (A) at the first level, that is there are $N + 1$ subproblems.

4. See Fry and Sage (1973) for the problem (D) case.

Ray and Szekely (1973) reference the work of Aris and Wilde on decomposing nonserial problems to serial subsystem problems in order that dynamic programming may be used at the lower level. Mention is also given of the work of Jackson, Denn and Lee on feasible and nonfeasible methods as they relate to the discrete maximum principle.

The distributed parameter optimal control problem using multilevel techniques has been discussed by Wismer (1969, 1971b, 1973).

Chapter **12**

Lyapunov Theory in Design

12.1 INTRODUCTION

Lyapunov's second (or direct) method may be used as a basis for the optimization of structures where stability with respect to time is required. In particular optimal stiffness/damping/mass properties may be determined for structures subjected to initial disturbances and for an integral square error (or deviation) criterion of the form

$$J = \int_0^\infty x^{\mathrm{T}}(t)Qx(t)\,\mathrm{d}t \tag{12.1}$$

where Q is some symmetric matrix. For a structure with an initially perturbed state $x(0)$ and equilibrium state $x_e = 0$ (assumed without loss of generality), such criteria measure how quickly the system goes from $x(0)$ to x_e.

This chapter first discusses Lyapunov's second or direct method in a qualitative and introductory fashion (section 12.2). It then goes on to use the theory in the above synthesis format where the structural system is designed according to a response criterion while maintaining specified dynamic stability properties. The design of a single degree of freedom structure is given as an illustration (section 12.3). Finally a brief mention is given of the use of mathematical programming as an aid to stability *analysis* in the sense of Lyapunov (section 12.4). Section 12.5 gives the associated notes, comments and bibliography.

12.2 STABILITY IN THE SENSE OF LYAPUNOV

Lyapunov's method enables the stability evaluation of systems modelled in standard first order state equation form. For the analysis problem

$$\dot{x} = f(x,t) \quad \text{or} \quad x(k+1) = F[x(k),k] \tag{12.2}$$

Considering the continuous time case, the stability of $x(t)$ about x_e

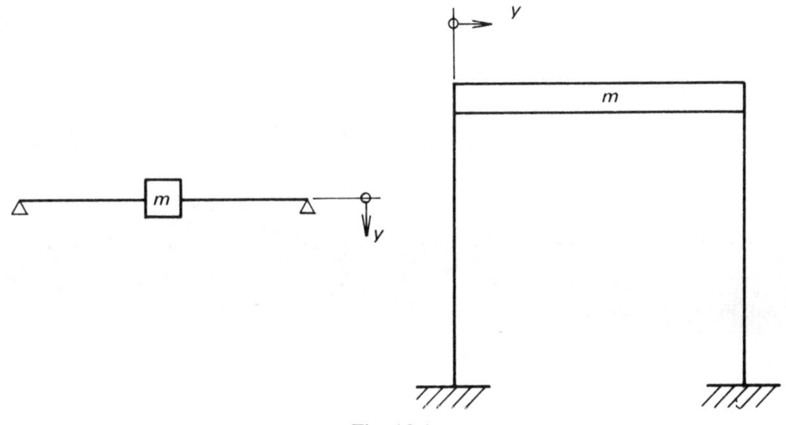

Fig. 12.1

may be evaluated via the introduction of a Lyapunov function, $V(x)$, and an examination of the characteristics of this positive definite function and its time derivative $\dot{V}(x)$ (the total derivative of V with respect to time). The method avoids obtaining explicit forms for the solution $x(t)$.

As an introduction consider a single degree of freedom system (Fig. 12.1), with equation of motion (free vibration)

$$m\ddot{y} + c\dot{y} + ky = 0 \quad \text{or} \quad \begin{cases} \dot{x}_1 = x_2 \\ \dot{x}_2 = \dfrac{1}{m}[-cx_2 - kx_1] \end{cases}$$

where x_1 is displacement and x_2 velocity.

The solution of these equations is

$$x_1 = e^{-\beta t}\left[\frac{x_2(0) + \beta x_1(0)}{\omega_d} \sin \omega_d t + x_1(0) \cos \omega_d t\right]$$

where $\beta = c/2m$, a damping coefficient and ω_d is the damped natural circular frequency. This is plotted in Fig. 12.2 for (a) given initial displacement, and (b) given initial velocity. Figure 12.2(c) is the phase plane representation for given initial displacement.

The system is globally asymptotically stable. The equilibrium position is $x_e = (0, 0)^T$.

Introduce an (energy) function

$$V = \tfrac{1}{2}kx_1^2 + \tfrac{1}{2}mx_2^2.$$

Differentiating (to give a rate of change of energy term)

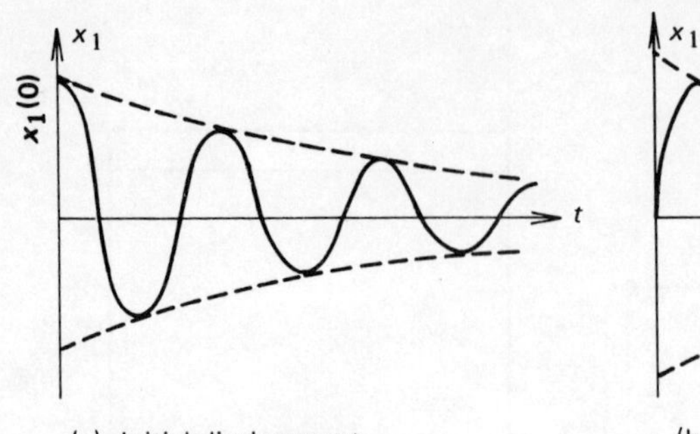

(a) initial displacement

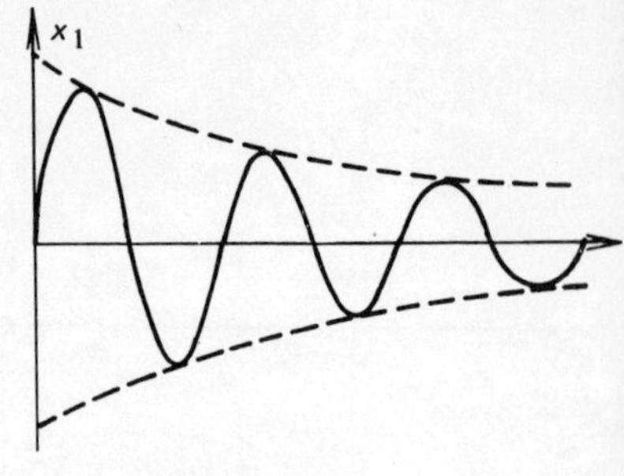

(b) initial velocity

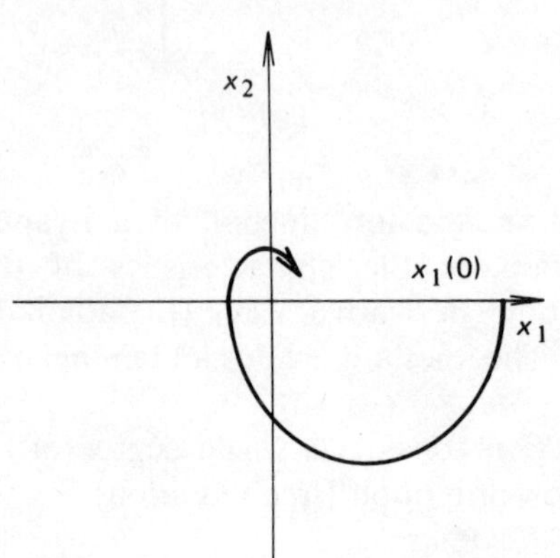

(c) phase/state trajectory in the phase plane

Fig. 12.2

$$\begin{aligned}\dot{V} &= kx_1\dot{x}_1 + mx_2\dot{x}_2\\ &= -cx_2^2.\end{aligned}$$

Plots of V and $\dot{V}$ are given in Fig. 12.3.

Note that $\dot{V}$ is always negative, V decreases with time and V equals zero only when x_1 and x_2 equal zero (at x_e). With V as an energy function, the implication is that the properties of V indicate the form of stability of the system. This result may be generalized, *inter alia* beyond considering V as energy, and proven, and constitutes the basis of Lyapunov's second or direct method.

For time invariant (stationary) systems, for example,

(a) the solution is stable if $\dot{V}(x)$ is negative semi-definite. Stable implies the solution remains within a given set of bounds if the initial disturbances are small enough.
(b) the solution is asymptotically stable if $\dot{V}(x)$ is negative definite. Asymptotic stability implies $\| x(t) - x_e \| \to 0$ as $t \to \infty$.

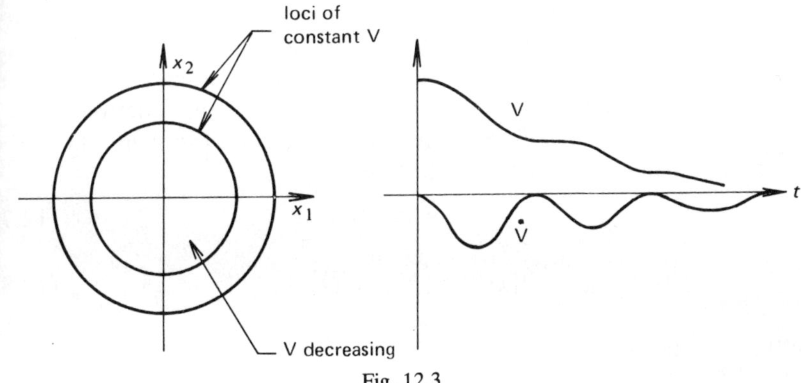

Fig. 12.3

Related theorems may be stated on instability and for time variant (nonstationary) systems, nonlinear systems and periodic systems. See the referenced works in the bibliography for a complete application of Lyapunov's method to dynamic systems. Topics of boundedness of the solutions, the converse of the stability theorems, nonlinear systems and discrete systems are covered.

The distinguishing feature of the Lyapunov approach to the stability analysis problem is that the analysis is not concerned with the solution of the system state equations, a feature which makes the approach attractive particularly for nonlinear systems.

12.3 STRUCTURAL DESIGN USING LYAPUNOV'S METHOD

12.3.1 A Design Interpretation of the Stability Results

For linear system equations

$$\dot{x}(t) = Ax(t) \tag{12.3}$$

a suitable choice for a Lyapunov function is a quadratic

$$V(x) = x^{\mathrm{T}}Px. \tag{12.4}$$

Here A is an $n \times n$ transition matrix and P is a symmetric positive definite matrix.

The time derivative of V is given by

$$\begin{aligned} \dot{V}(x) &= x^{\mathrm{T}}(A^{\mathrm{T}}P + PA)x \\ &= -x^{\mathrm{T}}Qx \end{aligned} \tag{12.5}$$

using (12.3), where

$$Q = -(A^{\mathrm{T}}P + PA) \tag{12.6}$$

a positive definite symmetric matrix.

If the result (12.6) holds, then the characteristics of V and $\dot{V}$ are such as to ensure that the system will be asymptotically stable. This implies, for the analysis problem, determining whether the P matrix, which is the solution of (12.6) for any given Q, is positive definite.

This result may be reinterpreted for the design problem where the system and criterion are given respectively by

$$\dot{x}(t) = A(\alpha)x(t) \tag{12.7}$$

$$J[x(0), \alpha] = \int_0^\infty x^T Q x \, dt. \tag{12.8}$$

Here $\alpha = [\alpha_1, \ldots, \alpha_m]^T$ is a vector of design variables (equivalently control variables).

Asymptotic stability implies $V(\infty) = 0$. Integrating the right-hand side of (12.8)

$$J[x(0), \alpha] = x^T(0)Px(0). \tag{12.9}$$

Using the conventional theory of extrema, the design variables follow from the minimization of J. The result yields a minimum for the criterion (12.8) while the system (12.7) is asymptotically stable.

12.3.2 Example: Single Degree of Freedom System

Consider the design of a single degree of freedom system with state equations

$$\begin{bmatrix} \dfrac{dx_1}{dt} \\ \dfrac{dx_2}{dt} \end{bmatrix} = \begin{bmatrix} 0 & 1 \\ -\dfrac{k}{m} & -\dfrac{c}{m} \end{bmatrix} \begin{bmatrix} x_1 \\ x_2 \end{bmatrix}$$

where x_1 is displacement and x_2 is velocity.

Assume a criterion of the form

$$J[x(0), \alpha] = \int_0^\infty (x_1^2 + \lambda x_2^2) \, dt$$

where λ is a weighting factor. This is a particular form of (12.8) and is used only as an example.

Assume the damping c and stiffness k to be the design variables. Make the substitution

$$\alpha_1 \triangleq \frac{c}{m}, \qquad \alpha_2 \triangleq \frac{k}{m}.$$

The state equations imply

$$A = \begin{bmatrix} 0 & 1 \\ -\alpha_2 & -\alpha_1 \end{bmatrix}$$

and the criterion implies

$$Q = \begin{bmatrix} 1 & 0 \\ 0 & \lambda \end{bmatrix}.$$

Substituting in (12.6) and solving for P gives

$$P = \begin{bmatrix} \dfrac{\alpha_1}{2\alpha_2} + \dfrac{\alpha_2}{2\alpha_1}\left[\lambda + \dfrac{1}{\alpha_2}\right] & \dfrac{1}{2\alpha_2} \\ \dfrac{1}{2\alpha_2} & \dfrac{1}{2\alpha_1}\left[\lambda + \dfrac{1}{\alpha_2}\right] \end{bmatrix}$$

which is positive definite, and from (12.9)

$$J[x(0), \alpha] = \left[\frac{\alpha_1}{2\alpha_2} + \frac{\alpha_2}{2\alpha_1}\left[\lambda + \frac{1}{\alpha_2}\right]\right] x_1^2(0) + \frac{1}{\alpha_2} x_1(0) x_2(0) + \frac{1}{2\alpha_1}\left[\lambda + \frac{1}{\alpha_2}\right] x_2^2(0).$$

For stationary values of J with respect to α_1 and α_2

$$\left.\frac{\partial J}{\partial \alpha_1}\right|_{\hat{\alpha}} = 0 = \left[\frac{1}{2\alpha_2} - \frac{\alpha_2}{2\alpha_1^2}\left[\lambda + \frac{1}{\alpha_2}\right]\right] x_1^2(0) - \frac{1}{2\alpha_1^2}\left[\lambda + \frac{1}{\alpha_2}\right] x_2^2(0)$$

$$\left.\frac{\partial J}{\partial \alpha_2}\right|_{\hat{\alpha}} = 0 = \left[-\frac{\alpha_1}{2\alpha_2^2} + \frac{\lambda}{2\alpha_1}\right] x_1^2(0) - \frac{1}{\alpha_2^2} x_1(0) x_2(0) - \frac{1}{2\alpha_1\alpha_2^2} x_2^2(0).$$

These last two equations may be solved for the optimal values of α and will depend on the initial state conditions, a property which may or may not be satisfactory for a given problem. For the case $\lambda = 0$ and $x_2(0) = 0$,

$$\hat{\alpha}_1 = (\hat{\alpha}_2)^2 \quad \text{or} \quad \hat{k} = \hat{c}^2/m.$$

Other results may be similarly derived. The asymptotic stability property naturally derives from the inclusion of damping in this example.

12.4 STABILITY ANALYSIS AS AN OPTIMIZATION PROBLEM

The problems of the choice of a Lyanpunov function and the determination of the regions of attraction and ultimate confinement, return times, time constants and global stability questions may be cast as nonlinear programming problems. Refer the bibliography. This is related to the analysis problem and is outside the scope of the present work.

12.5 NOTES, COMMENTS AND BIBLIOGRAPHY

[12.1] Lyapunov (alternative spelling Liapunov) in the 1890s outlined two approaches to the theory of stability of motion for the solution of ordinary differential equations. The so called 'first method' was quantitative and the 'second method' qualitative. The theory has since been developed, but only in the last 20 years or so, in the fields of analytical dynamics, differential equations, mechanics and control systems.

For a very readable treatment of the theory of stability for dynamic systems see Willems (1970). See also Hahn (1963, 1967), LaSalle and Lefschetz (1961), Zubov (1964), Kalman and Bertram (1960a, b), Tomovic (1963) and Liapunov (1966).

Introductions to Lyapunov theory may be found in Elgerd (1967), Porter (1969) and Ogata (1967).

The application of Lyapunov theory to structural design is treated in Carmichael (1979a). The application to the analysis problem can be found in numerous publications; see, for example, Holzer (1970, 1971, 1972a, b, 1974), Holzer and Eubanks (1969), Lee and Hsu (1972), Hsu (1966), Plaut and Infante (1972), Infante and Plaut (1969), Infante (1973), Plaut (1971), Ahmadi and Mostaghel (1978), Leipholz (1971, 1972, 1974, 1975a, b, c, 1976a, b), Parks (1966), Walker (1972, 1973), Dym (1974a), Hegemier (1967), Lepore and Stoltz (1974), Lepore and Shah (1968) and Vol'mir and Kul'terbaev (1974) among others and their bibliographies.

A note on terminology: In the stability literature 'autonomous' implies time independence whereas in the control literature it implies an unforced system. The word is not used in the present work because of this double meaning. In the stability literature the term 'discrete' is synonomous with the present 'lumped parameter' term usage while 'continuous' is synonomous with the present 'distributed parameter' term usage. Lumped and distributed parameter terminology is consistent with control theory usage where discrete implies sampled data or discrete time while continuous implies continuous with time. Control theory terminology is preferred in the present work.

[12.2] The prime difficulty in applying Lyapunov's method is the determination of a suitable Lyapunov function (scalar) although many functions have been catalogued for various system types. See for example Letov (1964) and Elgerd (1967). No general method exists for constructing Lyapunov functions although there is much flexibility in the choice of the function. Different functions will give different information on the stability of the solution. If a particular function does not indicate stability of the system, this does not imply necessarily that the system is unstable. Further functions should be tried. The Lyapunov theorems on stability of nonlinear systems only give sufficient conditions. In the structural mechanics case energy type expressions are usually suitable Lyapunov functions.

The extension of Lyapunov stability theory to distributed parameter systems is given by Zubov (1964), Movchan (1959a, b, 1960). See Dym (1974a) and Knops and Wilkes (1966). The Lyapunov function becomes a functional.

[12.3] The design problem associated with a general multidegree of freedom structure is solved in Carmichael (1979a). The relevant theory is covered in Meerov (1961), Grayson (1965), Ogata (1967), and Kalman and Bertram (1960a).

[12.4] Optimization formats and discussion in relation to the stability analysis problem have been given by Kalman and Bertram (1960a, b), Ogata (1967), Fisher and Goh (1977) and LaSalle and Lefschetz (1961) among others.

Chapter **13**

Energy and 'Optimality Criteria' Based Design

13.1 NOTES, COMMENTS AND BIBLIOGRAPHY

Publications using energy formulations, resulting in 'optimality criteria', or being based on 'optimality criteria' occupy a substantial portion of the structural optimization literature. Brief mention will be given here of these approaches and their 'equivalence' (section 13.2) to the approaches of the foregoing chapters for completeness; only references will be given to the detail of the approaches. It is noted that the approaches of the foregoing chapters favour using mathematical models of constitutive/equilibrium/compatibility relationships in contrast to energy or variational formulations, while the emphasis in optimization has been on direct synthesis rather than iterative analysis with updating.

The term 'optimality criterion' is used to describe a set of conditions governing the behaviour of the optimum structure and may be in terms of strength, stiffness, stability or other specified design requirements. It is placed inside ' ' to distinguish it from the earlier usage of optimality criterion which is a value judgement by the designer. Historically early examples of designs using 'optimality criteria' were the fully stressed designs, uniform strength designs (where the stresses are at their limiting values at least under one loading set) and simultaneous failure mode designs. Berke and Venkayya (1974) comment on the relationship of these to minimum weight design and uniform strain energy density design. See also Razani (1965) and Gallagher (1973) among others. Uniform strength design is a minimum weight design for isotropic material, uniform allowable stresses and a single load set without geometric constraints.

Extensive work has been done in the area of 'optimality criteria' by Prager, Taylor, Sheu, Shield, Chen, Huang, Martin, Dupuis, Dafalias and many others. Their work particularly relates to the case of generalized compliance constraints. (Generalized compliance is the virtual work of a fictitious load set when it is subjected to the displacement field of the actual loading.)

Extensive related work may be found in the publications of Barnett, Masur, Huang, Icerman, Plant, Vepa, Popelar, Olhoff, Mroz, Save, Karihaloo, Plaut, Niordson and others. See also Rozvany (1976), Sheu and Prager (1968), and Wasiutynski and Brandt (1963).

Generally this work is restricted to conventional structures and the emphasis is on the development of neat closed form optimality conditions. Simultaneously attention has been given by other researchers to the development of numerical algorithms (often based on these closed form optimality conditions) attacking quite complicated structures. In this latter area there also exists a considerable volume of literature. Some overviews are given in Berke and Venkayya (1974), Venkayya (1978), Gellatly and Berke (1973), and Khot *et al.* (1979). Contributions to the field have been by Venkayya, Khot, Berke, Tischler, Gellatly, Reddy, Dwyer, Emerton, Ojalvo, Johnson, Taig, Kerr, Levy, Melosh, Nagtegaal, Kiusalaas, Gwin, Haftka, Starnes, Barton, Taylor, Mistree, Thierauf and many others.

The 'optimality criteria' result is generally coupled with a finite element analysis package and the optimization carried out in an iterative analysis sense. The 'optimality criterion' on which the resizing is done in the computational algorithm, is related to the behaviour of the structure. Satisfying the 'criterion' gives the optimum solution. 'Optimality criteria' based algorithms are specifically written for a definite type of structural behaviour, and while losing generality as compared to say mathematical programming based algorithms, computational efficiency can often be attained. (Frequently the term direct method is used to describe mathematical programming based algorithms while the term indirect method is used to describe 'optimality criteria' based algorithms. This terminology is not used here as it duplicates the same terminology used to distinguish between conventional optimizations.) The problem formulations are inherently discrete.

The algorithms as mentioned iterate on the analysis problem with the control variables updated, using the 'optimality criterion' or are determined by the constraints on the problem. The state variables change in the analysis stage or are determined by the constraints on the problem. Variables determined by the constraints are termed passive. Variables may change from active to passive and vice versa from one iteration to the next. Many variations on this theme exist, for example using a stress ratio approach for the initial iterations where the controls are changed in proportion to the ratio of actual stress to allowable stress for the particular members. Troubles with the solution converging to relative or local minima are also present in 'optimality criteria' based approaches as they are in mathematical programming. Nonuniqueness may also be present. Additional ideas such as using an 'envelope' are required to handle multiple 'criteria' corresponding to many design requirements.

13.2 EQUIVALENCE DERIVATIONS

13.2.1 General

'Equivalence' of the optimization techniques given in the previous chapters, namely mathematical programming, Pontryagin's principle, . . . , and 'optimality criteria' approaches may be shown. Several publications exist showing this 'equivalence'. In particular Templeman (1976) relates mathematical programming and 'optimality criteria' through the Lagrangian formulation and primal-dual arguments for truss structures. See also Kelly *et al*. (1977), Fleury and Geradin (1978) and others. Carmichael and Goh (1977) derive the 'optimality criteria' of Prager and Taylor for plate vibration problems using Pontryagin's principle. See Chapter 9. Carmichael (1979b) relates the results of Popelar and Masur to the necessary conditions for optimality of Pontryagin's principle. Carmichael and Clyde (1980) relate optimal flexure field theory to a control format. The essence of the arguments in Carmichael and Clyde (1980) and Carmichael (1979b) are given below in section 13.2.2 and section 13.2.3 and in Carmichael and Goh (1977) in Chapter 9. See also Lepik (1972, 1973, 1978).

Experience with the 'optimality criteria' approaches and energy approaches would indicate that structural optimization in the future will take the idiosyncrasies of structural mechanics into account in preference to relying on a pure mathematical formulation of the design problem.

By showing the 'equivalence' of the approaches it is emphasized that the usefulness or efficiency of the energy/'optimality criteria' techniques is not questioned for these specialized problems. The control approach enables new interpretations of the established formulations and results.

13.2.2 Optimum Flexure Fields

The theory of optimum flexure fields embraces the so-called optimal force transmission by flexure problem and the minimum moment volume problem. The relevant systems are transversely loaded planar systems such as grillages, fibre-reinforced plates and space frames of fixed depth. Rozvany (1973, 1975, 1976) and Rozvany and Hill (1976) give extensive treatments of the subject. Besides the energy approaches to this problem by Prager, Shield, Marcal, Mroz, Masur, Save and others, there have been approaches based on the calculus of variations, concave programming, beam analogy and neutral line methods by

Rozvany, Charrett, Melchers, Adidam, Gangadharaiah, Hill and Hemp, approaches by Morley and Heyman using reasoned arguments, approaches by Lowe and Melchers using 'load path' arguments, Hillerborg's strip theory of Sharpe and Clyde, and function theoretic methods of Hill.

For grillage-like continua, fibre-reinforced plates of constant thickness or similar structures, consider a lower bound plastic design. In particular consider the determination of a statically admissible stress field such that some quantity

$$I = \int_Y \Psi \mathrm{d}y$$

is minimized and also that yield is not violated. Y denotes the two dimensional domain of the structure, with coordinates y_1, y_2; $y = (y_1, y_2)^{\mathrm{T}}$ and $\Psi(y)$ is termed the specific cost or cost per unit volume, area or length. Further constraints related to geometry restrictions attempting to gain serviceable designs may also be included in the formulation. Conventional approaches (Rozvany and Hill 1976) assume $\Psi(y) = \Psi[Q(y)]$, where Q is a generalized stress vector.

Prager's school (Prager and Shield 1967, Marcal and Prager 1964) gives the optimality condition for optimal plastic design as (in the notation of Rozvany and Hill 1976)

$$q = \mathscr{G}\,[\Psi(q)]$$

where q denotes a generalized strain vector, and $\mathscr{G}$ is termed a generalized gradient operator. q and Q are kinematically and statically admissible respectively. This result was obtained through energy arguments. Variational results (Rozvany and Hill 1976) give the same result as a necessary condition for optimality; where Ψ is convex, this result can be shown to be a sufficient condition for optimality.

For the more specific 'minimum moment volume problem', that is the lower bound plasticity problem for which the minimum of the integral of the sum of the absolute values of principal moments is obtained, this optimality condition has been shown by Rozvany (1973) to reduce to

$$\begin{aligned} &\kappa_i = k \operatorname{sgn} M_i \quad &&\text{for} \quad M_i \neq 0 \\ &|\kappa_i| \leq k &&\text{for} \quad M_i = 0 \end{aligned} \qquad (*)$$

where $i = n$, t denotes the principal directions. This result implies that the curvatures are bounded by the constant k and also take the same direction as the statically admissible principal moments M_i. The term optimal flexure fields (Rozvany 1973, 1975) is given to moment and curvature fields satisfying (*).

The essential ideas behind showing the 'equivalence' of optimum flexure field theory and the results of optimal control theory are contained in the problem of the design of beams of constant preassigned depth but variable width. For background to the problem, see Charrett and Rozvany (1972) and Rozvany *et al*. (1971). The extensions of the present approach to sandwich beams, shells and continuous and variously loaded beams are given in Carmichael and Clyde (1980). The problem may be stated as follows.

The optimality criterion is one of volume or cost

$$\min V = \int_L A \, \mathrm{d}y$$

where y is the independent variable of distance, L is the length of the beam, A is the cross sectional area, $A = kM_0$, k is a constant and M_0 is a yield moment capacity.

The solution is required to satisfy equilibrium

$$\frac{\mathrm{d}^2 M(y)}{\mathrm{d}y^2} = -p(y) \quad \text{or} \quad \frac{\mathrm{d}M}{\mathrm{d}y} = S, \qquad \frac{\mathrm{d}S}{\mathrm{d}y} = -p$$

and the yield condition

$$|M(y)| - M_0 \leq 0.$$

Here M is the bending moment, S the shearing force, and p is the applied lateral load.

Applying the result (*) for the constraint active

$$\begin{array}{ll} M < 0 & \kappa = -k \\ M > 0 & \kappa = k \\ M = 0 & -k \leqslant \kappa \leq k. \end{array}$$

For the Hamiltonian

$$H = -kM_0 + \lambda_1 S - \lambda_2 p$$

the costate equations and associated boundary conditions are

$$\frac{\mathrm{d}\lambda_1}{\mathrm{d}y} = -\frac{\partial H}{\partial M} \qquad \frac{\mathrm{d}\lambda_2}{\mathrm{d}y} = -\frac{\partial H}{\partial S}$$

$$\delta M \lambda_1 \bigg|_{y=0,L} = 0 \qquad \delta S \lambda_2 \bigg|_{y=0,L} = 0$$

where δM and δS are small variations in M and S respectively.

The optimal solution is one in which the constraint is active, that is $M_0 = |M|$ (or $M_0 = M_0^{\min}$ where minimum geometry constraints are present in the problem formulation). This implies the plastic moment capacity of the beam follows the bending moment diagram.

Consider an elementary example of a beam fixed at both ends and with a distributed load. Other loadings and boundary conditions may be treated in a similar fashion. Symmetry may be recognized for a regularly distributed load, such that only half the beam need be considered. A negative moment region will exist near the support and a positive moment region near midspan with the junction at y'.

For the negative moment region

$$H = kM + \lambda_1 S - \lambda_2 p$$

$$\frac{d\lambda_1}{dy} = -k \qquad \frac{d\lambda_2}{dy} = -\lambda_1$$

$$\lambda_1(y') = -kL/2 + ky'$$

$$\lambda_2(y') = \lambda_2(L/2) - kL^2/8 + \alpha L/2 + ky^2/2 - \alpha y'.$$

For the positive moment region

$$H = -kM + \lambda_1 S - \lambda_2 p$$

$$\frac{d\lambda_1}{dy} = k \qquad \frac{d\lambda_2}{dy} = -\lambda_1$$

$$\lambda_1(y') = -ky'$$

$$\lambda_2(y') = -ky'^2/2 - \beta y'$$

where α and β are constants of integration.

Continuity of the costate variable λ_1 gives $y' = L/4$. Note that this result is independent of the loading and the continuity properties of the static variables M and S. With foresight to a physical interpretation of the costate variables to follow, this result is purely based on kinematic conditions.

The physical interpretation of the costate variables, alluded to above, may be made through either an examination of the costate boundary conditions or the associated flow law. Consider the former.

It may be observed that

(i) for pinned boundary conditions

$\delta M = 0$ slope $\frac{dw}{dy}$ – no information

δS – no information   deflection $w = 0$

(ii) for fixed boundary conditions

$$\delta M \text{ – no information} \qquad \text{slope } \frac{dw}{dy} = 0$$

$$\delta S \text{ – no information} \qquad \text{deflection } w = 0$$

(iii) for free boundary conditions

$$\delta M = 0 \qquad \text{slope } \frac{dw}{dy} \text{ – no information}$$

$$\delta S = 0 \qquad \text{deflection } w \text{ – no information.}$$

By inspection λ_1 is equivalent to a slope and λ_2 is equivalent to a deflection.

Now curvature is the rate of change of slope, implying curvature $\equiv d\lambda_1/dy$.

For the negative moment part of the beam

$$M < 0, \qquad M_0 = -M \quad \text{and} \quad d\lambda_1/d\lambda = -k \equiv \text{curvature.}$$

For the positive moment part of the beam

$$M > 0, \qquad M_0 = M \quad \text{and} \quad d\lambda_1/dy = k \equiv \text{curvature}$$

which is the result (*).

The problem may then be tackled in either of two fashions; in particular through a state/costate approach or as an analysis-type problem in terms of curvatures.

The above static/kinematic breakdown of the state/costate relationship highlights the adjoint property and the orthogonality or duality relationship of the optimization problem.

It is instructive for this illustration on the lower bound plasticity design of a beam of preassigned depth, to consider the related elastic beam. The relevant constitutive equation reads

$$\frac{d^2}{dy^2}\left(EI\,\frac{d^2w}{dy^2}\right) = -p$$

where EI denotes the rigidity of the beam. To convert this to a standard state equation form, set

$$x_1 \triangleq w, \qquad x_2 \triangleq \frac{dw}{dy}, \qquad x_3 \triangleq EI\,\frac{d^2w}{dy^2}, \qquad x_4 \triangleq \frac{d}{dy}\left(EI\,\frac{d^2w}{dy^2}\right).$$

The states are immediately recognizable as deflection, slope, bending moment and shear force respectively. Differentiating the states,

$$\left.\begin{aligned} \frac{\mathrm{d}x_1}{\mathrm{d}y} &= x_2 \\ \frac{\mathrm{d}x_2}{\mathrm{d}y} &= \frac{x_3}{EI} \\ \frac{\mathrm{d}x_3}{\mathrm{d}y} &= x_4 \\ \frac{\mathrm{d}x_4}{\mathrm{d}y} &= -p \end{aligned}\right\} \text{ or } \begin{aligned} \frac{\mathrm{d}w}{\mathrm{d}y} &= \theta \\ \frac{\mathrm{d}\theta}{\mathrm{d}y} &= \frac{M}{EI} = \kappa \\ \hline \frac{\mathrm{d}M}{\mathrm{d}y} &= S \\ \frac{\mathrm{d}S}{\mathrm{d}y} &= -p. \end{aligned}$$

The first two equations are the costate equations and the last two equations are the state equations of the lower bound plasticity problem. Hence the lower bound plasticity design equations (state plus costate) satisfy the elastic state equations. However, from inspection of the associated costate equations for the elastic problem with stress constraints it appears that in general the optimum elastic solution will not coincide with the optimum plastic solution. This is confirmed in the papers of Rozvany (1977, 1978).

The plasticity problems involving interior supports, simultaneous loadings and segmental design may be treated by the extensions to the basic optimization problem as given in Chapter 8. For example, multiple loadings (multipurpose design) give rise to several system equations which may be treated as additional path constraints, while interior supports represent interior boundary conditions or point constraints on the state variables.

Yield criteria are typically described in a state space and so the extension, also, to yield criteria other than considered here (for example Tresca, von Mises, . . .) is straightforward.

13.2.3 Optimum Design Against Buckling

Results have been derived in the structural optimization literature for the optimal design of thin-walled beams, plates and columns in lateral buckling. Energy ideas have been used in many of the derivations. See, for example, Popelar (1976, 1977), Olhoff and Taylor (1978) and Sheu and Prager (1968) among others for reviews of optimization results considering instability.

The arguments developed below indicate that these results satisfy the necessary conditions for optimality of Pontryagin's principle. A particular problem of beam instability is considered as an illustration but parallel arguments may be used to obtain optimality results for other structural elements and loading. (Chapter 8 considers the column instability problem using Pontryagin's principle and the calculus of variations.) The optimal control approach is general in that no distinction need be made between the statically indeterminate and the statically determinate cases. Further, constraints may be included with small modification to the computations.

As the illustration, consider a problem posed and solved by Popelar using both potential energy (Popelar 1976) and complementary energy (Popelar 1977). Masur (1975b) had previously considered the general optimum problem for structures undergoing buckling. In particular consider a thin-walled beam buckling laterally under uniform end moments where the least volume solution is required.

Timoshenko and Gere (1961) develop the relevant equations for minor axis bending and torsion as

$$EI_y \frac{\mathrm{d}^2 u}{\mathrm{d}z^2} - M_0 \phi = 0$$

$$GJ \frac{\mathrm{d}\phi}{\mathrm{d}z} - \frac{\mathrm{d}}{\mathrm{d}z}\left[EI_\omega \frac{\mathrm{d}^2\phi}{\mathrm{d}z^2}\right] + M_0 \frac{\mathrm{d}u}{\mathrm{d}z} = 0$$

or combined as

$$\frac{\mathrm{d}}{\mathrm{d}z}\left[GJ \frac{\mathrm{d}\phi}{\mathrm{d}z} - \frac{\mathrm{d}}{\mathrm{d}z}\left[EI_\omega \frac{\mathrm{d}^2\phi}{\mathrm{d}z^2}\right]\right] + \frac{M_0^2}{EI_y}\phi = 0$$

where EI_y is the minor axis flexural rigidity, EI_ω is the warping rigidity, GJ is the torsional rigidity, u is the lateral displacement, ϕ is the cross section rotation, M_0 is an applied end moment, and z is the independent variable of distance. The above relations assume that the major axis bending is small for $I_x \gg I_y$, and the cross section is doubly symmetric.

Boundary conditions on the latter relationship are

$$\phi = 0, \qquad EI_\omega \frac{\mathrm{d}^2\phi}{\mathrm{d}z^2} = 0 \qquad z = 0, l$$

where l is the beam length.

This fourth order differential equation in ϕ may be replaced by the equivalent state equations

$$\begin{bmatrix} \dfrac{dx_1}{dz} = x_2 \\ \dfrac{dx_2}{dz} = \dfrac{x_3}{EI_\omega} \\ \dfrac{dx_3}{dz} = GJx_2 - x_4 \\ \dfrac{dx_4}{dz} = \dfrac{-M_0^2}{EI_y} x_1 \end{bmatrix} \quad \text{with} \quad x_1 = 0, \quad x_3 = 0 \quad \text{at} \quad z = 0, l$$

where the states are defined as

$$x_1 \triangleq \phi, \qquad x_2 \triangleq \frac{d\phi}{dz}, \qquad x_3 \triangleq EI_\omega \frac{d^2\phi}{dz^2},$$

$$x_4 \triangleq GJ \frac{d\phi}{dz} - \frac{d}{dz}\left[EI_\omega \frac{d^2\phi}{dz^2}\right]$$

and the controls are the geometric properties of the cross section reflected in the terms I_ω, I_y, J or A, the cross sectional area which occurs in the criterion

$$\min V = \int_0^l A \, dz.$$

The Hamiltonian and costate equations follow automatically. In particular

$$H \triangleq -A + \lambda_1 x_2 + \frac{\lambda_2 x_3}{EI_\omega} + \lambda_3[GJx_2 - x_4] - \frac{\lambda_4 M_0^2 x_1}{EI_y}$$

$$\begin{bmatrix} \dfrac{d\lambda_1}{dz} = \dfrac{\lambda_4 M_0^2}{EI_y} \\ \dfrac{d\lambda_2}{dz} = -\lambda_1 - \lambda_3 GJ \\ \dfrac{d\lambda_3}{dz} = \dfrac{-\lambda_2}{EI_\omega} \\ \dfrac{d\lambda_4}{dz} = \lambda_3 \end{bmatrix} \quad \text{with} \quad \lambda_2 = 0, \quad \lambda_4 = 0 \quad \text{at} \quad z = 0, l$$

From inspection of the state and costate equations, and the

associated state and costate boundary conditions, it is seen that

$$\begin{bmatrix} \lambda_1 \\ \lambda_2 \\ \lambda_3 \\ \lambda_4 \end{bmatrix} = \frac{1}{\gamma^2} \begin{bmatrix} & & & -1 \\ & & -1 & \\ & 1 & & \\ 1 & & & \end{bmatrix} \begin{bmatrix} x_1 \\ x_2 \\ x_3 \\ x_4 \end{bmatrix}$$

where $1/\gamma^2$ is a constant.

For A unconstrained, a necessary condition for a stationary value of the Hamiltonian is

$$\frac{\partial H}{\partial A} = 0 = -\gamma^2 + \frac{x_3^2}{EI_\omega^2}\frac{\partial I_\omega}{\partial A} + x_2^2 G \frac{\partial J}{\partial A} + \frac{x_1^2 M_0^2}{EI_y^2}\frac{\partial I_y}{\partial A}$$

or replacing the states by their defined quantities

$$0 = -\gamma^2 + E\left[\frac{\mathrm{d}^2\phi}{\mathrm{d}z^2}\right]^2 \frac{\partial I_\omega}{\partial A} + G\left[\frac{\mathrm{d}\phi}{\mathrm{d}z}\right]^2 \frac{\partial J}{\partial A} + E\left[\frac{\mathrm{d}^2 u}{\mathrm{d}z^2}\right]^2 \frac{\partial I_y}{\partial A}$$

which agrees with the result of Popelar (1976, equation 31) and is one part of the complete set of necessary conditions for optimality of the problem.

Part D

Closure

The foregoing chapters have demonstrated that systems theory and in particular modern control theory offer a viable approach to the modelling and design of a broad range of structures. The approach is conceptually satisfying as at all times, appeal may be made to the physical interpretation of the components of the model and the design problem. As well, the approach offers certain computational advantages for both the closed form and numerical derivation of optimization results.

Part A outlined the basis for using control systems theory for the mathematical representation of structures. The fundamental ideas of state variables and control variables were described within standard or canonical state equation forms. This involved the recognition of the basic traits of structural systems and a reworking, into systematic forms, of the governing structural equations. The range of models covered ordinary differential equations, difference equations, several forms of partial differential equations and algebraic (non-difference) equations.

Control theory offers an alternative view to modelling, a view which leads to systematic and tidy thinking. Modelling is treated in a generalized form whereby whole classes of structures may be included under a single category. Similarly the characteristic descriptors of structures, namely their behaviour, geometry and material properties, may be grouped as states and controls. This generalization enables the system to be specified independently of particular cases which then only require the correct recognition of the system elements for definition. The framework of the modelling remains constant for all systems. The fundamental problems of analysis, synthesis and identification then take on precise forms and their solutions are embraced within the theory of control. Systems with probabilistic properties and stochastic problems require only a marginal extension of the basic deterministic ideas.

Conventional structural mechanics theory works with single level models although an hierarchy of levels has been demonstrated. Each subsystem level has its characteristic model (constitutive relationship) and subsystem interaction (equilibrium and compatibility relationships). Subsystems and subsystem interaction are fundamental to structures and the multilevel form of control theory exploits this. Such vertical decompositions can be complemented by horizontal decompositions and staging of subsystems.

Part B first established the logic of the conventional structural design process and indicated how economies may be achieved by regarding the design problem as a synthesis or optimization problem. Conceptually a synthesis approach is more rational than the conventional analysis based attack on the design problem. Historically, however, the synthesis approach has not been pursued and this is essentially because of the lack of suitable computational techniques. The development of this Part was a foundation for the later exposure of viable techniques for an optimization approach.

It was shown that the structural design problem logically has three components, namely a model of the structure, the design constraints and the design optimality criterion. Part A treated the modelling aspects according to a modern control systems theory format. Using the same general entities of state variables and control variables to describe the characteristics of the structure, general relationships were written for the constraints and the criterion. As with the modelling, the framework remains constant for all design problems and it only requires the correct recognition of the problem elements in particular cases. By systematically searching through a statement of a given design problem for the three fundamental problem components and completing their mathematical description in terms of state variables and control variables, objectivity and efficiency is given to design.

It is seen that the three fundamental design problem components define a problem in optimal control (leading logically to optimal control solution techniques, which exploit the composition of the design problem, in Part C). The mathematical characteristics of the optimal control problem, that is whether the relationships are algebraic equations, differential equations or difference equations, determine the appropriate optimization solution technique. General statements were given for problems amenable to solution by mathematical programming, Pontryagin's principle, the calculus of variations and dynamic programming. Indications were also given of the straightforward extensions of the problem statements to multicriteria and multilevel formats.

Having given general statements for a broad range of deterministic design problems in Part B, Part C gave the theory and algorithms required for the problem solutions. Structural examples were used throughout to illustrate the theory. The ideas of optimization were introduced through the elementary ideas of mathematical programming, leading to techniques that require more sophisticated mathematics and thinking.

Mathematical programming was developed from elementary calculus of extrema through to the Kuhn–Tucker conditions. Special forms of mathematical programming, namely linear, quadratic, separable and geometric were discussed and related to the overall body of mathematical programming literature. It was seen that by far the largest proportion of structural optimization publications have favoured the use of mathematical programming for several reasons; firstly because of the general availability of existing computer programs in all the various types of mathematical programming, secondly because the design problem formulation being in algebraic terms is uncomplicated and this corresponds to discrete model formulations in structural mechanics, thirdly because existing theory (most notably in linear programming) permits the solution of problems with a large number of variables and constraints, and lastly because most optimization problems can be transformed into a mathematical programming format. It was seen, however, that because the theory does not require any distinction between state variables and control variables, and between design constraints and the system model, a certain amount of untidyness of problem formulation has developed in the structural optimization literature.

Formulations were given for dynamic programming for system models that were in difference equation, ordinary differential equation, algebraic equation and partial differential equation form. Dynamic programming represents a solution philosophy rather than a distinct algorithm, as in the mathematical programming cases. The relationship to the calculus of variations and Pontryagin's principle was shown. To be amenable to solution by dynamic programming the system is required to have a staged organization, where the staging may be according to definite physical grounds or it may be conceptual. For certain problems the approach is powerful and neat, offering solutions to problems regarded as intractable by other methods. Dynamic programming offers most potential for the treatment of probabilistic optimization problems. Limitations on the method centre about computer requirements in the numerical case.

Pontryagin's principle or the calculus of variations, as with dynamic programming, provides neat solutions to a certain class of problems. The theory was given for systems with differential and difference equation models. Closed form solutions may be gained in many cases while numerous equation solving routines have been developed in the optimal control literature for the solution of the necessary conditions for optimality. Conceptually Pontryagin's principle is found useful for understanding the nature of decision (control) problems while a 'feel' for the solution of an optimization problem may be gained quickly though the exact solution may require considerable computation. The linear-quadratic problem, as in the case of dynamic programming, assumes a neat solution and this may be used as an approximation to a less tractable problem.

Additional necessary conditions for optimality are required when the problem is one of singular control. Several existing formulations in the structural optimization literature were shown to be singular control problems for which inadequate optimality conditions have been employed. To generally circumvent the occurrence of singular control problems it was suggested that structures be given models, and the variables chosen, with complete physical meaning in place of models and variables that satisfied the mathematical requirements of the problem formulation alone.

The essential theory behind mathematical programming, dynamic programming, Pontryagin's principle and the calculus of variations developed in Chapters 6 to 9, applied to problems in which there was a single optimality criterion and the system models were treated as a single level. Chapters 10 and 11 provided the extensions for the multicriteria and multilevel cases.

For the multicriteria case it was seen that existing approaches to the problem use as a basis (a) ideas related to penalty function or Lagrange multiplier arguments, (b) a trade off between the various criteria treated individually, or (c) the reduction of the problem to a single criterion problem. Pareto optimality concepts were introduced in order to attack structural design problems which are in general fundamentally multicriteria; the criteria may be commensurable or noncommensurable. Historically, however, it is the single criterion problem which has been the sole target in structural optimization.

The multilevel optimization treatment developed on the multilevel modelling of Part A. Any suitable optimization technique could be used in conjunction with the multilevel modelling ideas. Generally the procedure involved decomposing the single level problem into subproblems and iterative solution and coordination of the subproblems. That is, a series of small problems are solved many times in preference to one large problem. The approach appears attractive given that the present state of mathematical optimization enables the solution to be gained to small problems but confidence in the solution values for large problems is lacking. Where the subsystems are chosen with physical meaning, the approach appears to offer considerable potential for future development whether the problem is large or small. Computationally, at the present time however, forms of decomposition without physical meaning may be more rewarding for large problems but this approach does not appear to have the same future promise as decomposition chosen on physical grounds.

The systematic approaches to optimization presented in Chapter 6 to 11 may be complemented by an *ad hoc* technique involving the reworking of the equations of Lyapunov's direct method. A result was given whereby the parameters of a dynamic system may be chosen to give an optimal performance result while the associated optimal structure has asymptotic stability properties. This was a specialized result for a specialized problem and lacked the generality of the other optimization approaches. Within its domain of application, however, the technique is quite useful.

The final chapter attempted to tie together some of the structural optimization literature which has been approached from a structural mechanics viewpoint rather than a systems theory viewpoint. In particular it was shown through examples that results derived using energy and 'optimality criteria' arguments correspond with results which may be derived from the systems optimization techniques presented in the preceding chapters. Considerable success appears to have been obtained by researchers using energy and 'optimality criteria' approaches and generally the conclusions from that work support the philosophy repeatedly advanced in this book. In particular it is argued that designers should include as much knowledge of the mechanics of structural behaviour and physical meaning as possible in the optimization study and not rely purely on mathematical formulations of the optimization problem.

References

AGARD-AG-149-71 (1971), 'Structural Design Applications of Mathematical Programming Methods' (eds. G. G. Pope and L. A. Schmit), AGARDograph No. **149**.

AGARD-CP-36-70 (1970), 'Symposium on Structural Optimization'.

AGARD-CP-123 (1973), 'Second Symposium on Structural Optimization'.

AIAA (1972), Film on Structural Synthesis, *Astronautics and Aeronautics*, August.

Abadie, J. (1967) (ed.), *Nonlinear Programming*, Wiley.

Agrawal, G. K. (1978), Helical Torsion Springs for Minimum Weight by Geometric Programming, *JOTA*, **25**, 2, 307–310.

Ahmadi, G. and Mostaghel, N. (1978), On the Stability of Columns Subjected to Non-Stationary Random or Deterministic Support Motion, *Earthquake Eng. Struct. Dyn.*, **6**, 3, 321–326, May–June.

Ames, W. F. (1965), *Nonlinear Partial Differential Equations in Engineering: Vol I*, Academic Press.

Andreev, L. V., Mossakovskii, V. I. and Obodan, N. I. (1972), On Optimal Thickness of a Cylindrical Shell Loaded by External Pressure, *PMM*, **36**, 4, 717–725 (*App. Math. Mech.* 677–685).

Andreev, L. V., Mossakovskii, V. I. and Obodan, N. I. (1976), Maximum Principle in Problems of Optimal Design of Reinforced Shells for Nonuniform Loading, *PMM*, **40**, 3, 569–573 (*App. Math. Mech*, 522–526).

Angel, E. (1968a), Discrete Invariant Imbedding and Elliptic Boundary–Value Problems over Irregular Regions, *J. Math. Anal. Appl.*, **23**, 471–484.

Angel, E. (1968b), Dynamic Programming and Linear Partial Differential Equations, *J. Math. Anal. Appl.*, **23**, 628–638.

Angel, E. (1970), Inverse Boundary–Value Problems: Elliptic Equations, *J. Math. Anal. Appl.*, **30**, 86–98.

Angel, E. (1973), Irregular Regions and Constrained Optimization, *ASCE Eng. Mech. Div.*, **99**, EM3, 581–596.

Angel, E. and Bellman, R. (1972), *Dynamic Programming and Partial Differential Equations*, Academic Press.

Angel, E. and Distefano N. (1972), Invariant Imbedding and the Effects of Changes of Poisson's Ratio in Thin Plate Theory, *Int. J. Eng. Sci.*, **10**, 401–408.

Angel, E., Distefano, N. and Jain, N. (1971), Invariant Imbedding and the

Reduction of Boundary-Value Problems of Thin Plate Theory to Cauchy Formulations, *Int. J. Eng. Sci.*, **9**, 933–945.

Aoki, M. (1968), Control of Large Scale Systems by Aggregation, *IEEE Trans. Aut. Cont.*, **AC-13**, 3, 245–253.

Aoki, M. (1971), Aggregation, in *Optimization Methods for Large-Scale Systems* (ed. D. A. Wismer) ch 5, 191–232, McGraw-Hill.

Aris, R. (1964), *Discrete Dynamic Programming*, Blaisdell.

Aris, R., Nemhauser, G. L. and Wilde, D. J. (1964). Optimization of Multistage Cyclic and Branching Systems by Serial Procedures, *A.I.Ch.E. Jnl.*, **10**, 913–919.

Armand, J.-L.P. (1971), Minimum-Mass Design of a Plate-Like Structure for Specified Fundamental Frequency, *AIAA Jnl*, **9**, 1739–1745.

Armand, J.-L.P. (1972), Applications of the Theory of Optimal Control of Distributed-Parameter Systems to Structural Optimization, NASA CR-2044, June. (Ph.D. Thesis).

Armand, J.-L.P. (1975), Applications of Optimal Control Theory to Structural Optimization: Analytical and Numerical Approach, Proc. IUTAM Symp. on *Optimization in Structural Design* (eds. A. Sawczuk and Z. Mroz), Warsaw 1973, Springer-Verlag.

Armand, J.-L.P. (1976). Optimization of Structural Elements, in 'Optimization Techniques, Modelling and Optimization in the Service of Man', *Proc. 7th IFIP Conf. Nice*, Sept. 1975 (ed. J. Cea), Springer-Verlag.

Armand, J.-L. P. and Vitte, W. J. (1970), Foundations of Aeroelastic Optimization and Some Applications to Continuous Systems, Stanford Univ., Dept. Aero, Astron., Report 390.

Arora, J. S. and Govril, A. K. (1977), An Efficient Method for Optimal Structural Design by Substructuring, *Comp. and Struct.*, **7**, 507–515.

Arora, J. S., Haug, E. J. and Rim, K. (1971), Optimal Design of Trusses under Multiple Constraint Conditions of Mechanics, *Developments in Mechanics*, Vol. 6, Univ. Notre Dame Press, 831–834.

Arora, J. S., Haug E. J. and Rim K. (1975), Optimal Design of Plane Frames, *ASCE J. Struct. Div.*, **101**, ST10, 16 pp.

Arora, J. S. and Haug E. J. (1976), Efficient Optimal Design of Structures by Generalized Steepest Descent Programming, *Int. J. Num. Meth. Eng.*, **10**, 20 pp.

Arrow, K. J., Hurwicz, L. and Zawa, H. U., (1958), *Studies in Linear and Nonlinear Programming*, Stanford Univ. Press.

Ashley, H. and McIntosh, S. C. (1969), Application of Aeroelastic Constraints in Structural Optimization, in *Applied Mechanics* (eds. M. Hetenyi and W. G. Vincenti), Springer-Verlag, 100–113.

Athans, M. (1966), The Status of Optimal Control Theory and Applications for Deterministic Systems, *IEEE Int. Conv. Record*, Part 6, 100–124; also *IEEE Trans. Aut. Control*, **AC-11**, 580–596.

Athans, M. and Falb, P. L. (1966), *Optimal Control, An Introduction to the Theory and its Applications*, McGraw-Hill.

Athans, M. and Geering, H. P. (1973), Necessary and Sufficient Conditions for Differentiable Nonscalar-Valued Functions to Attain Extrema, *IEEE Trans. Aut. Control*, **AC-18**, 2.

Au, T. (1966). Heuristic Games for Structural Design, *ASCE J. Struct. Div.*, ST6, 499-509.

Baker, K. N., Carmichael, D. G. and Van der Meer, A. T. (1978), A Multilevel-Staged Approach to the Optimal Design of Industrial Portal

Frame Structures, Inst. Eng. Australia, Metal Structures Conference, Perth; Also *Trans. I.E. Aust.*, **CE22**, 2, 55–61, 1980.

Balakrishnan, A. V. (1963), An Operator Theoretic Formulation of a Class of Control Problems and a Steepest Descent Method of Solution, *SIAM J. Control*, **1**, 109–127.

Balakrishnan, A. V. (1965), Optimal Control Problems in Banach Spaces, *SIAM J. Control*, **3**, 152–179.

Balinski, M. L. (1965), Integer Programming: Methods, Uses, Computation, *Management Sci.*, **12**, 253–313.

Banichuk, N. V. (1973), On the Game Theory Approach to Problems of Optimization of Elastic Bodies, *App. Math. Mech. (PMM)*, **37**, 6, 1098–1108. (Trans. 1042–1052).

Banichuk, N. V. (1975), Game Problems in the Theory of Optimal Design, in *Optimization in Structural Design*, IUTAM Symp., Warsaw 1973 (eds. A. Sawczuk and Z. Mroz), Springer, 111–121.

Banichuk, N. V. (1976) Minimax Approach to Structural Optimization Problems, *JOTA*, **20**, 1, 111–127.

Banichuk, N. V. and Karihaloo, B. L. (1977), On the Solution of Optimization Problems with Singularities, *Int. J. Solids Structs.*, **13**, 725–733.

Barnett, R. L. (1966), A Survey of Optimum Structural Design, *Exp. Mech.*, **6**, 12, 19A–26A.

Bartel, D. L. and Marks, R. W. (1974), Optimum Design of Mechanical Systems with Competing Design Objectives, *J. Eng. Ind., ASME, Ser B*, **96**, 1, 171–178.

Bartel, D., Rim, K. and Haug, E. J. (1971), The Optimum Design of Spatial Frames Using the Method of Constrained Steepest Descent with State Equations, *ASME J. Basic Eng.*, Feb., 1261–1268.

Baty, J. P. and Williams, G. (1973), Graph-Theoretic Decomposition of Large Structural Network Systems, in *Decomposition of Large Scale Problems* (ed. D. M. Himmelblau), 307–322, North Holland.

Bauman, E. J. (1968a), Multilevel Optimization Techniques with Application to Trajectory Decomposition, in *Advances in Control Systems: Theory and Applications* (ed. C. T. Leondes), Vol. 6, 159–220.

Bauman, E. J. (1968b), Two Level Optimization Techniques for Dynamic Systems, *Int. J. Control*, **8**, 5, 473–481.

Bauman, E. J. (1971), Trajectory Decomposition, in *Optimization Methods for Large Scale Systems with Applications* (ed. D. A. Wismer), ch. 7, 275–290.

Beale, E. M. L. (1955), On Minimizing a Convex Function Subject to Linear Inequalities, *Jnl. Royal Stat. Soc. (B)*, **17**, 172–184.

Bell, D. J. (1975), Singular Problems in Optimal Control—a Survey, *Int. J. Control*, **21**, 2, 319–331.

Bell, D. J. and Jacobson, D. H. (1975), *Singular Optimal Control Problems*, Academic Press.

Bellamy, N. W. and West, M. J. (1969), Methods of Profile Optimisation by Iterative Analogue Computation, *Computer Jnl*, **12**, 132–138.

Beliveau, J.-G. (1977), Eigenrelations in Structural Dynamics, *A.I.A.A. Jnl.*, **15**, 7, 1039–1041.

Bellman, R. (1957), *Dynamic Programming*, Princeton University Press.

Bellman, R. (1961), *Adaptive Control Processes: A Guided Tour*, Princeton Univ. Press.

Bellman, R. (1963), Mathematical Model Making as an Adaptive Process, in

Mathematical Optimization Techniques (ed. R. Bellman), Univ. Calif. Press, 333–339.

Bellman, R. (1967), *Introduction to the Mathematical Theory of Control Processes, Vol. I*, Academic Press.

Bellman, R. and Dreyfus, S. E. (1962), *Applied Dynamic Programming*, Princeton University Press.

Bellman, R. and Kalaba, R. (1960), Dynamic Programming and Adaptive Processes, Mathematical Foundation, *IRE Trans. Aut. Control*, **5**, 5–10.

Bellman, R. and Kalaba, R. (1961), Reduction of Dimensionality, Dynamic Programming and Control Processes, *J. Basic Engng, ASME, Series D*, **83**, 82–84.

Bellman, R. and Kalaba, R. (1962), Dynamic Programming Applied to Control Processes Governed by General Functional Equations, *Proc. Nat. Acad. Sci. USA*, **48**, 1735–1737.

Bellman, R. and Kalaba, R. (1965), *Dynamic Programming and Modern Control Theory*, Academic Press.

Bellman, R. and Osborn, H. (1958), Dynamic Programming and the Variation of Green's Functions, *J. Math. Mech.*, **7**, 81–85.

Benders, J. F. (1962), Partitioning Procedures For Solving Mixed-Variables Programming Problems, *Numerische Math.*, **4**, 238–252.

Benton, S. H. (1977), *The Hamilton–Jacobi Equation: A Global Approach*, Academic Press.

Berke, L. and Venkayya, V. B. (1974), Review of Optimality Criteria Approaches to Structural Optimization, *ASME Struct. Opt. Symp.* (ed. L. A. Schmit), 23–34.

Berkovitz, L. D. (1961), Variational Methods in Problems of Control and Programming, *J. Math. Anal. Appl.*, **3**, 1, 145–169.

Berkovitz, L. D. (1962), On Control Problems with Bounded State Variables, *J. Math. Anal. Appl.*, **4**, 488–498.

Bertele, U. and Brioschi, F. (1972), *Nonserial Dynamic Programming*, Academic Press.

Beveridge, G. S. and Schechter, R. S. (1970), *Optimization: Theory and Practice*, McGraw-Hill.

Bharucha-Reid, A. T. (1960), *Elements of the Theory of Markov Processes and their Applications*, McGraw-Hill.

Bigelow, R. H. and Gaylord, E. H. (1967), Design of Steel Frames for Minimum Weight, *ASCE, J. Struct. Div.*, **93**, ST6, 109–131.

Birkeland, H. W. (1974), How to Design Prestressed Concrete Beams with Minimum Cross Section, *Jnl. A.C.I.*, December, 634–641.

Bliss, G. A. (1946), *Lectures on the Calculus of Variations*, Univ. of Chicago Press.

Blum, E. K. (1967), The Calculus of Variations, Functional Analysis and Optimal Control Problems, in *Topics in Optimization* (ed. G. Leitmann), Academic Press, 417–461.

Boltyanskii, V. G. (1971), *Mathematical Methods of Optimal Control*, Holt, Rinehart and Winston (Russian ed., 1965).

Bolza, O. (1931), *Calculus of Variations*, Chelsea.

Bolza, O. (1961). *Lectures on the Calculus of Variations*, Dover.

Boot, J. C. G. (1964), *Quadratic Programming*, North Holland.

Borges, J. F. and Castanheta, M. (1968), *Structural Safety*, 1st ed., Laboratorio Nacional de Engenharia Civil, Lisbon (2nd ed. 1971).

Borkowski, A. (1975), On Optimization of the Limit Load, *Bull. de. L'Acadamie Polonaise des Sciences*, **23**, 11, 525–530 (919–924).

Borkowski, A. and Atkociunas, J. (1975), Optimal Design for Cyclic Loading, in *Optimization in Structural Design* (eds. A. Sawczuk and Z. Mroz), Springer-Verlag, 433–440.

Boudarel, R., Delmas, J. and Guichet, P. (1971), *Dynamic Programming and its Application to Optimal Control*, Academic Press.

Boykin, W. H. and Sierakowski, R. L. (1972), Remarks on Pontryagin's Maximum Principle Applied to a Structural Optimisation Problem, *Aero Jnl of Royal Aero Soc.*, 175–176.

Bracken, J. and McCormick, G. P. (1968), *Selected Applications of Nonlinear Programming*, Wiley.

Bradley, J., Brown, L. H. and Feeney, H. (1974), Cost Optimization in Relation to Factory Structures, *Eng. Optimzn.*, **1**, 125–128.

Brogan, W. L. (1967a, b), Theory and Application of Optimal Control for Distributed Parameter Systems — I, Theory, *Automatica*, **4**, 107–120; II, Computational Results, *Automatica*, **4**, 121–137.

Brogan, W. L. (1968a), Dynamic Programming and a Distributed Parameter Maximum Principle, *J. Basic Engng, ASME, Series D*, **90**, 152–156.

Brogan, W. L. (1968b), Optimal Control Theory Applied to Systems Described by Partial Differential Equations, in *Advances in Control Systems: Theory and Applications*, Vol. 6 (ed. C. T. Leondes), 221–316, Academic Press.

Brotchie, J. F. (1962), Direct Design of Plate and Shell Structures, *ASCE, J. Struct. Div.*, **88**, 127–148, Dec.

Brotchie, J. F. (1963), A Concept for the Direct Design of Structures, *Civ. Eng. Trans., I. E. Aust.*, **CE5**, 2, 61–66, Sept.

Brotchie, J. F. (1964), Direct Design of Prestressed Concrete Flat Plate Structures, *Constructional Review*, **37**, 13–15, Jan.

Brotchie, J. F. (1967), On the Structural Design Problem, *Trans. I. E. Aust.*, **CE9**, 1, 151–156.

Brotchie, J. F. (1969), Criterion for Optimal Design of Plates, *ACI J.*, **66**, 11, 898–906.

Bryson, A. E. and Ho. Y.-C. (1969), *Applied Optimal Control*, Ginn and Co (2nd ed. Hemisphere 1975).

Budak, B. M. (1969), Difference Approximations in Optimal Control Problems, *SIAM J. Control*, **7**, 18–31.

Butkovskii, A. G. (1961), Optimum Processes in Systems with Distributed Parameters, *Automn Remote Control*, **22**, 13–21.

Butkovskii, A. G. (1962), The Maximum Principle for Optimum Systems with Distributed Parameters, *Automn Remote Control*, **22**, 1156–1169.

Butkovskii, A. G. (1969), *Distributed Control Systems* (Eng. Trans.), American Elsevier (Russian edition; Navka, Moscow, 1965).

Butkovskii, A. G., Egorov, A. I. and Lurie, K. A. (1968), Optimal Control of Distributed Systems (A Survey of Soviet Publications), *SIAM J. Control*, **6**, 437–476.

Butkovskii, A. G. and Lerner, A. Ya. (1960), The Optimal Control of Systems with Distributed Parameters, *Automn Remote Control*, **21**, 472–477.

Butkovskii, A. G. and Lerner, A. Ya. (1961), Optimal Control Systems with Distributed Parameters, *Soviet Phys. Dokl.*, **5**, 936–939.

Canon, M. D., Cullum, C. D. and Polak, E. (1970), *Theory of Optimal Control and Mathematical Programming*, McGraw-Hill.

Carmichael, D. G. (1975), Control Systems Theory and the Mathematical Modelling and Design of Structures, Univ. Canterbury, Dept. Civil Eng., Research Report 75–9.

Carmichael, D. G. (1977a), Singular Optimal Control Problems in the Design of Vibrating Structures, *Jnl. Sound Vibrn.*, **53**, 2, 245–253.

Carmichael, D. G. (1977b), On a Minimum Weight Disk Design Problem, *Trans. ASME, J. App. Mech., Ser. E*, **44**, 3, 506–507.

Carmichael, D. G. (1978a), Probabilistic Design of Structures in State Equation Form, *Eng. Optimzn.*, **3**, 2, 83–92.

Carmichael, D. G. (1978b), Optimal Control in the Design of Material Continua, *Archives of Mechanics (Arch. Mech. Stos.)*, **30**, 6, 743–755.

Carmichael, D. G. (1979a), Lyapunov Theory in Structural Design, *Eng. Optimzn*, **4**, 3, 159–163.

Carmichael, D. G. (1979b), On the Optimum Design of Structures Against Buckling, Univ. Western Australia, Civil Eng. Dept. Res. Report.

Carmichael, D. G. (1980), Computation of Pareto Optima in Structural Design, *Int. J. Num. Meth. Eng.*, **15**, 925–929.

Carmichael, D. G. and Clyde, D. H. (1975), A Basis for the Use of Control Systems Theory in the Mathematical Modelling of Structures, Fifth Australas. Conf. Mech. Struct. Mat., 47–62, Melbourne.

Carmichael, D. G. and Clyde, D. H. (1976), A Rational Approach to Design Code Formats, Metal Structures Conf., I. E. Aust., 104–108, Adelaide.

Carmichael, D. G. and Clyde, D. H. (1977), Observations on the Theory of Optimal Load Transmission by Flexure, Sixth Australas. Conf. Mech. Struct. Mat., Univ. Canterbury, N.Z., 383–390.

Carmichael, D. G. and Clyde, D. H. (1979), Multilevel Control Concepts in Relation to the Structural Design Problem, IUTAM Symp. on Structural Control, Univ. Waterloo; Also in *Structural Control* (ed. H. H. E. Leipholz), 171–198, North Holland, 1980.

Carmichael, D. G. and Clyde, D. H. (1980), On the Optimum Flexure Problem in Structural Mechanics, *Optimal Control Applic. Methods*, **1**, 143–154.

Carmichael, D. G. and Elms, D. G. (1975), Markovian Assumptions and Stochastic Structural Design, Fifth Australas. Conf. Mech. Struct. Mat., Univ. Melbourne, 63–78.

Carmichael, D. G. and Goh, B. S. (1977), Optimal Vibrating Plates and a Distributed Parameter Singular Control Problem, *Int. J. Control*, **26**, 1, 19–31.

Carver, D. R. (1967), Dynamic Programming and Mechanics, *Eng. Educ.*, May, 631–635.

Casti, J. L. (1977), *Dynamical Systems and Their Applications: Linear Theory*, Academic Press.

Cella, A. and Soosaar, K. (1973), Discrete Variables in Structural Optimization, in *Optimum Structural Design* (eds. R. H. Gallagher and O. C. Zienkiewicz), Wiley, 201–223.

Chan, H. S. Y. (1968a), Minimum Volume Design of Frameworks and Discs for Alternative Loading Systems, *Quart. Appl. Math.*, **25**, 4, 470–473.

Chan, H. S. Y. (1968b), Mathematical Programming in Optimal Plastic Design, *Int. J. Solids Struct.*, **4**, 9, 885–894.

Chang, S. S. L. (1960), Digitized Maximum Principle, *Proc. IRE*, 2030–2031.

Chang, S. S. L. (1961), *Synthesis of Optimum Control Systems*, McGraw-Hill.

Chang, S.S.L. (1962), Optimal Control in Bounded Phase Space, *Automatica*, **1**, 55–67.

Charrett, D. E. and Rozvany, G. I. N. (1972), Extensions of the Prager-Shield Theory of Optimal Plastic Design, *Int. J. Non-linear Mech.*, **7**, 1, 51–64.

Chaudhuri, A. K. (1965), Concerning Optimal Control of Linear Distributed Parameter Systems, *Int. J. Control*, **2**, 365–394.

Chen, R. M. M. and Perlis, H. J. (1967), The Application of Multi-level Techniques to the Identification of State Variables, *Proc. JACC,* 236–240.

Chern, J. M. and Prager, W. (1970), Optimal Design of Rotating Disk for Given Radial Displacement of Edge, *Jnl. Optimization Theory Appl.*, **6**, 2, 161–170.

Chu, K. C. (1970), On the Non-Inferior Set for Systems with Vector-Valued Objective Functions, *IEEE Trans. Aut. Cont.*, **AC-15**, 5.

Citron, S. J. (1969), *Elements of Optimal Control*, Holt, Rinehart and Winston.

Clyde, D. H. (1965), Discussion on 'Plastic Design of Slabs Using Equilibrium Methods', by R. H. Wood, *Flexural Mechanics of Reinforced Concrete*, ASCE, Miami, Fla., Nov. 10–12, 1964.

Clyde, D. H. (1970a), 'The Mechanics of Reinforced Concrete', Lectures 1 and 2, Graduate Course, The University of Sydney, School of Civil Engineering, July–August.

Clyde, D. H. (1970b), Unpublished graduate lecture notes, The University of Sydney, School of Civil Engineering.

Clyde, D. H. and Sharpe, R. (1965), Discussion on 'Optimum Synthesis of Prestressed Structures', by G. I. N. Rozvany, *ASCE, J. Struct. Div.*, **91**, ST4, 236–241.

Cochrane, J. L. and Zeleny, M. (eds.) (1973), *Multiple Criteria Decision Making*, Univ. Sth. Carolina Press.

Cohn, M. Z. (1965), Optimum Limit Design for Reinforced Concrete Continuous Beams, *Proc. ICE*, **30**, 4, 675–707, April.

Cohn, M. Z. (1968), (ed.), *An Introduction to Structural Optimization*, Study No. 1, Solid Mech. Div., Univ. Waterloo.

Cohn, M. Z. and Maier, G. (1977) (eds.), *Engineering Plasticity by Mathematical Programming*, NATO Advanced Study Institute, Univ. Waterloo (Pergamon, 1979).

Comite Europeen du Beton (1964), 'Recommendations for an International Code of Practice for Reinforced Concrete (English Trans.), C. and C.A., London.

Courant, R. and Hilbert, D. (1953 — vol. I, 1962 — vol II), *Methods of Mathematical Physics*, Interscience (Wiley).

Cox, H. L. (1965), *The Design of Structures for Least Weight,* Pergamon.

Cullum, J. (1969), Discrete Approximations to Continuous Optimal Control Problems, *SIAM J. Control*, **7**, 32–49.

Cullum, J., (1970), An Explicit Method for Discretizing Continuous Optimal Control Problems, *JOTA*, **5**.

Cyras, A. (1975), Optimization Theory in the Design of Elastic-Plastic Structures, 'Structural Optimization', CISM Courses and Lectures, No. 237, Springer-Verlag.

Da Cunha, N. O. and Polak, E. (1967), Constrained Minimization under Vector Valued Criteria in Finite Dimensional Spaces, *Jnl. Math. Anal. Appl.*, **19**, 1.

Daniel, J. W. (1971), *The Approximate Minimization of Functionals*, Prentice-Hall.

Dantzig, G. B. (1963), *Linear Programming and Extensions*, Princeton Univ. Press.

Dantzig, G. B. and Van Slyke, R. M. (1971), Generalized Linear Programming, in *Optimization Methods for Large Scale Systems* (ed. D. A. Wismer), 75–120, McGraw-Hill.

de Silva, B. M. E. (1969), The Application of Nonlinear Programming to the Automated Minimum Weight Design of Rotating Discs, in *Optimization* (ed. R. Fletcher), 115–150, Academic Press.

de Silva, B. M. E. (1970), Application of Pontryagin's Principle to a Minimum Weight Design Problem, *ASME Jnl. Basic Eng.*, **92**, 245–250.

de Silva, B. M. E. (1972), Optimal Vibrational Modes of a Disc, *J. Sound Vibrn.* **21**, 1, 19–34.

de Silva, B. M. E. (1975), Optimal Control Concepts in the Design of Turbine Discs and Blades, *Shock Vibrn. Digest*, **7**, 5, 63–76.

de Silva, B. M. E. and Grant, G. N. C. (1975), Optimal Frequency — Weight Computations for a Disc, *Int. J. Num. Methods Eng.*, **9**, 509–533.

de Silva B. M. E. and Grant, G. N. C. (1978), Comparison of Some Optimal Control Methods for the Design of Turbine Blades, *ASME J. Mech. Des.*, **100**, 1, 173–182.

de Silva, B. M. E., Green, D. R. and Grant, G. N. C. (1976), Two-Point Boundary Value Problems in the Optimal Control Design of Turbine Blades, *Shock Vibrn. Digest*, **8**, 6, 25–33.

de Silva, B. M. E., Negus, B. and Worster, J. (1976), Mathematical Programming Method for the Optimal Design of Turbine Blade Shapes, *J. Sound Vibrn.*, **46**, 501–514.

de Silva, C. W. (1975), A Technique to Model the Simply Supported Timoshenko Beam in the Design of Mechanical Vibrating Systems, *Int. J. Mech. Sci.*, **17**, 389–393.

de Silva, C. W. (1976), Dynamic Beam Model with Internal Damping Rotatory Inertia and Shear Deformation, *A.I.A.A. Jnl.*, **14**, 5, 676–680.

Den Hartog, J. P. (1952), *Advanced Strength of Materials*, McGraw-Hill.

Denn, M. M. (1966), Optimal Boundary Control for a Nonlinear Distributed System, *Int. J. Control*, **4**, 167–178.

Denn, M. M. (1969), *Optimization by Variational Methods*, McGraw-Hill.

Desoer, C. A. (1961), Pontryagin's Maximum Principle and the Principle of Optimality, *J. Franklin Inst.*, **271**, 5, 361–367.

Di Maggio, F. L. (1963), Statical Determinacy and Stability of Structures, *ASCE, J. Struct. Div.*, **89**, ST3, 63–75.

Distefano N. (1970), Invariant Imbedding, in 'Lecture Notes in Operations Research and Mathematical Systems', No. 52, Springer-Verlag, 118–148.

Distefano, N. (1971), Dynamic Programming and the Solution of the Biharmonic Equation, *Int. J. Num. Meth. Engg.*, **3**, 199–213.

Distefano, N. (1972a), Dynamic Programming and the Optimum Design of Rotating Disks, *J. Optimization Theory Appl.*, **10**, 2, 109–128.

Distefano, N. (1972b), Dynamic Programming and a Max-Min Problem in the Theory of Structures, *J. Franklin Inst.*, **294**, 5, 339–350.

Distefano, N. (1974a), *Nonlinear Processes in Engineering*, Academic Press.

Distefano, N. (1974b), Invariant Imbedding and the Solution of Finite Element Equations, *Jnl. Math. Anal. Appl.*, **46**, 2, 487–498.

Distefano, N. (1975), Dynamic Programming and the Optimization of Two-Point Boundary-Value Systems, *Jnl. Math. Anal. Appl.*, **52**, 1,142–150.

Distefano, N. and Bellows, G. (1977), Application of Coupled Dynamic Programming to Two-Point Boundary-Value Systems, *JOTA*, **23**, 1, 15–26.

Distefano, N. and Chiu, H. (1977), A One-Sweep Method in the Solution of Finite-Element Equations: An Application to the Vibration of Structures in Heavy Fluids, *JOTA*, **23**, 1, 27–40.

Distefano, N. and Jain, A. (1974), A One Sweep Method for Linear Elliptic Equations over Irregular Domains, *JOTA*, **14**, 6, 585–597.

Distefano, N. and Rath, A. (1975), A Dynamic Programming Approach to the Optimization of Elastic Trusses, *JOTA*, **15**, 1, 13–26.

Distefano, N. and Samartin, A. (1975), A Dynamic Programming Approach to the Formulation and Solution of Finite Element Equations, *Comp. Meth. App. Mech. Eng.*, **5**, 1, 37–52.

Distefano, N. and Schujman, J. (1971), Solutions of Elastic Plates by Invariant Imbedding, *ASCE, J. Eng. Mech. Div.*, EM5, 1349–1361.

Distefano, N. and Todeschini, R. (1972), Invariant Imbedding and Optimum Beam Design with Displacement Constraints, *Int. J. Solids Structs.*, **8**, 1073–1087.

Distefano N. and Todeschini R. (1975), A Quasilinearization Approach to the Solution of Elastic Beams on Nonlinear Foundations, *Int. J. Solids Struct.*, **11**, 89–97.

Dixon, L. C. W. (1967), Pontryagin's Maximum Principle Applied to the Profile of a Beam, *Aero Jnl of Royal Aero Soc.*, 513–515.

Dixon, L. C. W. (1968), Further Comments on Pontryagin's Maximum Principle Applied to the Profile of a Beam, *Aero Jnl of Royal Aero Soc.*, 518–519.

Dixon, L. C. W. (1972), *Nonlinear Optimisation*, The English Universities Press.

Doob, J. L. (1953), *Stochastic Processes*, Wiley.

Dorn, W. S., Gomory, R. E. and Greenberg, H. J. (1964), Automatic Design of Optimal Structures, *J. de Mecanique*, **3**, 1, 25–52.

Douty, R. (1966), Optimization of a Two-span Cover-plated Steel Beam, in *Computers in Engineering Design Education, III,* 34–50, Civil Engineering, University of Michigan, Ann Arbor.

Douty, R. T. (1972), Structural Optimization with Dynamic Programming Utility Tables, *Proc. Int. Symp. Computer Aided Structural Design,* Univ. Warwick, 10–14 July, A 2.18–A 2.31.

Dreyfus, S. E. (1965), *Dynamic Programming and the Calculus of Variations*, Academic Press.

Duffin, R. J., Peterson, E. L. and Zener, C. M. (1967), *Geometric Programming*, Wiley.

Dyer, P. and McReynolds, S. R. (1970), *The Computation and Theory of Optimal Control*, Academic Press.

Dym, C. L. (1974a), *Stability Theory and its Applications to Structural Mechanics*, Noordhoff.

Dym. C. L. (1974b), Some Recent Approaches to Structural Optimization, *J. Sound Vibrn*, **32**, 1, 49–70.

Egorov, A. I. (1963), On Optimum Control of Processes in Distributed Objects, *Appl. Math. Mech. (PMM)*, **27**, 1045–1058.

Egorov, A. I. (1964), Optimal Control by Processes in Certain Systems with Distributed Parameters, *Automn Remote Control*, **25**, 557–567.

Egorov, A. I. (1965 a,b), Optimal Processes in Systems Containing Distributed Parameter Plants, Parts I and II, *Automn Remote Control*, **26**, 972–988, 1178–1187.

Egorov, A. I. (1966), Optimal Processes in Distributed Parameter Systems and Certain Problems in Invariance Theory, *SIAM J. Control*, **4**, 601–661.

Egorov, A. I. (1967a), Necessary Optimality Conditions for Distributed Parameter Systems, *SIAM J. Control*, **5**, 352–408.

Egorov, A. I. (1967b), Optimality Conditions on Systems Containing Components with Distributed Parameters, *Mathematical Theory of Control* (eds. A. V. Balakrishnan and L. W. Neustadt), 322–329, Academic Press.

Egorov, Yu. V. (1963), Optimal Control in Banach Space, *Dokl. Akad. Nauk, SSSR*, **150**, 241–244; Translation in *Soviet Math. Dokl.*, **4**, 630–633, MR 26 # 7470.

Egorov, Yu. V. (1966), Necessary Conditions for the Optimality of Control in Banach Spaces, *Am. Math. Soc. Trans.*, **49**, Series 2, 63–85.

Elgerd, O. I. (1967), *Control Systems Theory*, McGraw-Hill.

Elsgolc, L. E. (1961), *Calculus of Variations* (Russian Trans.), Pergamon Press.

Erzberger, H. and Kim, M. (1966a), Optimum Distributed-Parameter Systems with Distributed Control, *Proc. IEEE*, **54**, 714–715.

Erzberger, H. and Kim, M. (1966b), Optimum Boundary Control of Distributed Parameter Systems, *Inform Control*, **9**, 265–278.

Falb, P. L. (1964), Infinite Dimensional Control Problems — I: On the Closure of the Set of Attainable States for Linear Systems, *J. Math. Anal. Appl.*, **9**, 12–22.

Fan, L. T. and Wang, C. S. (1964), *The Discrete Maximum Principle*, Wiley.

Fel'dbaum, A. A. (1965), *Optimal Control Systems*, Academic Press.

Fenves, S. J. (1966a), Structural Analysis of Networks, Matrices and Computers, *ASCE J. Struct. Div.*, **92**, ST1, 199–221.

Fenves, S. J. (1966b), Tabular Decision Logic for Structural Design, *ASCE, J. Struct. Div.*, **92**, ST6, 473–490.

Fenves, S. J. (1973), Decomposition of Provisions of Design Specifications, in *Decomposition of Large Scale Problems* (ed. D. M. Himmelblau), 43–56, North Holland.

Fenves, S. J. and Branin, F. H. (1963), Network-Topological Formulation of Structural Analysis, *ASCE J. Struct. Div.*, 483–514.

Fenves, S. J. and Gonzalez-Caro, A. (1971), Network-Topological Formulation of Analysis and Design of Rigid Plastic Framed Structures, *Int. J. Num. Meth. Eng.*, **3**, 425–441.

Fiacco, A. V. and McCormick, G. P. (1968), *Nonlinear Programming: Sequential Unconstrained Minimization Techniques*, Wiley.

Fisher, M. E. and Goh, B. S. (1977), Stability in a Class of Discrete Time Models of Interacting Populations, *J. Math. Biology*, **4**, 265–274.

Fleury, C. and Geradin, M. (1978), Optimality Criteria and Mathematical Programming in Structural Weight Optimization, *Comp. and Struct.*, **8**, 7–17.

Flugge, W. (1973), *Stresses in Shells*, 2nd ed., Springer-Verlag.

Foulkes, J. (1953), Minimum Weight Design and the Theory of Plastic Collapse, *Quart. Appl. Math.*, **10**, 347.

Foulkes, J. (1954), The Minimum Weight Design of Structural Frames, *Proc. Royal Soc., A*, **223**, 482.

Fox, R. L. (1971), *Optimization Methods for Engineering Design*, Addison-Wesley.

Francis, A. J. (1953), Direct Design of Elastic Statically Indeterminate Triangulated Frameworks for Single Systems of Loads, *Aust. J. App. Sci.*, **4**, 2, 175–185, June.

Francis, A. J. (1955), Direct Design of Non-Linear Redundant Triangulated Frameworks, *Aust. J. App. Sci.*, **6**, 1, 13–31, March.

Francis, R. (1973), Optimal Design of Prestressed Concrete Continuous Beams, Univ. Waterloo, Solid Mech. Div. Study No. 8 (ed. M. Z. Cohn), 441–470.

Freudenthal, A. M. (1950), *The Inelastic Behavior of Engineering Materials and Structures*, Wiley.

Freudenthal, A. M., Garrelts, J. M. and Shinozuka, M. (1966), The Analysis of Structural Safety, *ASCE J. Struct. Div.*, **92**, ST1, 267–326, Proc. Paper 4682.

Fry, C. M. and Sage, A. P. (1973), On Hierarchical Estimation and System Identification Using the MAP Criterion, *Comput. and Elec. Eng.*, **1**, 361–389.

Fuller, A. T. (1960a), Phase Space in the Theory of Optimum Control, *J. Elect. Control*, **8**, 5, 381–400.

Fuller, A. T. (1960b), Optimization of Nonlinear Control Systems with Random Inputs, *J. Elect Control*, **9**, 65–80.

Fung, Y. C. (1969), *A First Course in Continuum Mechanics*, Prentice-Hall.

Gabasov, R. and Kirillova, F. M. (1972), High Order Necessary Conditions for Optimality, *SIAM J. Control,* **10**, 1, 127–166.

Gabasov, R. and Kirillova, F. M. (1976), *The Qualitative Theory of Optimal Processes*, M. Dekker.

Gallagher, R. H. (1973), Fully Stressed Design, in *Optimum Structural Design* (eds. R. H. Gallagher and O. C. Zienkiewicz), Wiley, ch. 3, 19–32.

Gallagher, R. H. and Zienkiewicz, O. C. (1973) (eds.), *Optimum Structural Design*, Wiley.

Garfinkel, R. S. and Nemhauser, G. L. (1972), *Integer Programming*, Wiley.

Gass, S. I. (1969), *Linear Programming*, McGraw-Hill, 3rd ed.

Gelfand, I. M. and Fomin, S. V. (1963), *Calculus of Variations* (Trans. by R. A. Silverman), Prentice-Hall.

Gellatly, R. A. and Berke, L. (1973), Optimality-Criterion-Based Algorithms, in *Optimum Structural Design* (eds. R. H. Gallagher and O. C. Zienkiewicz), Wiley, ch 4, 33–50.

Geoffrion, A. M. (1968), Proper Efficiency and the Theory of Vector Maximization, *Jnl. Math. Anal. Appl.*, **22**, 3.

Geoffrion, A. M. (1971), Large-Scale Linear and Nonlinear Programming, in *Optimization Methods for Large Scale Systems* (ed. D. A. Wismer), 47–74, McGraw-Hill.

Gerard, G. (1966), Optimum Structural Design Concepts for Aerospace Vehicles, *J. Spacecraft Rockets*, **3**, 5–18.

Gero, J. S. (1975), Architectural Optimization — A Review, *Eng. Optimzn*, **1**, 3, 189–199.

Gero, J. S., Sheehan, P. J. and Becker, J. M. (1978), Building Design Using Feedforward Non-Serial Dynamic Programming, *Eng. Optimzn*, **3**, 4, 183–192.

Gnedenko, B. V., Belyayev, Yu. K. and Solovyev, A. D. (1969), *Mathematical Methods of Reliability Theory*, Academic Press.

Goble, G. G. and deSantis, P. V. (1966), Optimum Design of Mixed Steel Composite Girders, *ASCE, J. Struct. Div.*, **92**, ST6, 25–43.

Goble, G. G. and Lapay, W. S. (1971), Optimum Design of Prestressed Beams, *Jnl. ACI*, September, 712–718.

Goff, R.F.D.P. (1966), Decision Theory and the Shape of Structures, *J. Royal Aero Soc.*, **70**, 448–452.

Goh, B. S. (1966a), The Second Variation for the Singular Bolza Problem, *SIAM J. Control*, **4**, 309–325.

Goh, B. S. (1966b), Necessary Conditions for Singular Extremals Involving Multiple Control Variables, *SIAM J. Control*, **4**, 4, 716–731.

Goh, B. S. (1967), Optimal Singular Control for Multi-Input Linear Systems, *J. Math. Anal. Appl.*, **20**, 534–539.

Goh, B. S. (1969), Optimal Control of a Fish Resource, *Malay. Scientist*, **5**, 65–70.

Goh, B. S. (1973), Compact Forms of the Generalized Legendre Conditions and the Derivation of Singular Extremals, Proc. 6th Hawaii International Conference on System Sciences, 115–117.

Gosling, W. (1962), *The Design of Engineering Systems*, Heywood.

Gottfried, B. S. and Weisman, J. (1973), *Introduction to Optimization Theory*, Prentice-Hall.

Graves, R. L. and Wolfe, P. (1963) (eds.), *Recent Advances in Mathematical Programming*, McGraw-Hill.

Grayson, L. P. (1965), The Status of Synthesis using Liapunov's Method, *Automatica*, **3**, 91–121.

Greenberg, S. G. (1971), On Quadratic Optimization in Distributed Parameter Systems, *IEEE Trans. Aut. Control*, **AC-16**, 2, 153ff.

Gregory, M. S. (1963), Philosophy of Engineering Design of Structures, *ASCE, Jnl. Struct. Div*., ST6, 119–135.

Grundy, P. and Wathen, G. R. (1969), Minimum Cost Design of Portal Frame Buildings, *Steel Construction, Jnl. Aust. Inst. Steel Const*., **3**, 2, 2–9.

Guinzy, N. J. and Sage, A. P. (1973), System Identification in Large Scale Systems with Hierarchical Structures, *Comput. and Elect. Eng*., **1**, 23–42.

Haack, W. and Wendland, W. (1972), *Lectures on Partial and Pfaffian Differential Equations*, Pergamon Press.

Hadley, G. (1962), *Linear Programming*, Addison-Wesley.

Hadley, G. (1964), *Nonlinear and Dynamic Programming*, Addison-Wesley.

Hahn, W. (1963), *Theory and Application of Liapunov's Direct Method*, Prentice-Hall.

Hahn, W. (1967), *Stability of Motion*, Springer-Verlag.

Haimes, Y. Y. (1973), Integrated System Identification and Optimization, in *Control and Dynamic Systems: Advances in Theory and Applications* (ed. C. T. Leondes), vol. 10, 435–518.

Haimes, Y. Y. (1977), *Hierarchical Analyses of Water Resources Systems; Modeling and Optimization of Large-Scale Systems*, McGraw-Hill.

Haimes, Y. Y., Hall, W. A. and Freedman, H. T. (1975), *Multiobjective Optimization in Water Resources Systems*, Elsevier.

Halkin, H. and Neustadt, L. W. (1966), General Necessary Conditions for Optimization Problems, *Proc. Natl. Acad. Sci., USA*, **56**, 1066–1071.

Hall, A. D. (1962), *A Methodology for Systems Engineering*, Van Nostrand.

Hare, V. C. (1967), *Systems Analysis: a Diagnostic Approach*, Harcourt Brace and World.

Haug, E. J. (1969), Two Methods of Structural Design, in *Developments in Mechanics, Vol. 5*, Proc. 11th Midwestern Mechanics Conf., 847–860.

Haug, E. J. (1977), Review of Literature on Distributed Parameter Optimization Theory Related to Elastic Structural Optimization, Tech. Report No. 35, Division of Materials Engineering, Univ. Iowa.

Haug, E. J. and Arora, H. S. (1978), Design Sensitivity Analysis of Elastic Mechanical Systems, *Comp. Meth. App. Mech. Eng*., **15**, 1, 35–62.

Haug, E. J., Arora J. S. and Feng. T. T. (1978), Sensitivity Analysis and Optimization of Structures for Dynamic Response, *ASME J. Mech. Des*., **100**, 2, 311–318.

Haug, E. J., Arora, J. S. and Matsui, K. (1976). A Steepest Descent Method for Optimization of Mechanical Systems, *JOTA*, **19**, 3, 401–424.

Haug, E. J. and Feng, T. T. (1977), Optimization of Distributed Parameter Structures under Dynamic Loads, in *Control and Dynamic Systems* (ed. C. T. Leondes), **13**, 207–246.

Haug, E. J. and Feng, T. T. (1978), Optimization of Dynamically Loaded Structures, *Int. J. Num. Meth. Eng*., **12**, 2, 299–317.

Haug, E. J. and Kirmser, P. G. (1967), Minimum Weight Design of Beams with Inequality Constraints on Stress and Deflection, *Jnl. Appl. Mech., Trans ASME*, 999–1004.

Haug, E. J. and Komkov, V. (1977), Sensitivity Analysis in Distributed Parameter Mechanical Systems, *JOTA*, **23**, 3, 445–464.

Haug, E. J., Pan, K. C. and Streeter, T. D. (1972), A Computational Method for Optimal Structural Design I: Piecewise Uniform Structures, *Int. J. Num. Meth. Eng.*, **5**, 171–184.

Haug, E. J., Pan, K. C. and Streeter, T. D. (1975), A Computational Method for Optimal Structural Design II: Continuous Problems, *Int. J. Num. Meth. Eng.*, **9**, 649–667.

Hegemier, G. A. (1967), Stability of Cylindrical Shells Under Moving Loads by the Direct Method of Liapunov, *ASME, Jnl. App. Mech.* **34**, 4, 991.

Hemp, W. S. (1973), *Optimum Structures*, Clarendon.

Heyman, J. (1951), Plastic Design of Beams and Plane Frames for Minimum Material Consumption, *Quart. Appl. Math.*, **8**, 4, 373–381.

Heyman, J. (1953), Plastic Design of Plane Frames for Minimum Weight, *Struct. Engr.*, **31**, 125.

Heyman, J. (1958), Minimum Weight of Frames Under Shakedown Loading, *ASCE, J. Eng. Mech. Div.*, **84**, EM4.

Heyman, J. (1959), On the Absolute Minimum Weight Design of Framed Structures, *Quart. J. Mech. Appl. Math.*, **12**, 3, 314–324.

Heyman, J. (1960), On the Minimum Weight Design of a Simple Portal Frame, *Int. J. Mech. Sci.*, **1**, 121.

Heyman, J. (1971), *Plastic Design of Frames, Vol. 2*, Cambridge Univ. Press.

Heyman, J. and Prager, W. (1958), Automatic Minimum Weight Design of Steel Frames, *J. Franklin Inst.*, **266**, 339.

Hillerborg, A. (1956), Equilibrium Theory for Reinforced Concrete Slabs, *Betong Stockholm*, **41**, 4, 171.

Himmelblau, D. M. (1972), *Applied Nonlinear Programming*, McGraw-Hill.

Himmelblau, D. M. (ed.) (1973), *Decomposition of Large-Scale Problems*, American Elsevier.

Hinderer, K. (1970), *Foundations of Non-Stationary Dynamic Programming with Discrete Time Parameter*, Springer-Verlag.

Holzer, S. M. (1970), Stability of Columns with Transient Loads, *ASCE, J. Eng. Mech. Div.*, EM6, 913–930.

Holzer, S. M. (1971), Response Bounds for Columns with Transient Loads, *ASME, J. App. Mech., Series E*, **38**, 1, 157.

Holzer, S. M. (1972a), Stability and Boundedness via Liapunov's Direct Method, *ASCE, J. Eng. Mech. Div.*, **98**, EM5, 1273–1284.

Holzer, S. M. (1972b), Displacement-Energy Bound for Elastic Structures, *ASME, J. App. Mech.*, **39**, 816–817.

Holzer, S. M. (1974), Degree of Stability of Equilibrium, *J. Struct. Mech.*, **3**, 1, 61–75.

Holzer, S. M. and Eubanks, R. A. (1969), Stability of Columns Subject to Impulsive Loading, *ASCE, J. Eng. Mech. Div.*, **95**. EM4, 897–920.

Hornbuckle, J. C., Nevill, G. E. and Boykin, W. H. (1975), Structural Optimization Using the Finite Element Method Applied to a Beam, *Int. J. Num. Meth. Eng.*, **9**, 101–107.

Horne, M. R. (1971), *Plastic Theory of Structures*, Nelson.

Hsu, C. S. (1966), On Dynamic Stability of Elastic Bodies with Prescribed Initial Conditions, *Int. J. Eng. Sci.*, **4**, 1, 1–22.

Hu, T. C. (1969), *Integer Programming and Network Flows*, Addison-Wesley.

Huang, N. C. and Tang, H. T. (1969), Minimum Weight Design of Elastic Sandwich Beams with Deflection Constraints, *JOTA*, **4**, 4, 277–298.

Hughes, O. F. and Mistree, F. (1975), Least Cost Optimization of Large Steel Box Girder Structures, Fifth Australas. Conf. Mech. Struct. Mat., Univ. Melbourne, 279–299.

Hughes, O. F. and Mistree, F. (1977), A Comprehensive Automated Optimization of Ship Structures, University of New South Wales, School of Mechanical and Industrial Engineering Report Nav. Arch./3/77.

Hughes, O. F., Mistree, F. and Davies, J. (1977), Automated Limit State Design of Steel Structures, Sixth Australas. Conf. Mech. Struct. Mat., Univ. Canterbury, 98–106.

Infante, E. F. (1973), Stability Theory for General Dynamical Systems and Some Applications, in *Optimization and Stability Problems in Continuum Mechanics* (ed. P. K. C. Wang), 63–82, Springer-Verlag.

Infante, E. F. and Plaut, R. H. (1969), Stability of a Column Subjected to a Time-Dependent Axial Load, *AIAA Jnl*, **7**, 4, 766–768.

Jackson, R. (1966), Optimization Problems in a Class of Systems Described by Hyperbolic Partial Differential Equations, *Int. J. Control*, **4**, 127–136.

Jacobs, O. L. R. (1967), *An Introduction to Dynamic Programming; the Theory of Multistage Decision Processes*, Chapman and Hall.

Jacobson, D. H. (1971), Totally Singular Quadratic Minimization Problems, *IEEE Trans. Aut. Control*, **AC-16**, 6, 651–658.

Jacobson, D. H., (1977), *Extensions of Linear-Quadratic Control, Optimization and Matrix Theory*, Academic Press.

Jenkins, G. M. (1969), The Systems Approach, *J. Systems Engineering*, **1**, 1, 3–49.

John, F. (1948), Extremum Problems with Inequalities as Side Conditions, *Studies and Essays, Courant Anniversary Volume* (eds. K. O. Friedrichs, O. E. Neugebauer and J. J. Stoker), Wiley, 187–204.

Johnsen, E. (1968), *Studies in Multiobjective Decision Models*, Studentlitteratur.

Johnson, C. D. (1965), Singular Solutions in Problems of Optimal Control, in *Advances in Control Systems*, C. T. Leondes (ed.), **2**, Academic Press, 209–267.

Johnson, E. W., Rizzi, P., Ashley, H. and Segenreich, S. A. (1976), Optimization of Continuous One-Dimensional Structures under Steady Harmonic Excitation, *A.I.A.A. Jnl.*, **14**, 12, 1690–1698.

Johnson, F. R. (1972), An Interactive Design Algorithm for Prestressed Concrete Girders, *Comp. and Struct.*, **2**, 1075–1088.

Julian, O. G. (1957), Synopsis of First Progress Report of the Committee on Factors of Safety, *ASCE J. Struct. Div.*, **83**, ST4, July, Proc. Paper 1316.

Kalaba, R. (1961), Dynamic Programming and the Variational Principles of Classical and Statistical Mechanics, *Developments in Mechanics Vol. I*, Procs. 7th Midwestern Mech. Conf. (Michigan State Univ. eds. J. E. Lay and L. E. Malvern), 1–9, Plenum.

Kalaba, R. (1962), Design of Minimum Weight Structures for Given Reliability and Cost, *Jnl. Aerospace Sci.*, **29**, 355–356.

Kaliszky, S. (1965), Economic Design by Ultimate Load Method, *Concrete and Constructional Engineer*, **60**, 11, 424.

Kalman, R. E. (1962), Canonical Structure of Linear Dynamical Systems, *Proc. Nat. Acad. Sci., USA*, **48**, 596–600.

Kalman, R. E. (1963a), Mathematical Description of Linear Dynamical Systems, *SIAM J. Control*, **1**, 2, 152–192.

Kalman, R. E. (1963b), The Theory of Optimal Control and the Calculus of Variations, in *Mathematical Optimization Techniques* (ed. R. Bellman), Univ. Calif. Press, 309–331.

Kalman, R. E. (1964), When is a Linear Control System Optimal?, *J. Basic Engng, ASME, Series D*, **86**.

Kalman, R. E. and Bertram, J. E. (1960a), Control System Analysis and Design via the 'Second Method' of Lyapunov; I Continuous-Time Systems, *ASME J. Basic Eng.*, **82D**, 371–393, June.

Kalman, R. E. and Bertram, J. E. (1960b), Control System Analysis and Design via the 'Second Method' of Lyapunov; II Discrete-Time Systems, *ASME, J. Basic Eng.*, **82D**, 394–400, June.

Karihaloo, B. L. (1979a), On Minimum Weight Design of Multi-Purpose Structures, Proc. 7th Canadian Cong. App. Mech., Univ. Sherbrooke, 877–878.

Karihaloo, B. L. (1979b), Optimal Design of Multi-Purpose Tie Column of Solid Construction, *Int. J. Solids Structs.*, **15**, 103–109.

Karihaloo, B. L. (1979c), Optimal Design of Multi-Purpose Tie-Beams, *JOTA*, **27**, 3, 427–438.

Karihaloo, B. L. (1979d), Optimal Design of Multi-Purpose Structures, *JOTA*, **27**, 3, 449–461.

Karihaloo, B. L. and Parbery, R. D. (1979a), Optimal Design of Multi-Purpose Beam-Columns, *JOTA*, **27**, 3, 439–448.

Karihaloo, B. L. and Parbery, R. D. (1979b), The Optimal Design of Beam Columns, *Int. J. Solids Struct.*, **15**, 855–859.

Karihaloo, B. L. and Wood, G. L. (1979), Optimal Design of Multipurpose Sandwich Tie-Columns, *ASCE, Eng. Mech. Div.*, **EM3**, 465–469.

Katz, S. (1964), A General Minimum Principle for End-Point Control Problems, *J. Elect. Control*, **16**, 189–222.

Kavlie, D. and Powell, G. H. (1971), Efficient Reanalysis of Modified Structures, *ASCE, J. Struct. Div.*, ST1, 377–392.

Keeney, R. L. and Raiffa, H. (1976), *Decisions with Multiple Objectives: Preferences and Value Tradeoffs*, Wiley.

Kelley, H. J. (1962), Method of Gradients, in *Optimization Techniques* (ed. G. Leitmann), Ch. 6, Academic Press.

Kelley, H. J., Kopp, R. E. and Moyer, H. G. (1966), Singular Extremals, in *Topics in Optimization*, G. Leitmann (ed.), Ch. 3, Academic Press.

Kelly, D. W., Morris, A. J., Bartholomew, P. and Stafford, R. O. (1977), A Review of Techniques for Automated Structural Design, *Comp. Meth. Appl. Mech. Eng.*, **12**, 219–242.

Khachaturian, N. (1968), Optimization and Structural Design, ASCE Joint STD-EMD Speciality Conf. — 'Optimization and Nonlinear Problems', 75–90, April. See also, Basic Concepts in Structural Optimization, in *An Introduction to Structural Optimization* (ed. M. Z. Cohn), Univ. Waterloo Solid Mech. Div. Study No. 1, 1969, 1–18.

Khachaturian, N. and Haider, G. S. (1966), Probabilistic Design of Determinate Structures, *Proc. Specialty Conf., Eng. Mech. Div., ASCE*, 623–647, Oct.

Khatri, H. C. and Goodson, R. E. (1966), Optimal Feedback Solutions for a Class of Distributed Systems, *ASME Trans., J. Basic Engng*, **88**, 337–342.

Khot, N. S., Berke, L. and Venkayya, V. B. (1979), Comparison of Optimality Criteria Algorithms for Minimum Weight Design of Structures, *AIAA J.*, **17**, 2, 182–218.

Kim, M. and Erzberger, H. (1967), On the Design of Optimum Distributed

Parameter System with Boundary Control Function, *IEEE Trans. Aut. Control*, **AC-12**, 22–28.

Kim, M. and Gajwani, S. H. (1968), A Variational Approach to Optimum Distributed Parameter Systems, *IEEE Trans. Aut. Control*, **AC–13**, 191–193.

Kirsch, U. (1972), Optimum Design of Prestressed Beams, *Computers and Structures*, **2**, 573–583.

Kirsch, U. (1973), Optimum Design of Prestressed Plates, *J. Struct. Div. ASCE*, **89**, ST6, 1075–1090.

Kirsch, U. (1975), Multilevel Approach to Optimum Structural Design, *ASCE J. Struct. Div.*, **101**, ST4, 957–974.

Kirsch, U. and Moses, F. (1976), Formulation of Optimal Design in the Behavior Variables Space, *J. Struct. Mech.*, **4**, 4, 437–452.

Kirsch, U. and Moses, F. (1977), The Relationship Between Plastic and Prestressed Elastic Optimal Design, in *Mechanics in Engineering* (eds. R. N. Dubey and N. C. Lind), Univ. Waterloo Study No. 11, 207–222.

Kirsch, U. and Moses, F. (1979), Decomposition in Optimum Structural Design, *ASCE J. Struct. Div.*, **105**, ST1, 85–100.

Kirsch, U., Reiss, M. and Shamir, U. (1972), Optimum Design by Partitioning into Substructures, *ASCE J. Struct. Div.*, **98**, ST1, 249–267.

Kirsch, U. and Rubinstein M. F. (1972), Reanalysis for Limited Structural Design Modifications, *ASCE, J. Eng. Mech. Div.*, EM1, 61–70

Klinger, A. (1964), Vector Valued Performance Criteria, *IEEE Trans. Aut. Control*, **AC–9**, 1.

Klir, G. J. (1969), *An Approach to General Systems Theory*, Van Nostrand.

Klir, G. J. (1972). *Trends in General Systems Theory*, Wiley.

Knops, R. J. and Wilkes, E. W. (1966), On Movchan's Theorems for Stability of Continuous Systems, *Int. J. Eng. Sci.*, **4**, 303–329.

Kolmogorov, A. N. (1956), *Foundations of Probability Theory*, Chelsea 2nd ed. (English) (1st ed. 1931).

Kowalik, J. (1966), 'Nonlinear Programming Procedures and Design Optimization', Acta Polytechnica Scandinavica, Math. and Comput. Machinery, Series NR13, 47 pp.

Kuhn, H. W. and Tucker, A. W. (1951), Nonlinear Programming, Procs. Second Berkeley Symposium on Mathematical Statistics and Probability, Univ. California Press, 481–492.

Kumar, I., Singh, K. and Raman, N. V. (1967), Application of Linear Programming to Optimisation of Structures, *Indian Concrete J.*, **41**, 10, 378–382.

Kunzi, H. P., Krelle, W. and Oettli, W. (1966), *Nonlinear Programming*, Blaisdell.

Lanczos, C. (1962), *The Variational Principles of Mechanics*, Univ. of Toronto Press (1st ed. 1949).

Larson, R. E. (1964), *State Increment Dynamic Programming*, American Elsevier.

LaSalle, J. P. and Lefschetz, S. (1961), *Stability by Liapunov's Direct Method With Applications*, Academic Press.

Lasdon, L. S. (1968), Duality and Decomposition in Mathematical Programming, *IEEE Trans. Syst. Man. Cybern.*, **SMC–4**, 2, July.

Lasdon, L. S. (1970), *Optimization Theory for Large Systems*, Macmillan.

Lee, E. B. and Markus, L. (1967), *Foundations of Optimal Control Theory*, Wiley.

Lee, R. C. K. (1964), *Optimal Estimation, Identification and Control,* M.I.T. Research Monograph No. 28, M.I.T. Press.

Lee, T. H. and Hsu, C. S. (1972), Liapunov Stability Criteria for Continuous Systems Under Parametric Excitation, *ASME, J. App. Mech., Series E*, 244–250, March.

Legerer F. (1970), Code Theory — A New Branch of Engineering Science, Univ. Waterloo, Solid Mechanics Division Study No. 3 (ed. N. C. Lind), 113–128.

Leipholz, H. H. E. (1971), Application of Liapunov's Direct Method to the Stability Problem of Rods Subjected to Follower Forces, in *Instability of Continuous Systems* (ed. H. H. E. Leipholz), Springer-Verlag, 1–10.

Leipholz, H. H. E. (1972), Dynamic Stability of Elastic Systems, in *Stability*, University of Waterloo Solid Mechanics Div. Study No. 6, 243–279.

Leipholz, H. H. E. (1974), On Conservative Elastic Systems of the First and Second Kind, *Ingenieur-Archiv.*, **43**, 255–271.

Leipholz, H. H. E. (1975a), *Six Lectures on Stability of Elastic Systems*, Solid Mechanics Division, University of Waterloo.

Leipholz, H. H. E. (1975b), Aspects of Dynamic Stability of Structures, *ASCE, J. Eng. Mech. Div.,* EM2, 109–124.

Leipholz, H. H. E. (1975c), Stability of Elastic Rods via Liapunov's Second Method, *Ing. Arch.*, **44**, 21–26.

Leipholz, H. H. E. (1976a), Liapunov's Second Method and its Application to Continuous Systems, *S. M. Archives,* **1**, 367–444.

Leipholz, H. H. E. (1976b), Some Remarks on Liapunov Stability of Elastic Dynamical Systems, in *Buckling of Structures* (ed. B. Budiansky), Springer-Verlag (IUTAM Symp. Cambridge, Mass. 1974).

Leitmann, G. (ed.) (1962), *Optimization Techniques*, Academic Press.

Leitmann, G. (1966), *An Introduction to Optimal Control*, McGraw-Hill.

Leitmann, G. (ed.) (1976), *Multicriteria Decision Making and Differential Games*, Plenum.

Leitmann, G. (1977), Some Problems of Scalar and Vector-Valued Optimization in Linear Viscoelasticity, *JOTA*, **23**, 1, 93–99.

Leitmann, G. and Marzollo, A. (eds.) (1975), *Multicriteria Decision Making*, Springer-Verlag.

Lepik, U. (1972), Minimum Weight Design of Circular Plates with Limited Thickness, *Int. J. Nonlinear Mech.*, **7**, 353–360.

Lepik, U. (1973), Application of Pontryagin's Maximum Principle for Minimum Weight Design of Rigid-Plastic Circular Plates, *Int. J. Solids Struct.*, **9**, 5, 615–624.

Lepik, U. (1978), Optimal Design of Beams with Minimum Compliance, *Int. J. Nonlinear Mech.*, **13**, 33–42.

Lepore, J. A. and Shah, H. C. (1968), Dynamic Stability of Axially Loaded Columns Subject to Stochastic Excitations, *AIAA Jnl.*, **6**, 8, 1515–1521.

Lepore, J. A. and Stoltz, R. A. (1974), Stability of Cylindrical Shells Under Random Excitation, *ASCE, J. Eng. Mech. Div.*, **100**, EM3, 531–546.

Letov, A. M. (1964), Liapunov's Theory of Stability of Motion, in *Disciplines and Techniques of Systems Control* (ed. J. Peschon), Ch. 6, Blaisdell.

Lewis, A. D. (1966), Optimal Design of Structural Steel Framing for Tier-type Buildings, in *Computers in Engineering Design Education*, *III*, 64–88, Civil Engineering, University of Michigan, Ann Arbor.

Liapunov, A. M. (1966), *Stability of Motion*, Academic Press (English Translation).

Lin, T. Y. (1961), A New Concept for Prestressed Concrete, in Proc. Symp. Prestressed Concrete, Sydney; see also *Constructional Review*, **34**, 21–31, Sept., and *J. PCI*, **6**, 36–52, December.

Lin, T. Y. (1963), Load-Balancing Method for the Design and Analysis of Prestressed Concrete Structures, *J. ACI*, 719–732, June (*Proc. ACI*, **60**.).

Lind, N. C. (1962), Analysis of Structures by System Theory, *ASCE J. Struct. Div.*, 1–22.

Lions, J. L. (1968), *Optimal Control of Systems Governed by Partial Differential Equations*, Dunod Gauthier-Valliars.

Lipson, S. L. and Russel, A. D. (1971), Cost Optimization of Structural Roof System, *ASCE J. Struct. Div*. **97**, 2057–2071.

Livesley, R. K. (1956), The Automatic Design of Structural Frames, *Quart. J. Mech. Appl. Math.*, **9**, 257.

Livesley, R. K. (1959), Optimum Design of Structural Frames for Alternative Systems of Loading, *Civil Engineering*, **54**, 737.

Livesley, R. K. (1964), *Matrix Methods of Structural Analysis*, Pergamon.

Livesley, R. K. (1973), Linear Programming in Structural Analysis and Design, ch. 6 in *Optimum Structural Design* (eds. R. H. Gallagher and O. C. Zienkiewicz), Wiley.

Llewellyn, R. W. (1964), *Linear Programming*, Holt, Rinehart and Winston.

Luenberger, D. G. (1969), *Optimization by Vector Space Methods*, Wiley.

Lurie, K. A. and Cherkaev, A. V. (1976), Prager Theorem Application to Optimal Design of Thin Plates, *Mekhanika Tverdogo Tela*, **11**, 6, 157–159.

Lurie, K. A. (1963), The Mayer-Bolza Problem for Multiple Integrals and the Optimization of the Performance of Systems with Distributed Parameters, *Appl. Math. Mech. (Prikl. Math. Mekh.)* **27**, 5, 1284–1299, March. See also in, The Mayer-Bolza Problem for Multiple Integrals: Some Optimum Problems for Elliptic Differential Equations Arising in Magnetohydrodynamics, in *Topics in Optimization*, Ch. 5, 147–198 (ed. G. Leitmann), Academic Press, 1967.

MacFarlane, A. G. J. (1970), *Dynamical System Models*, Harrap.

Mahmoud, M. S. (1977a), Multilevel Systems Control and Applications: A Survey, *IEEE Trans. Syst. Man and Cybern*, **SMC–7**, 3, 125–143.

Mahmoud, M. S. (1977b), A Class of Optimization Techniques for Linear State-Regulators, *Int. J. Systems Sci.*, **8**, 5, 513–537.

Mahmoud, M. S., Vogt, W. G. and Mickle, M. H. (1977a), Multilevel Control and Optimization Using Generalized Gradients Technique, *Int. J. Control*, **25**, 4, 525–543.

Mahmoud, M. S., Vogt, W. G. and Mickle, M. H. (1977b), Feedback Multilevel Control for Continuous Dynamic Systems, *J. Franklin Inst.*, **303**, 5, 453–471.

Maier, G. (1973), Limit Design in the Absence of a Given Layout: A Finite Element, Zero-One Programming Problem, in *Optimum Structural Design* (eds. R. H. Gallagher and O. C. Zienkiewicz), Wiley, 223–240.

Majid, K. I. (1972), *Non-Linear Structures*, Butterworths.

Majid, K. I. (1974), *Optimum Design of Structures*, Butterworths.

Mangasarian, O. L. and Fromovitz, S. (1967), The Fritz John Necessary Optimality Conditions in the Presence of Equality and Inequality Constraints, *J. Math. Anal. Appl.*, **17**, 37–47.

Marcal, P. V. and Prager, W. (1964), A Method of Optimal Plastic Design, *J. de Mecanique*, **3**, 509–530.

Masur, E. F. (1975a), Optimality in the Presence of Discreteness and

Discontinuity, in *Optimization in Structural Design* (eds. A. Sawczuk and Z. Mroz), IUTAM Symposium, Warsaw 1973, Springer-Verlag, 441–453.

Masur, E. F. (1975b), Optimal Placement of Available Sections in Structural Eigenvalue Problems, *JOTA*, **15**, 69–84.

McCart, B. R., Haug, E. J. and Streeter, T. D. (1970), Optimal Design of Structures with Constraints on Natural Frequency, *AIAA Jnl*, **8**, 6, 1012–1019.

McIntosh, S. C. (1974), Structural Optimization via Optimal Control Techniques; A Review, in *Structural Optimization Symposium*, ASME, New York (ed. L. A. Schmit), 49–64.

McIntosh, S. C., Weisshaar, T. A. and Ashley, H. (1969), Progress in Aeroelastic Optimization — Analytical versus Numerical Approaches, Stanford Univ., Dept. Aero. Astron., Report 383.

McShane, E. J. (1939), On Multipliers for Lagrange Problems, *Amer. J. Math.*, **61**, 809–19.

McShane, E. J. (1978), The Calculus of Variations from the Beginning Through Optimal Control Theory, in *Optimal Control and Differential Equations* (eds. A. B. Schwarzkopf, W. G. Kelley and S. B. Eliason), Academic Press, 3–50.

Meerov, M. V. (1961), *Introduction to the Dynamics of Automatic Regulating of Electrical Machines* (Russian edition 1956), Butterworths.

Merriam, C. W. (1964), *Optimization Theory and the Design of Feedback Control Systems*, McGraw-Hill.

Mesarovic, M. D. (1971), Multilevel Systems Theory, State of the Art 1971, in *Multivariable Technical Control Systems* (ed. H. Schwarz), V.4, 115–132, Proc. 2nd IFAC Symp., Duesseldorf, Oct 11–13, 1971, North Holland Pub. Co. Amsterdam, Amer. Elsevier.

Mesarovic, M. D. (1973), on Vertical Decomposition and Modelling of Large Scale Systems, in *Decomposition of Large-Scale Problems* (ed. D. M. Himmelblau), 323–340, North Holland.

Mesarovic, M. D., Macko, D. and Takahara, Y. (1970), *Theory of Hierarchical, Multilevel Systems*, Academic Press.

Mesarovic, M. D. and Takahara, Y. (1975), *General Systems Theory: Mathematical Foundations*, Academic Press.

Michell, A. G. M. (1904), The Limits of Economy of Material in Frame-structures, *Phil. Mag., 5.6.*, **8**, 47, November.

Miele, A. (1962a), Extremization of Linear Integrals by Green's Theorem, in *Optimization Techniques with Applications to Aerospace Systems* (G. Leitmann, ed.), Ch. 3, 69–98, Academic Press.

Miele, A. (1962b), The Calculus of Variations in Applied Aerodynamics and Flight Mechanics, in *Optimization Techniques with Applications to Aerospace Systems* (G. Leitmann, ed.), ch. 4, 100–170. Academic Press.

Mitten, L. G. and Nemhauser, G. L. (1963), Multistage Optimization, *Chem. Eng. Progress*, **59**.

Mohler, R. R. (1973), *Bilinear Control Processes*, Academic Press.

Morris, D. (1978), Prestressed Concrete Design by Linear Programming, *ASCE, J. Struct. Div., March* (Discussion, ST10, ST12).

Moses, F. (1964), Optimum Structural Design Using Linear Programming, *ASCE, J. Struct. Div.*, **90**, ST6, 90–104.

Moses, F. (1974), Mathematical Programming Methods for Structural Optimization, in *Structural Optimization Symposium* (ed. L. A. Schmit), ASME Meeting New York, November, 35–48.

Moses, F. and Kinser, D. E. (1967), Optimum Structural Design with Failure Probability Constraints, *AIAA J.*, **5**, 6, 1152–1158.

Movchan, A. A. (1959a), Concerning the Straightforward Method of Liapunov in Problems of Stability of Elastic Systems, *App. Math. Mech.*, **23**, 483–493.

Movchan, A. A. (1959b), The Direct Method of Liapunov in Stability Problems of Elastic Systems, *App. Math. Mech. (PMM)*, **23**, 3, 686–700.

Movchan, A. A. (1960), Stability Processes with Respect to Two Metrics, *App. Math. Mech. (PMM)*, **24**, 6, 1506–1524.

Mroz, Z. (1958), Design of Technically Orthotropic Plates, Symposium on Non-homogeneity in Elasticity and Plasticity, Warsaw, Pergamon.

Munro, J. and Smith, D. L. (1972), Linear Programming Duality in Plastic Analysis and Synthesis, Proc. Int. Symp. Computer-Aided Struct. Design, Univ. Warwick.

Naaman, A. E. (1976), Minimum Cost Versus Minimum Weight of Prestressed Slabs, *J. Struct. Div., ASCE*, ST7, 1493–1505.

Nagy, D. A. (1971), Some System Identification and Optimization Procedures in Structural Mechanics, Ph. D. Dissertation, University of California, Berkeley.

Nagy, D. and Distefano, N. (1972), A Dynamic Programming Approach to Optimal Disc Design, Proc. Intnl. Conf. Variational Methods Engng., Southampton Univ., Intnl. Assoc. for Shell Struct., Southampton, 11/13-11/25.

Neal, B. G. (1963), *The Plastic Methods of Structural Analysis*, Chapman and Hall, 2nd ed.

Nemhauser, G. L. (1966), *Introduction to Dynamic Programming*, Wiley.

Neustadt, L. W. (1966, 1967), An Abstract Variational Theory with Applications to a Broad Class of Optimization Problems, *J. SIAM Control*, part I: General Theory, **4**, 505–527; part II: Applications, **5**, 90–137.

Neustadt, L. W. (1969), A General Theory of Extremals, *J. Computer Syst. Sci.*, **3**, 57–92.

Niordson, F. I. and Pedersen, P. (1973), A Review of Optimal Structural Design, Proc. 13th Int. Congress of Theor. App. Mechanics, Moscow 1972 (eds. E. Becker and G. K. Mikhailov), Springer-Verlag.

Noton, A. R. M. (1965), *Introduction to Variational Methods in Control Engineering*, Pergamon.

Noton, A. R. M. (1971), A Two-Level Form of the Kalman Filter, *IEEE Trans. Aut. Cont.*, **AC–16**, 128–132.

Ogata, K. (1967), *State Space Analysis of Control Systems*, Prentice-Hall.

Ogata, K. (1970), *Modern Control Engineering*, Prentice-Hall.

Olhoff, N. (1976), A Survey of the Optimal Design of Vibrating Structural Elements, Part I Theory, **8**, 8, 3–10; Part II Applications, **8**, 9, 3–10, *Shock Vibrn. Digest*.

Olhoff, N. and Taylor, J. E. (1978), Designing Continuous Columns for Minimum Total Cost of Material and Interior Supports, DCAMM Report No. 135, Tech. Univ. Denmark.

Owen, J. B. B. (1965), *The Analysis and Design of Light Structures*, Arnold.

Paiewonsky, B. (1965), Optimal Control: A Review of Theory and Practice, *AIAA Jnl*, **3**, 11, 1985–2006.

Palmer, A. C. (1968a), Optimal Structure Design by Geometric Programming, *ASCE, J. Struct. Div.*, August.

Palmer, A. C. (1968b), Optimum Structure Design by Dynamic Programming, *ASCE, J. Struct, Div.*, **94**, ST8, 1887–1906.

Palmer, A. C. (1969), Limit Analysis of Cylindrical Shells by Dynamic Programming, *Int. J. Solids and Struct*., **5**, 289–302.

Palmer, A. C. (1973), Dynamic Programming and Structural Optimization, in *Optimum Structural Design* (eds. R. H. Gallagher and O. C. Zienkiewicz), 179–200, Wiley.

Palmer, A. C. and Sheppard, D. J. (1970), Optimizing the Shape of Pin-Jointed Structures, *Proc. ICE*, **47**, 363–376.

Parks, P. C. (1966), A Stability Criterion for a Panel Flutter Problem via the Second Method of Liapunov, *AIAA Jnl*. **4**, 1, 175–178.

Pearson, J. D. (1971), Dynamic Decomposition Techniques, in *Optimization Methods for Large Scale Systems* (ed. D. A. Wismer), 121–188, McGraw-Hill.

Pestel, E. C. and Leckie, F. A. (1963), *Matrix Methods of Elastomechanics,* McGraw-Hill.

Pierre, D. A. (1969), *Optimization Theory with Applications*, Wiley.

Pierson, B. L. (1972a), A Survey of Optimal Structural Design Under Dynamic Constraints, *Int. Jnl. Num. Meth. Eng*., **4**, 491–499.

Pierson, B. L. (1972b), Discrete Variable Approximation to Minimum Weight Panels with Fixed Flutter Speed, *A.I.A.A. Jnl.,* **10**, 9, 1147–1148.

Pierson, B. L. (1975a), Panel Flutter Optimization by Gradient Projection, *Int. J. Num. Meth. Eng*., **9**, 2, 271–296.

Pierson, B. L. (1975b), Aeroelastic Panel Optimization with Aerodynamic Damping, *A.I.A.A. Jnl*., **13**, 4, 515–517.

Pierson, B. L. (1977), An Optimal Control Approach to Minimum-Weight Vibrating Beam Design, *J. Struct. Mech*., **5**, 2, 147–178.

Pierson, B. L. and Genalo, L. J. (1977), Minimum Weight Design of a Rectangular Panel Subject to a Flutter Speed Constraint, *Comp. Meth. App. Mech. and Eng.,* **10**, 45–62.

Pierson B. L. and Hajela, P. (1979), Optimal Aeroelastic Design of an Unsymmetrically-Supported Panel, to appear, *J. Struct. Mech.*

Pierson, B. L. and Russell, S. S. (1973), Further Discrete Variable Results for a Panel Flutter Optimization Problem, *Int. J. Num. Meth. Eng*., **7**, 4, 537–543.

Pister, K. S. (1972), Mathematical Modelling for Structural Analysis and Design, *Nuclear Engineering and Design*, **18**, 353–375.

Plane, D. R. and McMillan, C. (1971), *Discrete Optimization*, Prentice-Hall.

Plaut, R. H. (1971), Displacement Bounds for Beam-Columns with Initial Curvature Subjected to Transient Loads, *Int. J. Solids Structs*, **7**, 9, 1229.

Plaut, R. H. and Infante, E. F. (1972), Bounds on Motions of Some Lumped and Continuous Dynamics Systems, *ASME, J. App. Mech., Series E*, 251–256, March.

Polak, E., Pister, K. S. and Ray, D. (1976), Optimal Design of Framed Structures subjected to Earthquakes, *Eng. Optimizn*., **2**, 65–71.

Pontryagin, L. S. (1962), *Ordinary Differential Equations*, Addison-Wesley.

Pontryagin, L. S., Boltyanskii, V. G., Gamkrelidze, R. V. and Mishchenko, E. F. (1962), *The Mathematical Theory of Optimal Processes*, Wiley.

Popelar, C. H. (1976), Optimal Design of Beams Against Buckling: A Potential Energy Approach, *J. Struct. Mech*., **4**, 2, 181–196.

Popelar, C. H. (1977), Optimal Design of Structures Against Buckling: A Complementary Energy Approach, *J. Struct. Mech*., **5**, 1, 45–66.

Porter, B. (1969), *Synthesis of Dynamical Systems*, Nelson.

Porteus, E. (1975), An Informal Look at the Principle of Optimality, *Management Sci.*, **21**, 1346–48.

Prager, W. (1956), Minimum Weight Design of a Portal Frame, *ASCE, J. Eng. Mech. Div.*, **82**, EM4, 1073.1–1073.10.

Prager, W. (1968), Optimality Criteria in Structural Design, *Proc. Nat. Acad. Sci. USA*, **61**, 3, 794–796.

Prager, W. (1969), Optimality Criteria Derived from Classical Extremum Principles, in *An Introduction to Structural Optimization* (ed. M. Z. Cohn), Univ. Waterloo S. M. Study No. 1, 165–178.

Prager, W. (1974), 'Introduction to Structural Optimization', Int. Centre for Mechanical Sciences Courses and Lectures No. 212, Udine, Springer-Verlag.

Prager, W. and Shield, R. T. (1967), A General Theory of Optimal Plastic Design, *J. Applied Mech., Proc. ASME*, **34**, 1, 184–186.

Prager, W. and Taylor, J. E. (1968), Problems of Optimal Structural Design, *J. App. Mech., ASME, Ser. E*, **35**, 102–106.

Przemieniecki, J. S. (1968), *Theory of Matrix Structural Analysis*, McGraw-Hill.

Pugsley, A. G. (1966), *The Safety of Structures*, Arnold.

Raiffa, H. (1970), *Decision Analysis*, Addison-Wesley.

Raiffa, H. and Luce, R. D. (1958), *Games and Decisions*, Wiley.

Ray, W. H. and Szekely, J. (1973), *Process Optimization*, Wiley.

Razani, R. (1965), Behavior of Fully Stressed Design of Structures and its Relationship to Minimum Weight Design, *AIAA J.*, **3**, 12, 2262–2268.

Razani, R. and Goble, G. G. (1966), Optimum Design of Constant Depth Plate Girders, *ASCE, J. Struct. Div.*, **92**, ST2, 253–281.

Reid, R. W. and Citron, S. J. (1971), On Non-Inferior Performance Index Vectors, *JOTA*, **7**, 1.

Reinschmidt, K. F., Cornell, C. A. and Brotchie, J. F. (1966), Iterative Design and Structural Optimization, *ASCE, J. Struct. Div.*, **92**, ST6, 281–317.

Ridha, R. A. and Wright, R. N. (1967), Minimum Cost of Frames, *ASCE, J. Struct. Div.*, **93**, ST4, 165–183.

Robinson, A. C. (1971), A Survey of Optimal Control of Distributed Parameter Systems, *Automatica*, **7**, 371–388.

Rosenblueth, E. (1973), Ethical Optimization in Engineering, *Engineering Issues, Proc. ASCE*, **100**, EI1, April, 223–243. Discussion January 1974, 88–93.

Rowe, R. E. (1970), Current European Views on Structural Safety, *ASCE, J. Struct. Div.*, **96**, ST3, 461ff.

Rozonoer, L. I. (1959), L. S. Pontryagin's Maximum Principle in the Theory of Optimum Systems — Parts I, II and III, *Automn Remote Control*, **20**, 10, 1288–1302, Oct; **20**, 11, 1405–1421, Nov; **20**, 12, 1517–1532, Dec.

Rozvany, G. I. N. (1964), Optimum Synthesis of Prestressed Structures, *J. Struct. Div., ASCE*, **90**, ST6, 189–211.

Rozvany, G. I. N. (1966a), Analysis versus Synthesis in Structural Engineering, *Trans. I. E. Aust.*, **CE8**, 2, 158–164.

Rozvany, G. I. N. (1966b), Rational Approach to Plate Design, *Jnl. ACI*, **63**, 10, 1077–1094.

Rozvany, G. I. N. (1973), Optimal Force Transmission by Flexure — The Present State of Knowledge, *Proc. IUTAM Symp. On Optimiz. in Struct. Design* (eds. A. Sawczuk and Z. Mroz), Warsaw.

Rozvany, G. I. N. (1975), Recent Advances in Structural Optimization by Analytical Methods, Proc. 5th Australas. Conf. Mech. Struct. Mater., Melbourne, 439–456.

Rozvany, G. I. N. (1976), *Optimal Design of Flexural Systems*, Pergamon.

Rozvany, G. I. N. (1977), Elastic versus Plastic Optimal Strength Design, *J. Eng. Mech. Div. ASCE*, **103**, EM1, 210–214.

Rozvany, G. I. N. (1978), Optimal Elastic Design for Stress Constraints, *Comp. and Struct.*, **8**, 3–4, 455–463.

Rozvany, G. I. N. and Adidam, S. R. (1972), Dual Formulation of Variational Problems in Optimal Design, *ASME J. Eng. for Industry*, **94**, Ser. B., 2, 409–418.

Rozvany, G. I. N. *et al.* (1971), On the Foundations of Plastic Optimal Design, Proc. 3rd Australas. Conf. Mech. Struct. Mater., Auckland.

Rozvany, G. I. N. and Cohn, M. Z. (1970), A Lower Bound Approach to the Optimal Design of Concrete Structures, *J. Eng. Mech. Div., ASCE*, **96**, EM6, 1013–1030, Dec.

Rozvany, G. I. N. and Hampson, A. J. K. (1963), Optimum Design of Prestressed Plates, *Jnl. ACI*, **60**, 1065–1082.

Rozvany, G. I. N. and Hill, R. (1976), The Theory of Optimal Load Transmission by Flexure, *Advances in Applied Mechanics*, **16**, 183–308.

Rubinstein, M. F. (1975), *Patterns of Problem Solving*, Prentice-Hall.

Rubinstein, M. F. and Karagozian, J. (1966), Building Design Using Linear Programming, *ASCE, J. Struct. Div.*, **92**, ST6, 223–245.

Rubio, J. E. (1971), *The Theory of Linear Systems*, Academic Press.

Sage, A. P. (1968), *Optimum Systems Control*, Prentice-Hall.

Sage, A. P. (1977), *A Methodology for Large-Scale Problems*, McGraw-Hill.

Sage, A. P. and Chaudhuri, S. P. (1967), Gradient and Quasi-linearization Techniques for Distributed Parameter Systems, *Int. J. Control*, **6**, 1, 81–98.

Sage, A. P. and Melsa, J. L. (1971), *System Identification*, Academic Press.

Sage, A. P. and White, C. C. (1977), *Optimum Systems Control*, Prentice-Hall.

Sakawa, Y. (1964), Solution of an Optimal Control Problem in a Distributed–Parameter System, *IEEE Trans. Aut. Control*, **AC–9**, 420–426.

Sakawa, Y. (1966), Optimal Control of a Certain Type of Linear Distributed–Parameter System, *IEEE Trans. Aut. Control*, **AC–11**, 35–41.

Salonen, E. M. (1976), An Iterative Penalty Function Method in Structural Analysis, *Int. J. Num. Meth. Eng.*, **10**, 413–422.

Savage, G. J. and Roe, P. H. (eds.) (1978), *Large Engineering Systems 2*, Sandford.

Save, M. A. and Massonet, C. E. (1972), *Plastic Analysis and Design of Plates, Shells and Disks*, North Holland.

Sawczuk, A. and Mroz. A. (1975) (eds.), *Optimization in Structural Design*, IUTAM Symp. Warsaw 1973, Springer-Verlag.

Schmidt, L. C. (1958), Fully-Stressed Design of Elastic Redundant Trusses Under Alternative Load Systems, *Aust. J. App. Sci.*, **9**, 4, 337–348, Dec.

Schmidt, R. M. and Brotchie, J. F. (1973), Design Sensitivity Studies on Simple Span Prestressed Concrete Beam and Slab Highway Bridge Super-structures, CSIRO (Aust.) Div. Building Research Paper No. 31.

Schmit, L. A. (1969a), Structural Synthesis 1959–1969, A Decade of Progress, Japan-U.S. Seminar on Matrix Methods of Structural Analysis and Design, Tokyo Japan, August 25–30.

Schmit, L. A. (1969b), Structural Engineering Applications of Mathematical Programming Techniques, Preprint; AGARD Conf. Proc. No. 36, Istanbul, Turkey, Oct. 6–8.

Schmit, L. A. (1969c), Problem Formulation, Methods and Solutions in the Optimum Design of Structures, in *An Introduction to Structural Optimization* (ed. M. Z. Cohn), Study No. 1, Solid Mech. Div., Univ. Waterloo, 19–46.

Schmit, L. A. (1974) (ed.), Structural Optimization Symposium, ASME, New York, November.

Schmit, L. A. and Farshi, B. (1974), Some Approximation Concepts for Structural Synthesis, *AIAA Jnl.*, **12**, 5, 692–699.

Schoeffler, J. D. (1971a), Static Multilevel Systems, in *Optimization Methods for Large Scale Systems* (ed. D. A. Wismer), 1–46, McGraw-Hill.

Schoeffler, J. D. (1971b), On-Line Multilevel Systems, in *Optimization Methods for Large Scale Systems* (ed. D. A. Wismer), 291–330, McGraw-Hill.

Segenreich, S. A., Johnson, E. H. and Rizzi, P. (1976), Three Contributions to Minimum Weight Structural Optimization with Dynamics and Aeroelastic Constraints, Stanford University SUDAAR 501 (Ph. D. Dissertations).

Seinfeld, J. H. and Lapidus, L. (1968), Singular Solutions in the Optimal Control of Lumped and Distributed Parameter Systems, *Chem. Engg. Sci.*, **23**, 1485–1499; and **23**, 1461–1484.

Sharpe, R. (1969), The Optimum Design of Arch Dams, Proc. ICE, Paper 7200S, Suppl. Vol., 73–98.

Sharpe, R. and Clyde, D. H. (1967), The Rational Design of Reinforced Concrete Slabs, *Trans. I. E. Aust.*, **CE9**, 209–216.

Sheppard, D. J. and Palmer, A. C. (1972), Optimal Design of Transmission Towers by Dynamic Programming, *Computers and Structures*, **2**, 455–468.

Sheu, C. Y. and Prager, W. (1968), Recent Developments in Optimal Structural Design, *Appl. Mech. Rev.*, **21**, 985–992.

Siljak, D. D. (1978), *Large Scale Dynamic Systems (Stability and Structure)*, North Holland.

Simonnard, M. (1966), *Linear Programming*, Prentice-Hall.

Singaraj, N. M. and Rao, J. K. S. (1972), Control Theory Formulation for Nonlinear Elastic Analysis of Trusses, *A.I.A.A. Jnl.*, **10**, 4, 527–529.

Singaraj, N. M. and Rao, J. K. S. (1975), Optimization in Trusses Using Optimal Control Theory, *ASCE, J. Struct. Div.*, ST5, 1037–1051.

Singh, M. G. (1977), *Dynamical Hierarchical Control*, North Holland.

Singh, M. G., Drew, S. A. W. and Coales, J. F. (1975), Comparisons of Practical Hierarchical Control Methods for Interconnected Dynamical Systems. *Automatica*, **11**, 4, 331–350.

Sirazetdinov, T. K. (1964), On the Theory of Optimal Processes with Distributed Parameters, *Automn Remote Control*, **25**, 431–440.

Smith, D. L. and Munro, J. (1976), Plastic Analysis and Synthesis of Frames Subjected to Multiple Loadings, *Eng. Optimizn*, **2**, 145.

Smith, N. J. and Sage, A. P. (1973a), An Introduction to Hierarchical Systems Theory, *Comput. and Elect. Eng.*, **1**, 55–71.

Smith, N. J. and Sage, A. P. (1873b), A Sequential Method for System Identification in Hierarchical Structure, *Automatica*, **9**, 677–688.

Snow, D. R. (1965), Singular Optimal Controls for a Class of Minimum Effort Problems, *SIAM J. Control*, **2**, 2, 203–219.

Sokolnikoff, I. S. (1956), *Mathematical Theory of Elasticity*, 2nd ed., McGraw-Hill.

Sokolnikoff, I. S. and Redheffer, R. M. (1966), *Mathematics of Physics and Modern Engineering*, 2nd ed, McGraw-Hill.

Speyer, J. L. and Jacobson, D. H. (1971), Necessary and Sufficient Conditions for Optimality for Singular Control Problems; A Transformation Approach, *J. Math. Anal. Appl.*, **33**, 163–187.

Spillers, W. R. (1963), Network Analogy for Linear Structures, *ASCE J. Eng. Mech. Div.*, 21–29.

Spillers, W. R. (1966), Artificial Intelligence and Structural Design, *ASCE J. Struct. Div.*, ST6, 491–497.

Spillers, W. R. (1971), Graph Theory, Switching Theory and Structural Design, *App. Mech. Reviews*, 501–504.

Spillers, W. R. (1972), *Automated Structural Analysis: An Introduction*, Pergamon.

Spillers, W. R. (1973), Applications of Graph Theory to Decomposition Problems of Structures, in *Decomposition of Large Scale Problems* (ed. D. M. Himmelblau), 285–306, North Holland.

Spillers, W. R. (1974), Some Problems of Structural Design, in *Basic Questions of Design Theory*, (ed. W. R. Spillers), North Holland, 103–120.

Spillers, W. R. (1975a), *Iterative Structural Design*, North Holland.

Spillers, W. R. (1975b), A Graph Problem of Structural Design, in *Optimization in Structural Design* (eds. A. Sawczuk and Z. Mroz), IUTAM Symp. Warsaw 1973, Springer-Verlag, 3–14.

Spillers, W. R. and Friedland, L. (1972), On Adaptive Structural Design, *ASCE J. Struct. Div.*, ST10, 2155–2163.

Spunt, L. (1971), *Optimum Structural Design*, Prentice-Hall.

Stadler, W. (1977a), Natural Structural Shapes of Shallow Arches, *J. Appl. Mech., Trans ASME, Ser. E*, **44**, 2, 291–298.

Stadler, W. (1977b), Uniform Shallow Arches of Minimum Weight and Minimum Maximum Deflection, *JOTA*, **23**, 1, 137–165.

Stadler, W. (1978), Natural Structural Shapes (The Static Case), *Quart. J. Mech. Appl. Math.*, **31**, 2, 169–217.

Stark, R. M. and Nicholls, R. L. (1972), *Mathematical Foundations for Design, Civil Engineering Systems*, McGraw-Hill.

Sugar, R. D. (1974a), Decomposition Technique for Minimum Time Trajectories, *Jnl. Opt. Theory. Appl.*, **14**, 2, 233–250.

Sugar, R. D. (1974b), Multilevel Optimization of Multiple Arc Trajectories, in *Advances in Control Systems: Theory and Applications* (ed. C. T. Leondes), **11**, 145–254.

Synge, J. L. (1960), Classical Dynamics, 1–225, Vol. III/1 Handbuch der Physik, ed. by S. Flugge, Springer-Verlag.

Szefer, G. (1971), Deformable Material Continuum as a Control System with Spatially Distributed Parameters, *Archives of Mechanics (Arch. Mech. Stos.),* **23**, 6, 927–952.

Szefer, G. (1975), Optimal Control of the Consolidation Process, in *Optimization in Structural Design*, IUTAM Symp. Warsaw 1973 (eds. A. Sawczuk and Z. Mroz), Springer-Verlag.

Tabak, D. and Kuo, B. C. (1969), Application of Mathematical Programming in the Design of Optimal Control Systems, *Intern, J. Control,* **10**, 545–552.

Tabak, D. and Kuo, B. C. (1971), *Optimal Control by Mathematical Programming*, Prentice-Hall.

Tabarrok, B. and Simpson, A. (1968), On Kron's Piecewise Method of Structural Analysis, *J. Franklin Inst.*, **286**, 6, 632–633.

Templeman, A. B. (1970), Structural Design for Minimum Cost using the Method of Geometric Programming, *Proc. ICE*, **46**, 459–472. Discussion in **48**, 691–702, 1971.

Templeman, A. B. (1972), Geometric Programming with Examples of the Optimum Design of Floor and Roof Systems, Procs. Int. Symp. on Computer-Aided Structural Design, Univ. Warwick.

Templeman, A. B. (1975), Optimum Truss Design Using Approximating

Functions, 327–349, in *Optimization in Structural Design*, IUTAM Symposium Warsaw 1973 (eds. A. Sawczuk and Z. Mroz), Springer-Verlag.

Templeman, A. B. (1976), A Dual Approach to Optimum Truss Design, *J. Struct. Mech.*, **4**, 3, 235–255.

Thakkar, M. C. and Rao, J. K. S. (1974), Optimal Design of Prestressed Concrete Pipes Using Linear Programming, *Computers and Structures*, **4**, 373–380.

Thiriez, H. and Zionts, S. (eds.) (1976), 'Multiple Criteria Decision Making', Lecture Notes in Economics and Mathematical Systems, No 130, (Proc. Conf. Jouy-en-Josas, France, May, 1975), Springer-Verlag.

Thoma, M. (1971), Optimal Multivariable Control Systems Theory: A Survey, in *Multivariable Technical Control Systems* (ed. H. Schwartz), v.4, 79–114, Proc. 2nd IFAC Symp., Duesseldorf, Oct 11–13, 1971, North Holland Pub. Co., Amsterdam, Amer. Elsevier.

Timoshenko, S. P. and Gere, J. M. (1961), *Theory of Elastic Stability,* McGraw-Hill.

Timoshenko, S. P. and Woinowsky-Krieger, S. (1959), *Theory of Plates and Shells*, 2nd ed., McGraw-Hill.

Toakley, A. R. (1968a), The Optimum Design of Triangulated Frameworks, *Int. J. Mech. Sci.*, **10**, 2, 115–128.

Toakley, A. R. (1968b), Some Computational Aspects of Optimum Rigid Plastic Design, *Int. J. Mech. Sci.*, **10**, 6, 531–538.

Toakley, A. R. (1968c), Optimum Design Using Available Sections, *J. Struct. Div., ASCE*, **94**, ST5, 1219.

Toakley, A. R. (1970), Axial Load Effects in Optimum Rigid–Plastic Design, *Build Sci.*, **5**, 111–115.

Tomovic, R. (1963), *Sensitivity Analysis of Dynamic Systems*, McGraw-Hill.

Torres, G. G. B., Brotchie, J. F. and Cornell, C. A. (1966), A Program for the Optimum Design of Prestressed Concrete Highway Bridges, *J. PCI*, **11**, 63–71.

Tou, J. T. (1964), *Modern Control Theory*, McGraw-Hill.

Touma, A. and Wilson, J. F. (1973), Design Optimization of Prestressed Concrete Spans for High Speed Ground Transportation, *Computers and Structures*, **3**, 265–279.

Trahair, N. S. and Booker, J. R. (1970), Optimum Elastic Columns, *Int. J. Mech. Sci.*, **12**, 973–983.

Traum, E. and Zalewski, W. (1968), Conceptual Rather than 'Exact' Structural Design, *Civil Engg*, July.

Truesdell, C. and Toupin, R. A. (1960), The Classical Field Theories, 226–793, Vol III/1 Handbuch der Physik, ed. S. Flugge, Springer-Verlag.

Tsypkin, Ya. Z. (1971), *Adaptation and Learning in Automatic Systems*, Academic Press.

Twisdale, L. A. and Khachaturian, N. (1973), Absolute Minimum Weight Structures by Dynamic Programming, *ASCE, J. Struct. Div.*, **99**, ST11, 2339–2344.

Twisdale, L. A. and Khachaturian, N. (1975a), Application of Dynamic Programming to Optimization of Structures, in *Optimization in Structural Design,* IUTAM Symp. Warsaw 1973 (eds. A. Sawczuk and Z. Mroz), 122–141.

Twisdale, L. A. and Khachaturian, N. (1975b), Multistage Optimization of Structures, *ASCE, J. Struct. Div.*, ST5, 1005–1020.

Vajda, S. (1961), *Mathematical Programming*, Addison-Wesley.

Valentine, F. A. (1937), The Problem of Lagrange with Differential Inequalities as Added Side Conditions, in *Contributions to the Calculus of Variations 1933—1937*, Univ. Chicago Press, 407–448.

Van der Neut. A. (1949), Design of Structures Based on Assumed Deformations, in *Engineering Structures*, Butterworths, 229–240.

Vanderplaats, G. N. and Moses, F. (1972), Automated Design of Trusses for Optimum Geometry, *ASCE J. Struct. Div.*, **98**, ST3, 671–690.

Vavrick, D. J. and Warner, W. H. (1978a), Minimum Mass Design with Torsional Frequency and Thickness Constraints, *J. Struct. Mech.* **6**, 2, 211–232.

Vavrick, D. J. and Warner, W. H. (1978b), Duality Among Optimal Design Problems for Torsional Vibration, *J. Struct. Mech.*, **6**, 2, 233–246.

Venkayya, V. B. (1978), Structural Optimization: A Review and Some Recommendations, *Int. J. Num. Meth. Eng.*, **13**, 2, 203–228.

Venkayya, V. B. and Khot N. S. (1974), Structural Optimization, *Structural Mechanics Computer Programs: Surveys, Assessments and Availability*, Univ. Press of Virginia, Charlottesville.

Vepa, K. (1973a), On the Existence of Solutions to Optimization Problems with Eigenvalue Constraints, *Quart. App. Math.*, **31**, 3, 329–341.

Vepa, K. (1973b), Generalization of an Energetic Optimality Condition for Non-Conservative Systems, *J. Struct. Mech.*, **2**, 3, 229–257.

Vepa, K. and Roorda J. (1973), Optimality Criteria for Stability Problems Using Pontryagin's Maximum Principle, Fourth CANCAM, 365–366.

Vitiello, E. (1977), Standardization and Optimum Structural Design by Dynamic Programming, *JOTA*, **23**, 1, 183–191.

Vitte, W. J., McIntosh, S. C. and Ashley, H. (1968), Applications of Aeroelastic Constraints in Structural Optimization, Stanford University SUDAAR Report.

Vol'mir, A. S. and Kul'terbaev, K. P. (1974), Stochastic Stability of Forced Nonlinear Shell Vibrations, *App. Math. Mech. (PMM)*, **38**, 5, 840–846.

Von Neumann, J. and Morgenstern, O. (1953), *Theory of Games and Economic Behavior*, Princeton Univ. Press, 3rd ed.

Walker, J. A. (1972), Liapunov Analysis of the Generalized Pfluger Problem, *ASME, J. App. Mech., Series E*, **39**, 4, 935–938, December.

Walker, J. A. (1973), Stability of a Pin-Ended Bar in Torsion and Compression, *ASME, J. App. Mech. Series E*, 405–408, June.

Wang, P. K. C. (1964), Control of Distributed Parameter Systems, in *Advances in Control Systems; Theory and Applications* (ed. C. T. Leondes), **1**, 75–172, Academic Press.

Wang, P. K. C. (1968), Theory of Stability and Control for Distributed Parameter Systems (a Bibliography), *Int. J. Control*, **7**, 2, 101–116.

Wang, P. K. C. and Tung, F. (1964), Optimum Control of Distributed–Parameter Systems, *Trans ASME, J. Basic Engng*, **86D**, 67–79.

Warner, R. F., Rangan, B. V. and Hall, A. S. (1976), *Reinforced Concrete*, Pitman.

Wasiutynski, F. and Brandt, A. (1963), The Present State of Knowledge in the Field of Optimum Design of Structures, *Appl. Mech. Rev.*, **16**, 5, 341–349.

Weisshaar, T. A. (1970), An Application of Control Theory Methods to the Optimisation of Structures Having Dynamic or Aeroelastic Constraints, Stanford Univ., Dept. Aero. Astron., Report 412 (Ph.D. Thesis).

Weisshaar, T. A. (1976), Panel Flutter Optimization — A Refined Finite Element Approach, *Int. J. Num. Meth. Eng.*, **10**, 77–92.

Wilde, D. J. and Beightler, C. S. (1967), *Foundations of Optimization*, Prentice-Hall.

Willems, J. L. (1970), *Stability Theory of Dynamical Systems*, Nelson.

Wismer, D. A. (1969), An Efficient Computational Procedure for the Optimization of a Class of Distributed Parameter Systems, *Jnl. Basic Eng., ASME, Series D*. **91**, 2, 190–194.

Wismer, D. A. (ed.) (1971a), *Optimization Methods for Large Scale Systems*, McGraw-Hill.

Wismer, D. A. (1971b), Distributed Multilevel Systems, ch. 6 in *Optimization Methods for Large-Scale Systems with Applications* (ed. D. A. Wismer), 233–273, McGraw-Hill.

Wismer, D. A. (1973), Decomposition and the Optimization of Distributed Parameter Systems, in *Decomposition of Large-Scale Problems* (ed. D. M. Himmelblau), 251–271, North Holland.

Wismer, D. A. and Chattergy, R. (1978), *Introduction to Nonlinear Optimization*, North Holland.

Wittler, M. and Shen, C. N. (1969), A Multiplier Rule for a Functional Subject to Certain Integrodifferential Constraints, *Trans ASME, Series D, J. Basic Engng*, **91**, 185–189.

Wolfe, P. (1959), The Simplex Method for Quadratic Programming, *Econometrica*, **27**, 382–398.

Wolfe, P. (1961), A Duality Theorem for Nonlinear Programming, *Quart. Appl. Math*., **19**, 239–244.

Wong, A. K. C. and Bugliarello, G. (1970), Artificial Intelligence in Continuum Mechanics, *ASCE, J. Eng. Mech. Div*., **96**, 1239–1265.

Wong, E. (1971), *Stochastic Processes in Information and Dynamical Systems*, McGraw-Hill.

Wood, R. H. (1961), *Plastic and Elastic Design of Slabs and Plates*. Thames and Hudson.

Wood, R. H. (1963), Demonstration of Hillerborg's Strip Method, Bulletin d'Information, No. 36, Comite Europeen du Beton, May.

Wood, R. H. and Jones, L. L. (1967), *Yield Line Analysis of Slabs*, Thames and Hudson and Chatto and Windus Ltd.

Yavin, Y. and Sivan, R. (1967), The Optimal Control of Distributed Parameter Systems, *IEEE Trans. Aut. Control*, **AC–12**, 758–761.

Yavin, Y. and Sivan, R. (1968), The Bounded Energy Optimal Control for a Class of Distributed Parameter Systems, *Int. J. Control*, **8**, 525–536.

Zadeh, L. A. (1958), What is Optimal?, *IEEE Trans. Inform Theory*, **IT–4**, 1, 3.

Zadeh, L. A. (1962), An Introduction to State Space Techniques, *Joint Aut. Control Conf. AIEE*, paper 10.1, 1–5.

Zadeh, L. A. (1963), Optimality and Non-Scalar Valued Performance Criteria, *IEEE Trans. Aut. Cont*., **AC–8**, 1, 59–60.

Zadeh, L. A. and Desoer, C. A. (1963), *Linear System Theory*, McGraw-Hill.

Zadeh, L. A. and Polak, E. (1969), (eds.), *System Theory*, McGraw-Hill.

Zangwill, W. I. (1969), *Nonlinear Programming*, Prentice-Hall.

Zavelani, A., Maier, G. and Binda, L. (1975). Shape Optimization of Plastic Structures by Zero-One Programming, in *Optimization in Structural Design* (eds. A. Sawczuk and Z. Mroz), IUTAM Symposium, Warsaw 1973, Springer-Verlag, 541–554.

Zeleny, M. (1974), *Linear Multiple Objective Programming*, Lecture Notes in Economics and Mathematical Systems, No. 95, Springer-Verlag.

Zener, C. (1971), *Engineering Design by Geometric Programming*, Wiley.
Zionts, S. (1974), *Linear and Integer Programming*, Prentice-Hall.
Zoutendijk, G. (1960), *Methods of Feasible Directions*, American Elsevier.
Zubov, V. I. (1964), *The Methods of Liapunov and Their Applications*, (Leningrad Univ. Press 1957) Noordhoff.

Index